ELEMENTS OF CHEMICAL REACTOR DESIGN AND OPERATION

ELEMENTS OF
CHEMICAL REACTOR DESIGN
AND OPERATION

by

H. KRAMERS and K.R. WESTERTERP
Technical University, Delft, The Netherlands

1963

ACADEMIC PRESS INC. - NEW YORK

PUBLISHED IN U.S.A. AND CANADA BY

ACADEMIC PRESS Inc.
111 Fifth Avenue
NEW YORK 3, New York

PRINTED IN THE NETHERLANDS BY

NEDERLANDSE BOEKDRUK INRICHTING N.V., 's-HERTOGENBOSCH

PREFACE

The chemical reactor is a vital element in every chemical manufacturing process. Chemical as well as physical phenomena take place in it and its final design and construction are determined by mechanical factors. The art of the design, construction and economic operation of a reactor can, therefore, be seen as a synthesis of the principles of chemistry, physics, mechanics and economics.

The design and operation of reactors has received much attention in the past decade and it is rapidly developing from an empirical art towards a synthetic and rational activity. In chemical engineering the physical operations have already gone through such a development. The systematics of the physical transport phenomena and of the physical separation processes have reached a state of maturity by way of the "unit operations". Compared to this development the chemical reactor aspects of a manufacturing process have lagged behind. The concept of "unit processes" has had certain advantages in bringing some system into the technical organic chemistry. It does not, however, provide a basis for a systematic treatment of chemical reactors since other aspects, such as heat effects and states of aggregation and of dispersion, may equally be determining factors. Therefore, the approach adopted in this book is rather based on physical considerations, as will be explained below.

For a process which has to be developed commercially or which has to be improved in actual operation, it must be assumed that, as a result of chemical research, information regarding the chemistry of the process will be available. This information is specific of the process and relates to equilibria, heat effects, conversion rates of desired and undesired reactions under various conditions, the influence of impurities, the behaviour of catalysts, etc. When such data have been supplied in a more or less complete form, the chemical engineer has to consider the following questions:
– What manner of operation has to be adopted?
– What reactor type is the most suitable?
– What reactor dimensions are required?
An answer to these questions should ultimately lead to a reactor design or a strategy of operation by means of which the desired materials can be manufactured at the desired rate and at the lowest cost.

The underlying philosophy of this book is that the above questions can be treated by methods which are not specific, but general. Accordingly, the text is limited to a discussion of the non-specific aspects of chemical reactors. As a starting point, the isothermal operation of a few model reactor types has been selected. Subsequently, the various complications are discussed which are connected with the flow phenomena in actual reactors, the heat effect of the reaction, the state of dispersion of the reaction mixture and the economic requirements of a manufacturing process, respectively.

This limitation to the engineering principles of chemical reactors implies that for a complete development and design of an industrial reactor supplementary information of a more specific nature will be necessary. Although this kind of information is not treated in this book, its importance cannot be overemphasized. This not only applies to chemical and physico-chemical data, the principles of which have been described in many excellent textbooks on chemical thermodynamics and kinetics, but also to data regarding materials of construction, corrosion, strength of material and costs. Evidently, in acquiring such information the chemical engineer has to rely on the work of a number of specialists.

Since this book has evolved from a lecture course for senior chemical engineering students at the Technical University of Delft, it has the character of a textbook. Accordingly, many illustrative examples have been included. At the same time, the authors address themselves to chemical engineers and chemists in practice who, in the authors' experience, sometimes get wrapped up in specific reactor problems to such an extent that some reminder as to the reactor engineering principles may be useful. No attempt was made to make a complete survey of the existing literature in the field. In elucidating the principles, a number of papers has been referred to which may be consulted for further study. Throughout the book, calculations have been made in MKS (meter, kilogramme, second) units, with the degree Kelvin as a unit of temperature difference and the kilomol as a unit of the amount of substance. This system has been recommended by the *Conférence Générale des Poids et Mesures* in 1960; conversion tables to other systems are readily available. It has been attempted to use throughout the book a consistent set of symbols as indicated in the list of symbols on page XIV.

Summarizing the contents of the book, it may be said that in Chapter I some of the basic data needed for our purposes are reviewed. In particular, the formalism of conversion rates and degrees of conversion is discussed at some length; in our opinion much confusion still prevails with respect to the definitions used for these important properties of a reaction mixture.

In Chapter II the material balance is applied to various basic reactor types working under isothermal conditions. The reactor types discussed are "model" reactors which, however, are often closely approached in practice. The special properties of these reactors are demonstrated with respect to the degree of conversion and the capacity, and to the selectivity and the yield.

The residence time distribution and the degree of mixing in continuous flow reactors are discussed in Chapter III. On the basis of these flow phenomena a comparison can be made between the performance of actual reactors and that of the model reactors.

In Chapter IV the heat balance is taken into account along with the material balance for the treatment of non-isothermal reactor operation. The autothermal operation of reactor systems is discussed at some length because of its importance for the heat economy of a plant. The occurrence of "hot spots" in tubular reactors is described and the relativity of the concept of "maximum allowable temperature" is demonstrated.

Chapter V has been devoted to the various ways in which diffusion and mass transfer may influence the conversion rate, the selectivity and the yield of reactions carried out in heterogeneous systems. Since this field of combined chemical reaction and physical transport phenomena is extremely extensive, the text has been limited to several demonstrative subjects which can be used as a basis for further study.

The subject of Chapter VI, the optimization of chemical reactors, is at present rapidly expanding. We have limited ourselves to the economic and technical principles and to the description of a few practical results. Some of the mathematical methods of optimization have been mentioned at the end of this chapter.

In many places the economic background of reactor design and operation has been emphasized. Two subjects which could not well be fitted into the systematics given above have been briefly discussed in the two appendices. The first contains recommendations for obtaining dependable conversion
amic behaviour of cooled tank

x either direct or indirect. Only The well-known text "Chemical K. M. WATSON and the pioneer-FRANK-KAMENETSKI have great- DENBIGH's early contributions on engineering were very stimu-naterial which was brought to-tional symposium on Chemical 7 and 1960, respectively, which opean Federation of Chemical frequent contacts with the main . W. VAN KREVELEN and J. C. we had fruitful discussions on ish to mention Professor R. B. lessor P. LE GOFF, Dr. C. VAN

HEERDEN, Dr. J. W. HIBY, Dr. H. HOFMANN, Mr. P. J. HOFTIJZER, Dr. F. HORN, Professor M. LETORT, Dr. B. H. MESSIKOMMER, Professor R. L. PIGFORD, Professor K. RIETEMA, Professor K. SCHOENEMANN and Professor E. WICKE. In particular, we gratefully acknowledge the assistance of Dr. W. J. BEEK in the preparation of Chapter VI and Appendix 2. Finally, we wish to express our gratitude to our wives who witnessed the writing of this book with much patience and understanding.

December 1962

H. KRAMERS
Technical University, Delft, The Netherlands

K. R. WESTERTERP
N.V. Petrochemie AKU-Amoco, Arnhem, The Netherlands

CONTENTS

LIST OF ILLUSTRATIVE EXAMPLES

Chapter IV

Chapter V

Chapter VI

LIST OF SYMBOLS

Symbol	Quantity	Units
a	activity	–
A	heat or mass transfer area	m^2
A_v	interfacial area per unit volume	m^2/m^3
A_i	internal surface area per unit porous particle volume	m^2/m^3
c	total molar concentration	$kmol/m^3$
c_J	molar concentration of species J	$kmol/m^3$
c_p, c_v	heat capacity per unit mass, at constant pressure and volume, respectively	$J/kg\ °C$
C_p, C_v	molar heat capacity, at constant pressure and volume, respectively	$J/kmol\ °C$
d	characteristic dimension, diameter	m
d_p	particle diameter	m
d_t	tube diameter	m
D	coefficient of molecular diffusion	m^2/s
D_i	coefficient of internal diffusion in porous particle	m^2/s
D_t	coefficient of transverse dispersion	m^2/s
D_l	coefficient of longitudinal dispersion	m^2/s
e	relative excess of one reactant with respect to the other reactant	–
E	activation energy	$J/kmol$
E_J	extraction factor $= K_J \Phi_{vg}/\Phi_{vf}$	–
f	Fanning friction factor	–
$F(\tau)$	residence time distribution function	–
F_A	chemical acceleration factor (Section V.3)	–
g	acceleration by gravity, 9.81	m/s^2
G	free enthalpy, $H - TS$	J
G_J	molar free enthalpy of species J	$J/kmol$
h	enthalpy per unit mass	J/kg
H	hold-back (Eq. III-15)	–
H	enthalpy	J
H_J	molar enthalpy of species J	$J/kmol$

Symbol	Quantity	Units
ΔH_r	heat of reaction at constant pressure associated with stoichiometric equation	J
$(\Delta H_r)_J$	heat of reaction at constant pressure for the conversion of or to one molar unit of J	J/kmol
$(\Delta h_r)_J$	heat of reaction for the conversion of or to one mass unit of J	J/kg
j	mass flux	kg/m²s
J	molar flux	kmol/m²s
k	homogeneous reaction velocity constant	f(conc.)/s
k'	surface reaction velocity constant	f(conc.) $\times$ m/s
K	chemical equilibrium constant	–
K_J	distribution coefficient for species J	–
L	length	m
m	total mass of a system	kg
m_J	mass of species J in a system	kg
m_s	mass of solid or catalyst in a system	kg
M	average molar mass of a reaction mixture	kg/kmol
M_J	molar mass of species J	kg/kmol
M, M^*	objective function (Section VI.4)	
n	sequence number of a tank reactor in a cascade	–
N	total number of tank reactors in a cascade	–
N'	$\langle v \rangle L/2D_l$	–
N_{ad}, N_c	parameters used in Eq. IV-9	–
p	total pressure	N/m²
p_J	partial pressure of species J	N/m²
p	degree of polymerization (Ill. III. 8)	–
q	heat flux	W/m²
Q	amount of heat	J
$\dot{Q}$	heat flow	W
r	cylindrical or spherical coordinate	m
r_J	mass rate of production of J per unit volume	kg/m³s
$r_J{}^*$	production rate of J per unit volume by homogeneous chemical reaction	kg/m³s
$|r|_J$	mass rate of conversion per unit volume	kg/m³s
$|r_s|_J$	mass rate of conversion per unit mass of solids (e.g. catalyst)	kg/kg s
$|r'|_J$	mass rate of conversion per unit surface area	kg/m²s
R_J	molar rate of production of J per unit volume	kmol/m³s
$R_J{}^*$	production rate of J per unit volume by homogeneous chemical reaction	kmol/m³s
$|R|_J$	molar rate of conversion per unit volume	kmol/m³s

Symbol	Quantity	Units
$\lvert R\rvert_{sJ}$	molar rate of conversion per unit mass of solid	kmol/kg s
$\lvert R'\rvert_{J}$	molar rate of conversion per unit surface area	kmol/m²s
R	gas constant, 8.315×10^3	J/kmol°K
R	radius of spherical particle	m
R_h	hydraulic radius = cross-sectional area divided by circumference	m
s	selectivity parameter, k_1/k_2	–
S	cross-sectional area	m²
S	entropy	J/°K
t	time	s
T	temperature, absolute or centigrade	°K or °C
ΔT_{ad}	adiabatic temperature rise of reaction mixture after complete conversion (Eq. IV-17)	°C
u	internal energy per unit mass	J/kg
U	internal energy	J
U_J	molar internal energy of species J	J/kmol
ΔU_r	heat of reaction at constant volume associated with stoichiometric equation	J
$(\Delta U_r)_J$	heat of reaction at constant volume for the conversion of or to one molar unit of J	J/kmol
$(\Delta u_r)_J$	heat of reaction at constant volume for the conversion of or to one mass unit of J	J/kg
U	over-all heat transfer coefficient	W/m²°C
V	volume	m³
V_r	volume of reaction mixture	m³
v	fluid velocity, approach velocity in packed bed	m/s
$\langle v \rangle$	average actual fluid velocity (in packed bed $= v/\varepsilon$)	m/s
v_r	relative velocity	m/s
w_J	mass fraction of species J	–
W	amount of work	Nm = J
$\dot{W}$	rate of work done on surroundings	Nm/s = W
x_J	molar fraction of species J	–
y	coordinate perpendicular to interface	m
z	coordinate in the direction of flow	m
α	heat transfer coefficient	W/m²°C
β	mass transfer coefficient	m/s
γ	fugacity coefficient	–
δ	film thickness	m
ε	fractional volume of continuous phase	–

XVI

Symbol	Quantity	Units
η	yield, fraction of reactant fed which is converted to desired product (Eq. II-24)	–
$\bar{\eta}$	plant yield	–
ϑ	dimensionless temperature difference	–
ζ	relative degree of conversion, fraction of reactant converted (Eq. I-26)	–
$\varkappa$	dimensionless reaction velocity constant, k/k_R	–
λ	Lagrange parameter (Section VI.4)	–
λ	thermal conductivity	W/m °C
λ_t	effective thermal conductivity transverse to main flow	W/m °C
λ_0	thermal conductivity of packed bed without flow	W/m °C
μ	dynamic viscosity	Ns/m²
ν	kinematic viscosity	m²/s
ν_J	stoichiometric coefficient of species J	–
ξ_J	degree of conversion of species J (Eq. I-23)	–
ϱ	density, specific mass	kg/m³
ϱ_s	apparent density of solid (catalyst) particles	kg/m³
σ	selectivity, fraction of desired product in reaction products (Eq. II-23)	–
τ	age, residence time	s
$\bar{\tau}$	average residence time in reactor system	s
τ_L	residence time in tubular reactor	s
φ	parameter defined in Eq. V-16	–
φ'	parameter defined in Eq. V-30	–
Φ_v	volumetric flow rate	m³/s
Φ_m	mass flow rate	kg/s
Φ_P	production rate of P	kg/s, kmol/s
ψ	differential selectivity (Eq. VI-2)	–
ω	angular speed	1/s

	Subscripts
J	arbitrary species
A, B	reactants
P, Q	products
X, Y	side products
0	initial or feed conditions

1	output of one tank reactor
n	output of nth tank reactor in cascade
N	output of cascade of N tank reactors
L	output of tubular reactor
r	reaction
w	wall
i	interface
e	equilibrium
c	coolant
l	longitudinal
t	transverse
v	volumetric
f, g	phases
R	at reference temperature T_R

Dimensionless groups

Le	Lewis number	$\lambda/c_p \varrho D$
$P\acute{e}_l$	Péclet number for longitudinal dispersion	$\langle v \rangle d/D_l$
$P\acute{e}_t$	Péclet number for transverse dispersion	$\langle v \rangle d_p/D_t$
Pr	Prandtl number	$\mu c_p/\lambda$
Re	Reynolds number	vd/ν
Re_p	Reynolds number in packed bed	vd_p/ν
Sc	Schmidt number	ν/D
Sh	Sherwood number	$\beta d/D$

CHAPTER I

FUNDAMENTALS OF CHEMICAL REACTOR CALCULATIONS

I.1. Introduction

A rational approach to all problems relating to a physical or chemical change of matter must be based on the elementary physical conservation laws. The formulation of these laws is, therefore, the point of departure in any chemical engineering textbook, and it has been handled most systematically in, e.g., the book by BIRD, STEWART and LIGHTFOOT [1]. For the treatment of chemical reactors, the laws of conservation of matter and of energy are of primary importance; they will be consistently applied in this book. Flow phenomena, governed by the principle of conservation of momentum, naturally are equally important for chemical reactors; however, the reader is assumed to have a working knowledge of engineering fluid dynamics, so that it will be applied where necessary without further explanation.

The principle of conservation of energy is also expressed in the first law of thermodynamics, whereas the second law of thermodynamics is concerned with the degradation of energy associated with irreversible processes. The application of the first and second laws to the chemical transformation of matter, i.e. chemical thermodynamics, provides a consistent framework for the calculation of heats of transformation and for the relationships describing chemical equilibrium. Of the numerous textbooks in which this material is treated, we only mention those by HOUGEN, WATSON and RAGATZ [2] and by DENBIGH [3] since its use with reference to chemical reactors is implied.

The conservation laws and the relevant relationships supplied by chemical thermodynamics will be briefly reviewed in Sections I.2 and I.3.

The second kind of information needed for a quantitative treatment of chemical reactor problems is concerned with *rates*. The rate at which a reaction proceeds may not only be determined by the chemical kinetics of the reaction proper but also by physical transport phenomena (Section I.4). The interaction between chemical kinetics and physical transport rates has received considerable attention during the past decades. DAMKÖHLER [4] and particularly FRANK-KAMENETSKI [5] have systematically developed this field. The latter author distinguished in this respect "microkinetics" (i.e. chemical kinetics) and "macrokinetics" (i.e. physical rates). According to

VAN KREVELEN [6], several scales of scrutiny can be considered in macro-kinetics: the dimensions of the molecular mean free path (diffusion), of the dispersion in heterogeneous systems (transfer), and of the reactor as a whole (convection transport). Whereas for obtaining chemical kinetic data we still must entirely rely on experimental results relative to the particular reaction under consideration, it is possible to estimate physical transport and transfer rates on the basis of fluid properties, flow circumstances and the geometry of the system. Since the reader is supposed to be familiar with the concepts of diffusion, mass transfer and heat transfer, these will be used where necessary without prior discussion. Therefore, in Sections 3 and 4 of this chapter we shall only briefly mention a few facts about chemical kinetics and indicate which formulation will be used for the chemical conversion rate and the degree of conversion.

Section I.6 is meant to remind the reader of the fact that the ultimate judgment on the performance of a chemical reactor or a reactor section is based on economics. Although no physical conservation principle is here involved, we may speak of an economic balance which has to be taken into account for obtaining maximum profitability of any industrial operation.

Finally, for the reader's orientation, some remarks are made in Section I.7 on the great variety of chemical reactors. This leads to the three basic reactor types to be discussed further: the mixed batch reactor, and, for continuous operation, the stirred tank reactor and the tubular reactor.

I.2. The material and energy balance

Material balance

For any reactor calculation the application of the principle of conservation of matter is indispensable. A material balance may be set up for any molecular species taking part in the reaction. In words, such a balance over a system, e.g. for a component J, may be formulated in the following manner:

$$\begin{Bmatrix} \text{accumulation of} \\ \text{mass of J in the} \\ \text{system} \end{Bmatrix} = \begin{Bmatrix} \text{mass of J} \\ \text{into the} \\ \text{system} \end{Bmatrix} - \begin{Bmatrix} \text{mass of J} \\ \text{out of the} \\ \text{system} \end{Bmatrix} + \begin{Bmatrix} \text{mass of J} \\ \text{produced} \\ \text{by reaction} \end{Bmatrix}^{*}.$$

This equation can be set up for a certain time interval, in which case the terms are expressed in units of mass; in view of the applications, however, it is preferable to use units of mass per unit time, so that the terms represent mass rates of J.

The mathematical formulation of the material balance greatly depends on the nature of the system under consideration. As a basis for further calcula-

---

* In this section we have followed the systematic formulation of balances used by BIRD, STEWART and LIGHTFOOT [1].

tions we select as our system a volume V for which a material balance may be put into the form:

$$\frac{\mathrm{d}m_J}{\mathrm{d}t} = - \Delta\Phi_{mJ} + \langle r_J \rangle V, \text{ [kg/s]},$$ I-1

where
m_J = mass of J in the system,
$-\Delta\Phi_{mJ}$ = net inflow of J by convection and possibly also by a diffusional process,
r_J = mass rate of production of J by chemical reaction per unit volume,
$\langle r_J \rangle$ = space average of r_J.

The sum of the material balances for each chemical species gives the total material balance:

$$\frac{\mathrm{d}m}{\mathrm{d}t} = - \Delta\Phi_m, \text{ [kg/s]}.$$ I-2

Since we have expressed the amounts of the various components in units of mass, the production terms in Eq. I-1 cancel each other in this summation. This would, of course, not be generally so if other units were used (mols or units of volume). The necessity to make use of units of mass in the material balance, together with the theoretically well-founded practice of using molar quantities for chemical reactions, calls for much care (also see I.5).

Energy balance

The application of the principle of conservation of energy leads to an energy balance which in general states that:

$$\begin{Bmatrix} \text{rate of accumu-} \\ \text{lation of energy} \end{Bmatrix} = \begin{Bmatrix} \text{rate of} \\ \text{energy in} \end{Bmatrix} - \begin{Bmatrix} \text{rate of} \\ \text{energy out} \end{Bmatrix} + \begin{Bmatrix} \text{rate of ener-} \\ \text{gy production} \end{Bmatrix}.$$

Strictly speaking, all forms of energy must be taken into account: heat, kinetic energy, potential energy in a gravitational, electrical and magnetic field. For a complete formulation of the energy balance, the reader is referred to, e.g., [1] and [7]. In most reactor calculations the terms with thermal energy and work done on the surroundings are of main importance. Leaving out the other effects, the energy balance for a system in which reaction takes place, becomes:

$$\frac{\mathrm{d}(\langle u \rangle m)}{\mathrm{d}t} = - \Delta(h\Phi_m) + \dot{Q} - \dot{W}, \text{ [J/s = W]};$$ I-3

here
$\langle u \rangle m$ = total internal energy of the system,
$-\Delta(h\Phi_m)$ = net inflow of enthalpy,
$\dot{Q}$ = rate of heat supply from the surroundings,
$\dot{W}$ = rate of work done on the surroundings.

Note that for a closed system (i.e., no material flowing in or out) the second term in Eq. I-3 disappears; the resulting equation is the exact equivalent of

3

the first law of thermodynamics. Whenever effects of reaction heat come into play, the energy balance has to be taken into consideration (see Chapter IV).

I.3. Thermodynamic data; heat of reaction and chemical equilibrium

Heat of reaction

Generally there is a difference between the sum of absolute enthalpies of the reaction products and that of the reactants. For a reaction:

$$\nu_A A + \nu_B B + \ldots \rightarrow \nu_P P + \nu_Q Q + \ldots,$$

the corresponding heat of reaction, ΔH_r, is defined as the heat absorbed by the system when the reaction proceeds completely in the direction indicated by the arrow, at constant temperature and pressure. Hence:

$$\Delta H_r \equiv (\nu_P H_P + \nu_Q H_Q + \ldots) - (\nu_A H_A + \nu_B H_B + \ldots) =$$

$$= + \Sigma(\nu_J H_J)_{\text{prod}} - \Sigma(\nu_J H_J)_{\text{react}}. \qquad \text{I-4}$$

This result follows from the energy balance for a closed system which is identical with the first law of thermodynamics. ΔH_r is positive for an endothermic reaction and negative for an exothermic reaction.

For a certain reaction, ΔH_r can be calculated from the heat effects of other reactions, e.g. the heats of formation of the species involved, or the heats of combustion of these compounds. For obtaining the numerical value of ΔH_r, the stoichiometric equation, the direction of the reaction, the temperature, the pressure and the physical state of the components must be specified. When the reactants and the products are at standard conditions and the reaction proceeds under standard conditions, the standard heat of reaction is $\Delta H_{rs}{}^0 \star$.

Its value can than be derived from the standard heats of formation $(\Delta H_{fs}{}^0)_J$ according to:

$$\Delta H_{rs}{}^0 = \Sigma[\nu_J(\Delta H_{fs}{}^0)_J]_{\text{prod}} - \Sigma[\nu_J(\Delta H_{fs}{}^0)_J]_{\text{react}}, \qquad \text{I-5}$$

and from the standard heats of combustion $(\Delta H_{cs}{}^0)_J$ from:

$$\Delta H_{rs}{}^0 = \Sigma[\nu_J(\Delta H_{cs}{}^0)_J]_{\text{react}} - \Sigma[\nu_J(\Delta H_{cs}{}^0)_J]_{\text{prod}}. \qquad \text{I-6}$$

The standard pressure is generally 1 atmosphere and the standard temperature 18 or 25°C. Values of $\Delta H_{fs}{}^0$ and $\Delta H_{cs}{}^0$ can be found in the book by HOUGEN, WATSON and RAGATZ [7] and other sources.

The influence of pressure on the heat of reaction can be neglected for solids, liquids and ideal gases, so that $\Delta H_{rs}{}^0 = \Delta H_{rs}$. Corrections to be used for non-ideal gases can be found in the references [2], [8] and [9]; also see Illustration I.3a.

★ The index s refers to the standard temperature and the superscript 0 to the standard pressure and standard physical state.

The heat of reaction generally varies with temperature. The value of $\Delta H_r{}^0$ at a temperature T follows from $\Delta H_{rs}{}^0$ according to:

$$\Delta H_r^0 = \Delta H_{rs}^0 + \int_{T_s}^{T} \Delta C_p \, dT , \qquad\qquad \text{I-7}$$

where T_s is the standard temperature selected, and:

$$\Delta C_p = \Sigma(\nu_J C_{pJ})_{\text{prod}} - \Sigma(\nu_J C_{pJ})_{\text{react}}.$$

The molar specific heats, C_{pJ}, and hence ΔC_p are in general weak functions of temperature. Eq. I-7 is illustrated in Fig. I-1.

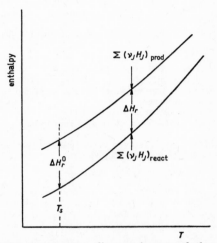

FIG. I-1. Enthalpy-temperature diagram for an endothermic reaction.

ILLUSTRATION I. 3a. *Calculation of a heat of reaction*

It is required to calculate ΔH_r for the reaction

$$\tfrac{1}{3}N_2 + H_2 \rightarrow \tfrac{2}{3}NH_3 ,$$

at 400°C, and for 1 and for 200 atmospheres of pressure.

ΔH_r at 1 atmosphere
The data given by HOUGEN, WATSON and RAGATZ [7] are used to calculate $\Delta H_r{}^0$ from the standard heats of formation, and ΔC_p from the specific heats of the three components. Both quantities refer to the amount reacting according to the above reaction formula, i.e. 1 kmol of H_2 converted. The heats of formation and the specific heats are:

component	$(\Delta H_f{}^0)_J$ kcal/kmol (18°C)	C_{pJ} kcal/kmol °K (T in °K)
P = NH₃(g)	− 11,000	$5.92 + 8.963 \times 10^{-3}T - 1.764 \times 10^{-6}T^2$
A = N₂(g)	0	$6.46 + 1.389 \times 10^{-3}T - 0.069 \times 10^{-6}T^2$
B = H₂(g)	0	$6.95 - 0.196 \times 10^{-3}T + 0.476 \times 10^{-6}T^2$

$$\Delta C_p = \tfrac{2}{3}C_{pP} - \tfrac{1}{3}C_{pA} - C_{pB} =$$
$$= -5.15 + 5.71 \times 10^{-3}T - 1.63 \times 10^{-6}T^2 \text{ kcal}/^\circ\text{K}$$
$$= -21.6 + 23.9 \times 10^{-3}T - 6.83 \times 10^{-6}T^2 \text{ kJ}/^\circ\text{K}.$$

$$\Delta H_{rs}^0 = -\tfrac{2}{3} \times 11{,}000 = -7{,}333 \text{ kcal}$$
$$= -30.73 \times 10^3 \text{ kJ}.$$

At 400°C and 1 atmosphere we find for ΔH_r:

$$\Delta H_r^0 = -30.73 \times 10^3 + \int\limits_{291.1}^{673.1} (-21.6 + 23.9 \times 10^{-3}T - 6.83 \times 10^{-6}T^2)\mathrm{d}T =$$
$$= (-30.73 - 8.49 + 4.40 - 0.63) \times 10^3 = -35.45 \times 10^3 \text{ kJ}.$$

It is seen that in this case the influence of temperature on ΔH_r is rather great.

ΔH_r at 200 atmospheres

In order to calculate ΔH_r at 200 atmospheres and 400°C with the use of the known value of ΔH_r at 1 atmosphere and 400°C, the following procedure is followed:

i. We imagine the reactant mixture ($\tfrac{1}{3}$ kmol N_2 + 1 kmol H_2) to expand isothermally at 400°C from 200 to 1 atmospheres;

ii. We let the reaction proceed at 400°C and 1 atmosphere;

iii. The product ($\tfrac{2}{3}$ kmol NH_3) is isothermally compressed at 400°C from 1 to 200 atmospheres.

If we call the enthalpy changes involved in the first and third processes ΔH_1 and ΔH_3 respectively, we have at 400°C and 200 atmospheres:

$$\Delta H_r = \Delta H_1 + \Delta H_r^0 + \Delta H_3.$$

The values of ΔH_1 and ΔH_3 can be found from a generalized graph where the enthalpy correction per kmol of a gas is given as a function of the reduced pressure, p_r, and the reduced temperature, T_r (see, e.g., HOUGEN, WATSON and RAGATZ [2], Fig. 141).

The critical pressure, p_c, and the critical temperature, T_c, of the reactant mixture are estimated as follows:

$$(p_c)_\text{react} = x_A p_{cA} + x_B p_{cB} = 0.25 \times 33.5 + 0.75 \times 12.8 = 18.0 \text{ atm},$$
$$(T_c)_\text{react} = x_A T_{cA} + x_B T_{cB} = 0.25 \times 126 + 0.75 \times 33.2 = 56.4 °\text{K}.$$

From this we find for the reactant mixture at 200 atmospheres and 400°C:

$$(p_r)_\text{react} = \frac{200}{18.0} = 11.1 \quad \text{and} \quad (T_r)_\text{react} = \frac{673.1}{56.4} = 11.9.$$

For these values Fig. 105 in [10] gives:

$$H(1 \text{ atm}) - H(200 \text{ atm}) = -3.2 \, (T_c)_\text{react} = -3.2 \times 56.4 = -181 \text{ kcal/kmol} =$$
$$= -756 \text{ kJ/kmol of reactant}.$$

Hence:

$$\Delta H_1 = -\frac{4}{3} \times 756 = -1010 \text{ kJ}.$$

Similarly, we find for the product (NH_3 = P), with $p_{rP} = 200/111.5 = 1.79$ and $T_{rP} = 673.1/405.5 = 1.66$:

$$H(200 \text{ atm}) - H(1 \text{ atm}) = -1.55 \, T_{cP} = -1.55 \times 405.5 = -629 \text{ kcal/kmol}$$
$$= -2630 \text{ kJ/kmol}.$$

Accordingly:

$$\Delta H_3 = -\tfrac{2}{3} \times 2630 = -1750 \text{ kJ}.$$

6

As a result, the heat of reaction at 400°C and 200 atmospheres is found to be:

$$\Delta H_r = -1010 - 35{,}450 - 1750 = -38.2 \times 10^3 \text{ kJ} .$$

Chemical equilibrium

A chemical reaction by itself proceeds in the direction in which the Gibbs free energy (or the free enthalpy), G, of the reaction mixture diminishes. When equilibrium is reached, this quantity has a minimum value. Hence, from the value of G as a function of the extent of the reaction it can be predicted whether the reaction will proceed in a certain direction, and what will be the composition of the reaction mixture at chemical equilibrium. This follows from the second law of thermodynamics, which also furnishes a relationship between the equilibrium constant K and the difference between the free enthalpies of the product mixture and of the reactant mixture, ΔG. When the reaction proceeds at a constant temperature T and the reactants and products remain at the standard state (denoted by superscript 0), this relationship is:

$$-RT \ln K = \Delta G^0 = \Delta H_r^0 - T\Delta S^0 . \qquad \text{I-8}$$

ΔG^0 can be calculated in various ways, see e.g. VAN KREVELEN and CHERMIN [11]. Also we have:

$$\Delta H_r^0 = \Delta H_{rs}^0 + \int_{T_s}^{T} \Delta C_p^0 dT , \qquad \text{I-9}$$

and

$$\Delta S^0 = \Delta S_s^0 + \int_{T_s}^{T} \frac{\Delta C_p^0}{T} dT , \qquad \text{I-10}$$

where the subscript s refers to the standard temperature.

K is the *true* equilibrium constant for the reaction:

$$\nu_A A + \nu_B B + \ldots \rightarrow \nu_P P + \nu_Q Q + \ldots \ *$$

and is defined as:

$$K = a_P^{\nu_P} a_Q^{\nu_Q} \ldots / a_A^{\nu_A} a_B^{\nu_B} \ldots . \qquad \text{I-11}$$

For ideal gases the activities a_J are proportional to the partial pressures of the corresponding species; in other cases, fugacities have to be used, see, e.g., HOUGEN, WATSON and RAGATZ [2]. The true equilibrium constant is only dependent on temperature. Modified equilibrium constants are frequently used, and they may depend on pressure and composition as well. Therefore, in using such equilibrium constants it is necessary to define them carefully.

---

* In chemistry the symbol ⇌ is used for the indication of an equilibrium reaction. However, we shall in general use only one arrow, which indicates in which direction the reaction proceeds. If the reaction is an equilibrium reaction, this will be automatically clear from the chemical reaction rate equation.

The variation of K with temperature follows from Eqs. I-8, 9 and 10:

$$\frac{d \ln K}{dT} = \frac{\Delta H_{rs}^0}{RT^2} + \frac{1}{RT^2} \int_{T_s}^{T} \Delta C_p^0 dT = \frac{\Delta H_r^0}{RT^2}. \qquad \text{I-12}$$

Accordingly, e.g. with an exothermic reaction, K decreases with increasing temperature.

Knowledge of the equilibrium composition of a reaction mixture makes it possible to determine whether a reaction can proceed in the desired direction; also, the circumstances can be predicted under which a desired product yield is obtainable. Not only the reaction temperature and pressure, but also the composition of the reaction mixture can be selected with the purpose of obtaining a favourable yield of products; examples of this are the use of high pressure in NH_3 synthesis, of excess air in the catalytic oxidation of SO_2 to SO_3, and of excess steam in the water-gas reaction ($H_2O + CO \rightarrow CO_2 + H_2$).

However, the degree to which the equilibrium is approached depends on the conversion *rate* and the time during which the volume elements of the reacting mixture are exposed to the reaction conditions. These factors determine to a great extent the reactor type and conditions needed for successful operation on an industrial scale. The degree of success is then mainly judged on the basis of the economics of the whole manufacturing unit, of which the reactor forms only a part.

ILLUSTRATION I. 3b. *Equilibrium constant in the synthesis of ammonia*

For the reaction:

$$\tfrac{1}{3}N_2 + H_2 \rightarrow \tfrac{2}{3}NH_3,$$

$$\text{(A)} \quad \text{(B)} \quad \text{(P)}$$

it is required to calculate at 400°C:
  i. the true equilibrium constant K;
  ii. the equilibrium composition as a function of pressure for an initial composition with a molar ratio $N_2 : H_2 = 1 : 3$;
  iii. the equilibrium composition at 200 atmospheres as a function of the initial composition.

i. The true equilibrium constant
  The standard molal entropies at 298.1°K are [2]:

$$N_2 \quad : 191.9 \text{ kJ/kmol °K};$$
$$H_2 \quad : 130.9 \text{ kJ/kmol °K};$$
$$NH_3 : 192.9 \text{ kJ/kmol °K}.$$

Hence:

$$\Delta S_s^0 = (\tfrac{2}{3} \times 192.9 - \tfrac{1}{3} \times 191.9 - 130.9) = -66.2 \text{ kJ/°K};$$

this is the entropy change for a complete conversion to NH_3 according to the above reaction equation, i.e. for the case where 1 kmol of H_2 is converted. With Eq. I-10 and with the C_p values given in Illustration I.3a, we find for the entropy change at 400°C:

$$\Delta S^0 = -66.2 + \left[-21.6 \ln T + 23.9 \times 10^{-3}T - 3.41 \times 10^{-6}T^2 \right]_{298.1}^{673.1} =$$

$$= -76.1 \text{ kJ/°K}.$$

8

With Eq. I-8 and the ΔH_r^0 value from Illustration I.2a, we have:

$$\ln K = \left(\frac{35.45 \times 10^3}{673.1} - 76.1\right)\frac{1}{8.315} = -2.79,$$

and:

$$K = \frac{a_P^{2/3}}{a_A^{1/3} a_B} = 0.062.$$

Note that the value of K is very sensitive to small errors in ΔH_r^0 and ΔS^0.

ii. The equilibrium composition as a function of pressure (400°C)

The activity of a component of a gas mixture is equal to the product of its fugacity coefficient γ, its mole fraction x and the total pressure p, here expressed in the number of atmospheres. Thus for component A:

$$a_A = \gamma_A x_A p.$$

Accordingly, the true equilibrium constant K for NH_3 synthesis can be written as:

$$K = \frac{\gamma_P^{2/3}}{\gamma_A^{1/3}\,\gamma_B} \times \frac{x_P^{2/3}}{x_A^{1/3}\,x_B} \times \frac{1}{p^{2/3}} = \frac{1}{p^{2/3}} K_\gamma K_x.$$

K_γ, which is unity for ideal gases, can be derived from the generalized relationship between γ, the reduced pressure p_r and the reduced temperature T_r (see, e.g., Fig. 142 in [2]). K_x can be expressed in terms of the ratio of the reactants and the degree of conversion of one of them; if we call the relative conversion of $H_2(B)$ ζ_B, we have for the stoichiometric ratio between N_2 and H_2:

$$x_A = \frac{0.25(1 - \zeta_B)}{1 - \tfrac{1}{2}\zeta_B}, \qquad x_B = \frac{0.75(1 - \zeta_B)}{1 - \tfrac{1}{2}\zeta_B}, \qquad x_P = \frac{\tfrac{1}{2}\zeta_B}{1 - \tfrac{1}{2}\zeta_B},$$

and

$$K_x = \frac{4}{3} \times \frac{\zeta_B^{2/3}(1 - \tfrac{1}{2}\zeta_B)^{2/3}}{(1 - \zeta_B)^{4/3}}.$$

The following results are obtained:

Atmospheres		10	50	100	200	400	600
N_2, T_r	= 5.34						
	p_r	0.30	1.50	2.99	5.97	11.94	17.91
	γ_A	1.00	1.00	1.02	1.08	1.20	1.30
H_2, T_r	= 20.3						
	p_r	0.78	3.91	7.81	15.63	31.25	46.88
	γ_B	1.00	1.00	1.04	1.10	1.15	1.35
NH_3, T_r	= 1.66						
	p_r	0.09	0.45	0.90	1.79	3.59	5.39
	γ_P	1.00	0.98	0.95	0.90	0.80	0.70
	K_γ	1.00	0.98	0.93	0.81	0.66	0.49
	$p^{2/3}$	4.65	13.6	23.0	34.2	54.2	71.0
$K p^{2/3}/K_\gamma = K_x$		0.288	0.827	1.52	2.63	5.10	9.00
equilibrium value of:							
	ζ_B	0.09	0.29	0.46	0.61	0.75	0.83
	x_P	0.047	0.17	0.30	0.44	0.60	0.71

9

The equilibrium mole fraction of NH$_3$, x_P, at 400°C is shown as a function of pressure in Fig. I-2.

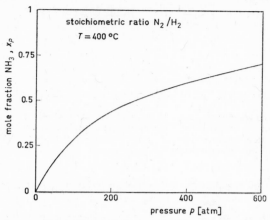

FIG. I-2. Equilibrium mole fraction of NH$_3$ as a function of pressure; Illustration I.3b.

iii. The equilibrium composition as a function of the initial composition (400°C, 200 atm)

From the preceding table it is seen that, at 400°C and 200 atm, $K_x = 2.63$. If the initial mole fractions of H$_2$ and N$_2$ are x_{B0} and $(1 - x_{B0})$, respectively, and the relative degree of conversion of H$_2$ is ζ_B, we have for the reaction mixture:

$$x_A = \frac{1 - x_{B0} - \frac{1}{3}x_{B0}\zeta_B}{1 - \frac{2}{3}x_{B0}\zeta_B}, \qquad x_B = \frac{x_{B0} - x_{B0}\zeta_B}{1 - \frac{2}{3}x_{B0}\zeta_B}, \qquad x_P = \frac{\frac{2}{3}x_{B0}\zeta_B}{1 - \frac{2}{3}x_{B0}\zeta_B}.$$

From the last expression we find for $x_{B0}\zeta_B$:

$$x_{B0}\zeta_B = \frac{3}{2}\frac{x_P}{1 + x_P},$$

so that K_x can be expressed in terms of x_{B0} and x_P. The result is that, for equilibrium at

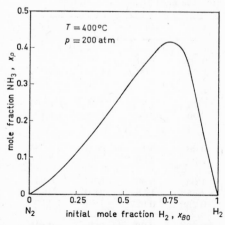

FIG. I-3. Equilibrium mole fraction of NH$_3$ as a function of initial composition; Illustration I.3b.

10

400 °C and 200 atm, the following relation must apply:

$$K_z = 2.63 = \frac{\left(\dfrac{x_P}{1+x_P}\right)^{2/3}\left(1 - \dfrac{x_P}{1+x_P}\right)^{2/3}}{\left(1 - x_{B0} - \dfrac{1}{2}\dfrac{x_P}{1+x_P}\right)^{1/3}\left(x_{B0} - \dfrac{3}{2}\dfrac{x_P}{1+x_P}\right)}.$$

The resulting dependence of the equilibrium value of x_P on x_{B0} is shown in Fig. I-3. The maximum of x_P is found at a stoichiometric composition of the initial reaction mixture.

I.4. Conversion rate and chemical reaction rate

For the application of the material balance to reactor problems (see, e.g., Eq. I-1) an expression must be available for the *chemical production rate* of the species for which the balance has been written down. For the production rate of a component J, the symbol r_J is used if it is expressed in units mass per unit time and volume; when molar units are used instead of mass units the symbol R_J is used. R_J and r_J are related according to the expression:

$$M_J R_J = r_J . \qquad\qquad \text{I-13}$$

When we have a reaction proceeding according to the reaction formula:

$$\nu_A A + \nu_B B \to \nu_P P + \nu_Q Q ,$$

the molar production rates of the components will be related to each other through the stoichiometric coefficients, according to:

$$\frac{R_A}{\nu_A} = \frac{R_B}{\nu_B} = -\frac{R_P}{\nu_P} = -\frac{R_Q}{\nu_Q} . \qquad\qquad \text{I-14}$$

Evidently, the production rate of a reactant is negative and that of a product is positive.

Now, it is often convenient to use the concept of the *chemical conversion rate*, which is always positive when the reaction proceeds in the direction of the arrow. If we denote by $|R|$ the number of moles of reactant converted or of product formed according to the stoichiometric formula, and per unit time and volume, we can write:

$$|R| = \frac{|R|_A}{\nu_A} = \frac{|R|_B}{\nu_B} = \frac{|R|_P}{\nu_P} = \frac{|R|_Q}{\nu_Q} . \qquad\qquad \text{I-15}$$

Thus the molar conversion rates, $|R|_J$, are the absolute values of the molar production rates, R_J; similarly, the mass conversion rates, $|r|_J$, are the absolute values of the mass production rates, r_J.

The conversion rate, $|r|$ or $|R|$, is to be considered as a phenomenological property of the reaction mixture under its operating conditions. It will generally depend on the composition, temperature and pressure, on the properties of a catalyst which may be involved, and in principle also on the conditions of flow, mixing, mass transfer and heat transfer in the reaction system. If one of these variables changes, it is manifested in a change of the

11

conversion rate. Since some of these variables will change from place to place in nearly all reactors, a proper knowledge of the relationship between the conversion rate and the pertinent variables is indispensable for integrating the material balance.

In this connection, it is important to note that in principle the *conversion rate is not identical with the chemical reaction rate*. The latter quantity only reflects the *chemical kinetics* of the system, i.e. the conversion rate measured under such conditions that it is not influenced by physical transport (diffusion and mass transfer) of reactants towards the reaction site or of products away from it. This situation is often encountered with homogeneous reactions in fluids where the reactants are well mixed on a molecular scale, and with reactions in heterogeneous systems which proceed slowly with respect to the potential physical transport. Thus, if we denote the chemical reaction rate with the symbol $|R^*|$, we have for these systems:

$$|R| = |R^*|.$$

On the other hand, with homogeneous reactions in a poorly mixed fluid and with relatively rapid reactions in heterogeneous systems, the physical transport phenomena may reduce the conversion rate, so that here in general:

$$|R| < |R^*| .$$

The latter aspect will be treated extensively in Chapter V, so that a few remarks on chemical kinetics properly speaking will suffice here. For further pertinent information, the reader is referred to the large number of available texts, of which we mention the books by HOUGEN and WATSON [12], JUNGERS and associates [13], SMITH [8] and the review article by LETORT [14].

In many cases the results of measurements of the chemical reaction rate can be described by means of properly chosen functions of temperature and composition in terms of concentration of the reaction mixture. Such expressions do not necessarily reflect the mechanism of the reaction proper, although their form often suggests, rightly or wrongly, a certain mechanism.

In the reaction rate expressions, the influence of temperature and composition can usually be represented separately. Thus, the influence of temperature is accounted for in the reaction velocity constant k which has the form:

$$k = k_\infty \exp(-E/RT) , \qquad\qquad \text{I-16}$$

where E is the activation energy of the reaction. The fact that k is currently called a "constant" only stems from the circumstance that it is not supposed to be a function of composition. For most reactions the activation energy lies in the range of $(10$ to $60) \times 10^3$ kcal/kmol [i.e. about $(40$ to $240) \times 10^3$ kJ/kmol], resulting in an increase of k by a factor of 1.2 to 2.5 for a temperature rise of 10°C. This increase naturally depends also on the temperature level involved.

The temperature dependence of the chemical reaction rate is determined by the manner in which the various velocity constants occur in the reaction rate expression. Thus, for a simple homogeneous reaction between A and B with a rate expression:

$$|R^*|_A = kc_A c_B, \qquad \text{I-17}$$

the value of $|R^*|_A$ will, at constant composition, be proportional to $\exp(-E/RT)$ (Fig. I-4, Curve 1). For an equilibrium reaction, the reaction rate is equal to the difference between a forward rate and a reverse rate, e.g.:

$$|R^*|_A = k_1 c_A c_B - k_2 c_P c_Q, \qquad \text{I-18}$$

and if E_2 is greater than E_1, $|R^*|_A$ will, at constant composition, pass through a maximum as a function of temperature; it will become zero for the temperature at which the reaction mixture is at equilibrium (Fig. I-4, Curve 2).

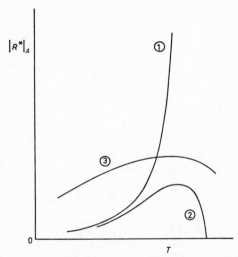

FIG. I-4. Possible temperature dependence of the chemical reaction rate at constant composition; 1—single forward reaction, 2—equilibrium reaction, 3—solid catalysed reaction, e.g. Eq. I-19.

With solid catalyzed reactions, a reaction rate expression is often encountered, e.g. of the following form:

$$|R^*|_A = \frac{kc_A c_B}{1 + K_A c_A + K_B c_B + K_{AB} c_A c_B}, \qquad \text{I-19}$$

where the K's in the denominator are constants describing the chemisorption equilibrium of A and B on the catalyst surface. Depending upon the influence of temperature on these equilibrium constants, $|R^*|_A$ may increase, remain constant, or even decrease when the temperature rises (Fig. I-4, Curve 3).

A further type of chemical rate equation is often encountered in homogeneous polymerization reactions; it may have the following form:

$$|R^*|_A = k_p \sqrt{\frac{k_i c_B}{k_t}} \times c_A \sqrt{\frac{K c_A}{1 + K c_A}}. \qquad \text{I-20}$$

Here c_A is the monomer concentration and c_B the catalyst concentration; k_p, k_i and k_t are the velocity constants for the propagation, initiation and termination reactions, respectively; K is an equilibrium constant. The temperature dependence of $|R^*|_A$ is determined by the activation energies of the constants involved.

As far as the influence of composition is concerned, it is often possible to approximate the chemical reaction rate of a single reaction by:

$$|R^*|_A = k c_A^\alpha c_B^\beta. \qquad \text{I-21}$$

It is then said that the reaction is of the order α with respect to A and of the order β with respect to B; the total order of the reaction is $\alpha + \beta$. The orders do not have to be whole numbers. With a rate equation of the form of Eq. I-19, both α and β may be < 1; the order with respect to A in Eq. I-20 will lie between 1 and 1.5, depending on the value of K, i.e. on the temperature level.

Finally it should be mentioned that, as the conversion rate becomes more determined by physical transport phenomena and less by chemical kinetics, the order of the reaction with respect to the reactant(s) approaches unity since the transport by diffusion and mass transfer is a linear function of concentration. At the same time, the temperature dependence of the conversion rate is sharply reduced; the apparent activation energy of the physical transport coefficients (e.g. the diffusivity) is one to two orders of magnitude smaller than the activation energies of the reaction velocity constants.

In conclusion it may be said that dependable expressions for production rates or conversion rates of the species involved must be available for reactor calculations. Throughout the following chapters it will be assumed that this condition has been met; whether the information is present in the form of an analytical expression or in that of a collection of experimental results is, in principle, immaterial. Since, however, the simple analytical formulation allows for a more general quantitative treatment, it will frequently be used in the following for demonstrating general principles in reactor calculations. The need of good chemical kinetic data and of an understanding of the interfering physical phenomena for the solution of actual reactor problems cannot be sufficiently stressed. Therefore, the requirements for obtaining adequate information on chemical reaction rates are discussed separately in Appendix 1, and the influence of physical transport phenomena is treated in Chapter V.

I.5. The degree of conversion

Since in the material balance the amounts of the chemical species involved in a reaction have to be expressed in mass units, the most logical variable for describing the composition is the *mass fraction w*. For a single reaction governed by a stoichiometric equation like:

$$\nu_A A + \nu_B B \rightarrow \nu_P P + \nu_Q Q \,,$$

the mass fractions of the reactants, w_A and w_B, decrease, and those of the products, w_P and w_Q, increase as the reaction proceeds from left to right. If no material is added to or withdrawn, during the reaction, from the amount of reaction mixture under consideration, we clearly have:

$$w_A + w_B + w_P + w_Q = \text{constant} \,,$$

or in general:

$$\Sigma(w_J)_{\text{react}} + \Sigma(w_J)_{\text{prod}} = \text{constant} \,. \qquad \text{I-22}$$

For such a system we can introduce the *degree of conversion, ξ*, which is a measure of the extent to which the reaction has proceeded. It is defined as the difference between the mass fraction of a component, w_J, and its initial mass fraction, w_{J0}, in such a way that ξ_J is always positive when a reagent has been converted or a product has been formed:

$$\xi_J \equiv |w_{J0} - w_J| \,. \qquad \text{I-23}$$

With Eq. I-22 we find for a reaction system without supply or removal of material during the reaction:

$$\Sigma(\xi_J)_{\text{react}} = \Sigma(\xi_J)_{\text{prod}} \,. \qquad \text{I-24}$$

The values of ξ of the different components taking part in a single reaction are also related to each other in consequence of the stoichiometric requirements; thus we have for the above reaction:

$$\frac{\xi_A}{\nu_A M_A} = \frac{\xi_B}{\nu_B M_B} = \frac{\xi_P}{\nu_P M_P} = \frac{\xi_Q}{\nu_Q M_Q}. \overset{\star}{} \qquad \text{I-25}$$

Accordingly, if in a single reaction the degree of conversion of one of the components is known, this is also the case for the other components. This does not apply to a system of simultaneous reactions.

Sometimes it is convenient to use the *relative degree of conversion* of a reactant, ζ_J, as a measure for the extent of the reaction. It can be quite generally defined as the fraction of the amount of a reactant fed prior to and during the reaction, which has been converted. For a reactor system without intermediate supply or removal of material, ζ_J can be expressed in terms of ξ_J:

$$[\zeta_J \equiv \xi_J/w_{J0} = 1 - w_J/w_{J0}]_{\text{react}} \,. \qquad \text{I-26}$$

$\star$ Note from Eqs. I-13 and 15 that a similar expression applies to $|r|_A$, etc.

From this equation and Eq. I-25 we also find that for such a system:

$$\frac{w_{A0}\zeta_A}{\nu_A M_A} = \frac{w_{B0}\zeta_B}{\nu_B M_B}. \qquad \text{I-27}$$

Now, the definitions of both ξ_J and ζ_J are based on *mass fractions*. On the other hand, the influence of the composition on the conversion rate is generally given in terms of *molar concentrations*, c_J, or of partial pressures (which can be easily converted to molar concentrations). Since there is a single relationship between the molar concentration and the mass fraction in a mixture:

$$c_J = \varrho w_J / M_J \qquad \text{I-28}$$

(where ϱ is the specific mass or density of the mixture), concentrations can be expressed in terms of conversions or vice versa. Some of these relationships, based on Eqs. I-23, 25, 26 and 28, are shown in Table I-1.

TABLE I-1

Relations between concentration and conversion

reactants	products
$c_A = \varrho\left(\dfrac{c_{A0}}{\varrho_0} - \dfrac{\xi_A}{M_A}\right)$	$c_P = \varrho\left(\dfrac{c_{P0}}{\varrho_0} + \dfrac{\xi_P}{M_P}\right)$
	$c_P = \varrho\left(\dfrac{c_{P0}}{\varrho_0} + \dfrac{\nu_P \xi_A}{\nu_A M_A}\right)^{\star}$
$c_A = \dfrac{\varrho}{\varrho_0} c_{A0}(1 - \zeta_A)$	$c_P = \dfrac{\varrho}{\varrho_0}\left(c_{P0} + c_{A0}\dfrac{\nu_P \zeta_A}{\nu_A}\right)^{\star}$
$c_B = \dfrac{\varrho}{\varrho_0}\left(c_{B0} - c_{A0}\dfrac{\nu_B \zeta_A}{\nu_A}\right)^{\star}$	

This table indicates that ζ has a slight advantage over ξ for expressing molar concentrations in terms of conversion. The above relationships may become rather complicated for systems with a variable density, since ϱ itself depends then on the degree of conversion.

ILLUSTRATION I. 5a. *Conversion rate as a function of the degree of conversion, liquid reaction*

For the homogeneous equilibrium reaction in the liquid phase:

alcohol (A) + acid (B) → ester (P) + water (Q) ,

the rate of conversion (= rate of chemical reaction in this case) is, under certain conditions, found to be:

$$|R|_A = |R|_B = k_1 c_B - k_2 c_P \ [\text{kmol/m}^3\text{s}] .$$

What are the expressions for r_A, r_B and r_P in terms of the conversion of the reaction, if the density ϱ remains constant and $c_{P0} = 0$?

$\star$ Only valid for single reactions

16

Taking the acid B as a reference component, we have from Table I-1:

$$c_B = c_{B0} - \frac{\varrho \xi_B}{M_B} = c_{B0}(1 - \zeta_B),$$

and

$$c_P = \varrho \xi_B / M_B = c_{B0}\zeta_B.$$

Consequently, the molar conversion rate of B is:

$$|R|_B = c_{B0}[k_1(1 - \zeta_B) - k_2\zeta_B].$$

The mass production rates of A, B and P are respectively:

$$r_A = -|R_B|M_A$$
$$r_B = -|R_B|M_B$$
$$r_P = |R_B|M_P.$$

ILLUSTRATION I. 5b. *Conversion rate as a function of the degree of conversion, gas reaction*

For the equilibrium reaction A → 2P in the gas phase the conversion rate is given by the formula:

$$|R|_A = k_1\left(\frac{p_A}{RT}\right) - k_2\left(\frac{p_P}{RT}\right)^2, \; [\text{kmol/m}^3\text{s}].$$

The gas can be considered to be ideal, and A and P are the only components present. The total pressure $p\,(= p_A + p_P)$ of the gas mixture is assumed to be constant, but the temperature may change with the progress of the reaction. Initially the gas consists of pure A, so that $w_{A0} = 1$ and $\xi_A = \zeta_A$. Express $|R|_A$ in terms of ξ_A.

With a degree of conversion ξ_A, $(1 - \xi_A)$ mols of 1 mol of A are left, while $2\xi_A$ mols of P have been produced. Hence, the mol fractions of A and P, which in this case are equal to the relative partial pressures, become:

$$\frac{p_A}{p} = \frac{1 - \xi_A}{1 + \xi_A} \quad \text{and} \quad \frac{p_P}{p} = \frac{2\xi_A}{1 + \xi_A}.$$

The rate expression then becomes:

$$|R|_A = k_1\frac{p}{RT}\frac{1 - \xi_A}{1 + \xi_A} - k_2\left(\frac{p}{RT}\right)^2\frac{4\xi_A^2}{(1 + \xi_A)^2}.$$

where k_1 and k_2 are still functions of temperature.

In this example, ξ_A, ζ_A and ξ_P go to unity on completion of the reaction. In practice, the quantity $\varrho \xi_A / \varrho_{A0}$ is sometimes used for indicating the degree of conversion. This quantity has the disadvantage that it does not range from 0 to 1. In our example we see that for $\xi_A = 1$ and at a temperature $T_1 : \varrho = pM_B/RT_1 = pM_A/2RT_1$, whereas at the initial temperature $T_0 : \varrho_{A0} = pM_A/RT_0$. Hence, for $\xi_A = 1 : \varrho \xi_A / \varrho_{A0} = T_0/2T_1$.

I.6. The economic balance

It is not only required from a design of a reactor system that the specifications demanded of the process can actually be realized; it is also important to know the production costs, the pay-out time and the return on investment for the installation considered. In general, therefore, each project is evaluated economically in an early stage of its development.

In the economic evaluation all costs involved in the production of a cer-

17

tain product are balanced against the total expected income (see, e.g., Schweyer [15]). When the income exceeds the production costs, a profit will result. The best (or optimum) design for a certain production will show the greatest profit *per unit time*. It will be clear that both an increase in income and a reduction of the production costs may cause the profit to rise.

The main factors which determine the economics of a *reactor* are: composition of the feed, pressure, temperature, reaction time and the materials of construction to be used. For the economics of a *production unit* as a whole, the plant yield, the costs of auxiliary equipment, e.g. for conditioning the feed and for isolating the desired product, are equally very important.

Since these many variables are to a great extent mutually dependent and since their influence on the performance of the plant is not generally known sufficiently beforehand, an exact prediction of the optimum solution is not feasible. In practice, near-to-optimum designs are arrived at from a combination of technical data obtained from the laboratory and pilot-plant units, of experience obtained with similar production units and of engineering common sense of the designers.

At several places in this book, the economic aspects of plant design and operation will be touched upon. An example of a simple economic consideration is given below.

ILLUSTRATION I. 6. *Influence of reactor yield on plant profitability*

A plant is making ethyl acetate from acetic acid and ethyl alcohol. The average annual price of the reactants (delivered to the plant, including storage charges) is:
acetic acid   1.172 MU/kg,★
ethyl alcohol   0.678 MU/kg.
The sales price of the product, after deduction of the sales expenses, is:
ethyl acetate   1.339 MU/kg.
It is assumed that 99% of the alcohol are converted in the installation but that the plant yield, $\bar{\eta}$ (calculated with respect to the acetic acid), is variable depending on operating conditions. It is furthermore assumed that the manufacturing costs are constant and amount to 0.100 MU/kg ethyl acetate. It is asked how the plant profitability depends on $\bar{\eta}$.

1 kg of ethyl acetate requires 0.682 kg of acetic acid and 0.523 kg of ethyl alcohol. The raw materials costs per kg of ethyl acetate are:

$$\frac{0.682 \times 1.172}{\bar{\eta}} + \frac{0.523 \times 0.678}{0.99} = \frac{0.799}{\bar{\eta}} + 0.358 \text{ MU/kg ethyl acetate.}$$

The gross profit, I, of the plant therefore is:

$$I = 1.339 - (0.100 + \frac{0.799}{\bar{\eta}} + 0.358) \text{ MU/kg ethyl acetate.}$$

This function is shown in Fig. I-5.

★ MU = monetary unit, approximately equal to one Dutch guilder.

18

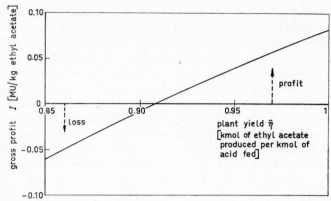

FIG. I-5. Influence of the plant yield $\bar{\eta}$ on the gross profit; Illustration **I.6**.

It can be deduced from the figure that, most probably due to the heavy competition between ethyl acetate manufacturers, a minimum plant yield of 0.907 is needed for marginal operation and that an increase of 1% in $\bar{\eta}$ already has a marked effect on the profitability. This example also illustrates, however, the importance of the commercial aspects; if the purchasing department manages to obtain a 2% reduction of the price of the reactants, the increase in profit is the same as that achieved by a technical staff member who improves the plant yield $\bar{\eta}$ by 3%.

I.7. Classification of chemical reactors

Chemical reactors exist in a wide range of forms and appearances. There is such a great variety of them that a complete systematic classification is impossible and that an attempt to do so is hardly justified.

There appears to be no correlation at all between the type of reaction to be carried out (e.g. oxidation, reduction, etc.) or the complexity of the reaction (e.g. consecutive, parallel and chain reactions) and the shape and operating conditions of the equipment in which the reaction is to be carried out. Nor is the heat effect of a reaction an important shape-determining factor, except for the fact that in many cases a sufficiently large heat transfer area must be available for reactions with a great heat effect; a reactor for which these requirements are extreme will be very similar to a heat exchanger.

A limited systematic survey of the reactors currently in use in the chemical industry can be made according to the two following criteria, which are related to the handling of reactants and products:

i. One or more phases are needed for carrying out the desired reaction; *homogeneous* and *heterogeneous* reaction systems, respectively, are then involved.

ii. The reaction mixture is processed in intermittent or in uninterrupted operation; if, in the former case, no material is supplied or withdrawn during the reaction cycle, the reaction is carried out *batch-wise*; the other case is that of the *continuous* flow reactor.

19

If we apply the second criterion to *homogeneous* reaction systems, we see that batch reactions in the fluid phase (mostly the liquid phase) are carried out in vessels, tanks or autoclaves in which the reaction mixture is agitated and mixed in a suitable manner. For example, glass beakers with stirrers are the most extensively used reactors in the chemical laboratory.

Continuous flow reactors for homogeneous reaction systems already show a much greater variety. Predominant forms are the *tubular reactor* and the mixed *tank reactor*, which have essentially different characteristics. These are shown in Fig. I-6 together with a few intermediate forms. As was indicated by VAN KREVELEN [6], a further distinction can be made according to the fact whether or not the feed streams are mixed prior to entering into the

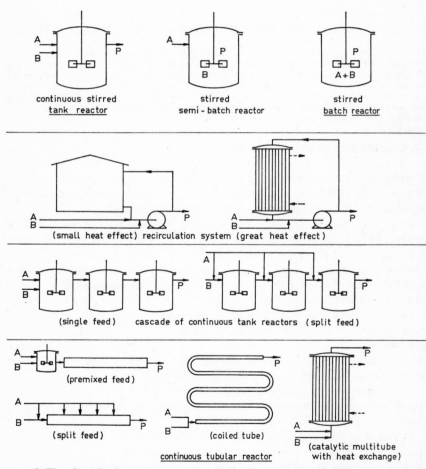

FIG. I-6. The three basic reactor types (underlined) and some related reactor systems for homogeneous or quasi-homogeneous reactions.

reactor.* In Chapter II, idealized forms of the batch reactor, the stirred tank reactor and the tubular reactor will be used as the primary models for isothermal reactor calculations.

The classification of reactors for *heterogeneous* systems (in which the reaction may still proceed in a homogeneous phase) shows a great number of possibilities: either one or more phases may be processed continuously and the flow of a phase may be more or less mixed in the direction of flow (corresponding with flow in a tank reactor and in a tubular reactor as extreme cases). Furthermore, there are several ways in which two or more phases can be dispersed into one another. WICKE [16] and VAN KREVELEN [6] have given a survey of the combinations of these possibilities which are frequently encountered in practice. In the first instance, the flow patterns of the two continuous model reactors (tank reactor and tubular reactor) can be traced in such systems. In a burning coal stove, for example, the gas flow is similar to that occurring in a tubular reactor. The coal is slowly consumed and the reaction zone moves slowly in the direction of the gas flow. If the coal is more or less continuously supplied (and the ashes removed), the situation with respect to coal can also be handled as that prevailing in a tubular reactor. In continuous gas-solid reactions in a rotating kiln, both phases are relatively little mixed in the direction of flow, as a first approximation; when a similar reaction is carried out in a fluidized bed, the solids are well mixed (tank reactor), and the behaviour of the gas flow will be intermediate between that in a tank reactor and a tubular reactor.

Actual reactors will not be described in this book; illustrative information of this kind is found in many articles and in books like those by BRÖTZ [17] and WALAS [18]. The following chapters are intended to give the principles of reactor design and operation, on the basis of which actual and more complicated reactor problems can be analysed and, to a certain extent, solved.

---

* This is particularly important in the case of rapid homogeneous reactions, such as the combustion of a gas.

CHAPTER II

ISOTHERMAL REACTOR CALCULATIONS

In this chapter the material balances are applied to isothermal reactions with known expressions for their conversion rates. The reactions are assumed to be carried out in reactor systems consisting of or derived from one of the three basic types of model reactors, i.e.:

i. The well-mixed reaction vessel with uniform composition, operated batchwise; it will be referred to as a "batch reactor".

ii. The continuously operated ideal tubular reactor in which piston flow of the reacting mixture is assumed and mixing or diffusion in the direction of flow does not occur.

iii. The continuously operated ideally mixed tank reactor in which the composition of the reaction mixture is assumed to be uniform and equal to the composition at the outlet.

As a consequence of the assumptions relating to these three model reactors, the reactor calculations remain relatively simple. This makes it possible, e.g., to investigate more complex reactions without undue complications arising from a possible departure from the ideality of the basic reactor types. The extent to which the fluid flow in actual reactors may depart from that in the models given above will be discussed in Chapter III.

The following concepts will be frequently used:

> reactor capacity = production rate of desired product per unit volume of reactor at a given conversion of key reactant;
> throughput, feed rate = volumetric or mass flow through reactor system;
> load = volumetric or mass flow per unit reactor volume or catalyst mass;
> yield = fraction of the feed which has been converted to desired product (see Eq. II-24).

II.1. The well-mixed batch reactor

No material is supplied to or withdrawn from the reactor during the reaction so that the total mass m of the reaction mixture remains constant, see Eq. I-2. The composition, which is assumed to be uniform, is only a function of time. Thus, for a component J the material balance I-1 becomes:

$$\frac{dm_J}{dt} = m \frac{dw_J}{dt} = r_J V_r ,$$

II-1

22

where V_r is the volume of the reaction mixture. Conversion of this equation to molar concentrations by means of Eq. I-28 introduces an additional term since, in principle, the density of the mixture, $\varrho = m/V_r$, is not constant:

$$\frac{dc_J}{dt} - \frac{c_J}{\varrho}\frac{d\varrho}{dt} = R_J . \qquad \text{II-2}$$

Only when the density of the mixture does not change with time, can Eq. II-2 be simplified. The result is, e.g. for a *reactant* A:

$$\frac{dc_A}{dt} = R_A = -|R|_A . \qquad \text{II-3}$$

It is from this expression that the current practice in physicochemical literature originates, according to which chemical reaction velocities or conversion rates are indicated by the symbol $-dc_A/dt$. In reactor calculations, however, this custom may cause confusion, especially when dealing with continuous operation in the steady state where concentrations are independent of time. The symbol dc_A/dt in Eq. II-3 is not a reaction velocity or a conversion rate; it is the rate of concentration change in a batch reactor as a result of a chemical reaction.

Eq. II-1 may also be rewritten in terms of the degree of conversion ξ defined by Eq. I-23; we thus have for any component of the mixture:

$$\frac{d\xi_J}{dt} = \frac{|r|_J}{\varrho} , \qquad \text{II-4}$$

from which the reaction time t needed for a certain degree of conversion can be obtained by integration:

$$t = \int_0^{\xi_J} \frac{\varrho\, d\xi_J}{|r|_J}. \qquad \text{II-5}$$

Other possible forms of Eq. II-5 may be obtained by introducing the relative degree of conversion of one of the reactants, ζ_A:

$$t = w_{A0} \int_0^{\zeta_A} \frac{\varrho\, d\zeta_A}{|r|_A} = \frac{c_{A0}}{\varrho_0} \int_0^{\zeta_A} \frac{\varrho\, d\zeta_A}{|R|_A}; \qquad \text{II-6}$$

these are greatly simplified if the density remains constant.

The general problem in design is to calculate the volume of a reactor for a certain average rate of production. The volume can be obtained from the required degree of conversion and the corresponding time (see Illustration II.1). This is possible since the reaction time is independent of the reactor volume; this is a consequence of the assumption that the reactor contents are well mixed and that all elements of volume behave identically. In practice, the size of a batch reactor may have some influence on the reaction time, because the conversion rate may be influenced by wall effects, mixing

23

intensity, degree of dispersion in heterogeneous systems, or temperature deviations near a heating or cooling surface.

ILLUSTRATION II. 1. *Production of ethyl acetate in a batch reactor*

A daily production of 50 tons of ethyl acetate from alcohol and acetic acid is required. The reaction proceeds according to:

$$C_2H_5OH\,(A) + CH_3COOH\,(B) \rightarrow CH_3COOC_2H_5\,(P) + H_2O\,(Q)\,.$$

The conversion rate in the liquid phase at 100°C is given by SMITH [19]:

$$|R|_A = k\left(c_A c_B - \frac{c_P c_Q}{K}\right),$$

where $k = 7.93 \times 10^{-6}$ m³/kmol s and $K = 2.93$. The molar conversion rates of all components are equal because of the equality of the stoichiometric coefficients.

The feed solution contains 23% by weight of acid, 46% by weight of alcohol and no ester. The required relative conversion of the acid is 35%. The density may be assumed to have a constant value of 1020 kg/m³. The plant must be operated day and night, and the time for the filling, emptying and cleaning operations of a reactor is 1 hour, irrespective of its size. What would be the required reaction volume if (a) one reactor vessel, (b) three reactor vessels are to be used?

The concentrations are expressed in terms of ζ_B, the relative conversion of the acid, with the following results:

compo-nent	M_J kg/kmol	composition at $t = 0$, $\zeta_B = 0$		at conversion ζ_B	at $\zeta_B = 0.35$
		w_{J0} kg/kg	c_{J0} kmol/m³	c_J kmol/m³	c_J kmol/m³
A	46	0.46	10.20	$10.20 - 3.91\zeta_B$	8.83
B	60	0.23	3.91	$3.91(1 - \zeta_B)$	2.54
P	88	0	0	$3.91\,\zeta_B$	1.37
Q	18	0.31	17.56	$17.56 + 3.91\,\zeta_B$	18.93

According to Eq. II-6 the reaction time t is given by:

$$t = c_{B0} \int_0^{0.35} \frac{d\zeta_B}{|R|_B}\,,$$

where $|R|_B$ is expressed in terms of ζ_B. The integration can best be carried out graphically. The result is $t = 7270$ s $\approx$ 2 hours so that $24/(2 + 1)$ batches can be processed per 24 hours. The daily ethyl acetate production per m³ of reactor volume is $8 \times 1.37 \times 88 = 965$ kg/m³ day. The total reaction volume required is $50,000/965 \approx 52$ m³.

It makes no difference for the total volume whether one reactor is used or three reactors in parallel. In the latter case some of the auxiliary equipment like pumps and storage vessels can be smaller, and by means of a proper time schedule the work of the operating personnel can be more evenly distributed. On the other hand, a small vessel is relatively more expensive per m³ than a large one, and three small tanks take more space and piping than one large tank having the same volume.

II.2. The continuously operated ideal tubular reactor

In the steady state, the conditions at any point in the reactor are independent of time, and the total mass flow Φ_m through any cross section of the reactor is the same. The composition of the reaction mixture depends on the distance z from the inlet point (see Fig. II-1). For the calculation of the concentration distributions the material balance has to be applied to a differential section $S\,dz$, where S is the area of the cross section occupied by reacting mixture.

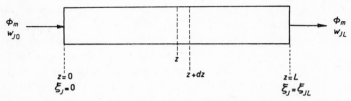

FIG. II-1. Tubular reactor with total reaction volume $V_r = SL$.

Under these conditions Eq. I-1 becomes for a component J:

$$0 = -\Phi_m \, dw_J + r_J S \, dz \, .$$
II-7

Introduction of the degree of conversion ξ_J yields:

$$0 = -\Phi_m \, d\xi_J + |r|_J S \, dz \, .$$
II-8

The reactor volume, $V_r = SL$, required for a conversion ξ_{JL} follows from integration of Eq. II-8:

$$V_r = \int_0^L S \, dz = \Phi_m \int_0^{\xi_{JL}} \frac{d\xi_J}{|r|_J} \, .$$
II-9

Note that the integral on the right-hand side also occurs in the calculation of the reaction time in a batch reactor (cf. Eq. II-5), provided the density is constant. Apparently, in that case:

$$\left(\frac{t}{\varrho}\right)_{\text{batch}} \triangleq \left(\frac{V_r}{\Phi_m}\right)_{\text{tubular}} , \quad \text{or} \quad (t)_{\text{batch}} \triangleq \left(\frac{\varrho V_r}{\Phi_m} = \tau_L\right)_{\text{tubular}} .$$

τ_L is the residence time of the reaction mixture in the tubular reactor for constant density. The correspondence between the reaction time for a batch reactor and the residence time for an ideal tubular reactor is also clear from a physical point of view; in the latter an element of volume is not supposed to mix with its surroundings. The requirement of constant density for this analogy to be valid rests in the fact that the volume of the reaction mixture in a batch reactor is in principle variable, whereas the volume of the tubular reactor has been assumed to be fixed.

If the reaction in a tubular reactor proceeds under the influence of a *solid catalyst*, e.g. in the form of a packed bed of catalyst pellets, the conversion rate is often given per unit mass of solids (e.g. $|r_s|_J$). In that case, the total mass of solids m_{sL} required for a certain degree of conversion ξ_{JL} can be obtained from:

25

$$m_{sL} = \Phi_m \int_0^{\xi_{JL}} \frac{d\xi_J}{|r_s|_J} \, . \qquad\qquad \text{II-10}$$

This expression is equivalent to Eq. II-9, and the reactor volume may be calculated from m_{sL} and the bulk density of the catalytic material. Since a heterogeneous reaction is involved, $|r_s|_J$ may in principle depend not only on composition and temperature, but also on the nature and size of the catalyst pellets and on the flow velocity of the mixture (see Section V.4).

With reactors where a solid catalyst is used, the reactor load is in practice often indicated by the term *space velocity, S.V.* It is defined as the volumetric flow at the inlet of the reactor divided by the reaction volume (or by the total mass of catalyst). Thus, for a tubular reactor:

$$S.V. \equiv \Phi_m/\varrho_0 V_r \text{ (or } \Phi_m/\varrho_0 m_{sL}) \, .$$

The density ϱ_0 at the inlet conditions is sometimes substituted by the density at other conditions (e.g., standard temperature and pressure). This may give rise to confusion, unless the definition used for $S.V.$ is properly specified.

The inverse value of the space velocity can have the dimension of time:

$$\frac{1}{S.V.} = \frac{\varrho_0 V_r}{\Phi_m} = \varrho_0 \int_0^{\xi_{JL}} \frac{d\xi_J}{|r|_J} \, .$$

Unless ϱ is constant, the value of $1/(S.V.)$ is different from the true residence time of the reaction mixture in a tubular reactor, τ_L. For the latter we have:

$$\tau_L = \int_0^{V_r} \frac{\varrho S \, dz}{\Phi_m} = \int_0^{\xi_{JL}} \frac{\varrho \, d\xi_J}{|r|_J} \, . \qquad\qquad \text{II-11}$$

In practice, tubular reactors are encountered which consist of one long single tube, such as in thermal cracking furnaces where the reactor may be up to 2 km long. Very often reactions are carried out in tube bundles, i.e. a number of parallel tubular reactors. These are used in cases where special heat transfer requirements have to be met (see also Section IV.4).

ILLUSTRATION II. 2a. *Production of ethyl acetate in the liquid phase in a tubular reactor*

It is requested to calculate the volume of an ideal tubular reactor for the same production and under the same conditions as given in Illustration II.1.

Since the density was assumed to be constant, the residence time in the tubular reactor must be equal to the time of reaction calculated in the foregoing example. Thus, we have:

$$\tau_L = \varrho V_r/\Phi_m = 7270 \text{ s} \, .$$

Since the product stream contains 1.37 kmol/m³ of ethyl acetate, the volumetric flow rate for a production of 50 tons/day is:

$$\Phi_m/\varrho = \frac{50{,}000}{24 \times 3600 \times 1.37 \times 88} = 4.80 \times 10^{-3} \, \text{m}^3/\text{s} \, .$$

From the two last formulae we find:

$$V_r = 7270 \times 4.80 \times 10^{-3} = 34.8 \text{ m}^3 .$$

We might have reached this result somewhat faster by realizing that we need the same reaction volume as in Illustration II.1. The volume calculated for the batch process was 52 m³, but about $\frac{1}{3}$ of the time was reserved for the operations between two batches. For a tubular reactor in which the continuous operation is not interrupted, the same production can be obtained with a volume $V_r \approx \frac{2}{3} \times 52 \approx 35$ m³.

ILLUSTRATION II. 2b. *Catalyzed gas reaction in a tubular reactor*

The reaction:

$$C_2H_5OH\,(A) + CH_3COOH\,(B) \rightarrow CH_3COOC_2H_5\,(P) + H_2O\,(Q)$$

is now carried out in the vapour phase at 277°C and at a pressure of 1 atmosphere. It is catalyzed by silica gel having a bulk density of 700 kg/m³. According to the literature [20], the molar conversion rate at 277°C is given by:

$$|R_s|_B = \frac{0.0415(0.3 + 0.9\,p_Q)(p_B - p_P p_Q/9.8\,p_A)}{3600(1 + 15.35\,p_P)} \left[\frac{\text{kmol}}{\text{kg/s}}\right],$$

where the partial pressures are expressed in atmospheres. What reactor volume is needed for the same production and the same feed composition as in Illustration II.1?

The reaction proceeds under isothermal conditions and the flow of moles remains constant; hence the density $\varrho = pM/RT$ does not change. The constant average molecular mass M is found to be 32.2 kg/kmol. The partial pressures can be expressed in terms of the relative conversion ζ_B of the acid B:

$$p_A = pMw_A/M_A, \quad p_B = pMw_B/M_B \text{ etc.,} \quad \text{and}$$
$$p_A = p_{A0} - p_{B0}\zeta_B, \quad p_B = p_{B0}(1 - \zeta_B) \text{ etc.}$$

Thus we have in this example:

component	M_J kg/kmol	w_{J0} kg/kg	p_J atm	p_J atm
		composition at $z = 0$, $\zeta_B = 0$		at conversion ζ_B
A	46	0.46	$0.322\,p$	$(0.332 - 0.123\,\zeta_B)p$
B	60	0.23	$0.123\,p$	$0.123(1 - \zeta_B)p$
P	88	0	0	$0.123\,\zeta_B p$
Q	18	0.31	$0.555\,p$	$(0.555 + 0.123\,\zeta_B)p$
total		1.00	p	p

From Eq. II-10 we derive for the total mass of catalyst:

$$m_{sL} = \frac{\Phi_m}{M_B} w_{B0} \int_0^{0.35} \frac{\mathrm{d}\zeta_B}{|R_s|_B} = \frac{\Phi_m p_{B0}}{Mp} \int_0^{0.35} \frac{\mathrm{d}\zeta_B}{|R_s|_B} .$$

For $p = 1$ atm graphic integration yields:

$$m_{sL} = 65.1 \times 10^3\,\Phi_m/M .$$

For the feed rate in kmol/s we have:

$$\Phi_m/M = \frac{50{,}000}{88 \times 24 \times 3600 \times 0.123 \times 0.35} = 0.155 \text{ kmol/s} ,$$

27

so that
$$m_{sL} = 65.1 \times 10^3 \times 0.155 = 10,100 \text{ kg,}$$
and
$$V_r = 10,100/700 = 14.5 \text{ m}^3 .$$

II.3. The continuously operated ideal tank reactor

The contents of the tank reactor are assumed to be "perfectly mixed" so that the conditions throughout the tank are the same and equal to the conditions at the outlet (see Fig. II-2). In the steady state, the material balance I-1 for one of the components becomes:

$$0 = \Phi_m(w_{J0} - w_{J1}) + r_{J1}V_r , \qquad \text{II-12}$$

where V_r is the constant volume of the reaction mixture. From eq. II-12 we find for any component:

$$V_r = -\Phi_m \frac{w_{J0} - w_{J1}}{r_{J1}} = \Phi_m \frac{\xi_{J1}}{|r|_{J1}} . \qquad \text{II-13}$$

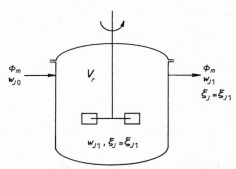

FIG. II-2. Continuously operated ideal tank reactor.

Note that the conversion rate has to be taken at the conditions in the outlet, which are the reactor conditions. Therefore, if the degree of conversion is high, the conversion rate throughout the reactor will be relatively low. As a consequence, the continuous tank reactor requires a larger volume than a tubular reactor for the same production rate.

In practice, a tank reactor may be approximately considered a perfectly mixed system when the mixing time is much smaller than the average residence time $\bar{\tau}$ of the mixture in the reactor. This average residence time is defined as:

$$\bar{\tau} = V_r \varrho_1/\Phi_m . \qquad \text{II-14}$$

ILLUSTRATION II. 3. *Production of ethyl acetate in a continuous tank reactor*

The 52 m³ vessel of Illustration II.1 is to be used as a continuous tank reactor. The feed composition and the desired relative conversion of 35% of the acetic acid remain the same as in the above example. What production rate of ethyl acetate will result in this case? What volume should the tank reactor have to maintain an ester production of 50 tons/day?

The table in Illustration II.1 contains the molar concentrations at $\zeta_B = 0.35$; they can be used for calculating $|R|_A$. For the mass production rate of ester (P) at the condition $\zeta_B = 0.35$ we find:

$$r_{P1} = M_P |R|_{A1} = 9.5 \times 10^{-3} \text{ kg/m}^3\text{s} .$$

The total production rate of P is obtained with Eq. II-13:

$$\Phi_m \xi_{P1} = V_T |r|_{P1} = 52 \times 9.5 \times 10^{-3} = 0.493 \text{ kg/s} ,$$

which is equivalent to 42.6 tons/day. For a production of 50 tons/day, the reactor volume would have to be $52 \times 50/42.6 = 61$ m³, i.e. much larger than the volumes calculated for the batch reactor and the continuous tubular reactor.

II.4. The cascade of tank reactors

Very often, continuous reactor operations are carried out in more than one tank reactor in cascade; this term is used to indicate that the product stream of one tank reactor is the feed stream of the next, and that the conditions

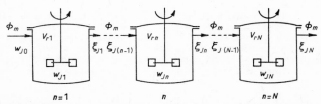

FIG. II-3. Cascade of tank reactors; N = total number of reactors.

in one of the reactors in the chain are not influenced by what happens in the reactors further downstream. The reactors are numbered 1, 2 . . ., n, . . ., N in the direction of flow, and the properties of the stream leaving the n-th reactor carry the index n (see Fig. II-3).

The steady state material balance II-12 over the n-th reactor gives for a component J:

$$w_{Jn} - w_{J(n-1)} = \frac{V_{rn}}{\Phi_m} r_{Jn} , \qquad \text{II-15}$$

or:

$$\xi_{Jn} - \xi_{J(n-1)} = \frac{V_{rn}}{\Phi_m} |r|_{Jn} , \qquad \text{II-16}$$

where $\xi_{Jn} = w_{Jn} - w_{J0}$. Summation over a cascade of N tank reactors yields for the degree of conversion obtained in the entire system:

$$\xi_{JN} = \frac{1}{\Phi_m} \sum_{n=1}^{n=N} V_{rn} |r|_{Jn} . \qquad \text{II-17}$$

In deriving Eq. II-17 we have assumed that no material is added to or withdrawn from the system between its inlet and its outlet.

29

It can be shown that as N approaches infinity (the total volume remaining finite), a cascade of tank reactors becomes identical with the ideal tubular reactor. For this purpose we put Eq. II-16 into the form:

$$\frac{\Delta \xi_{Jn}}{|r|_{Jn}} = \frac{V_{rn}}{\Phi_m}.$$

By summation and taking the limit for $N \to \infty$ or $\Delta \to 0$, we get:

$$\lim_{\Delta \to 0} \left[\sum_{n=0}^{n=N} \frac{\Delta \xi_{Jn}}{|r|_{Jn}} \right] = \int_0^{\xi_{Jn}} \frac{d\xi_J}{|r|_J} = \lim_{N \to \infty} \left[\frac{1}{\Phi_m} \sum_{n=0}^{n=N} V_{rn} \right] = \frac{V_r}{\Phi_m},$$

where V_r is the volume of the entire system. The resulting equation is the same as Eq. II-9. From this result it may be concluded that the behaviour of a cascade of tank reactors, depending upon the number N of reaction vessels into which the total reaction volume is divided, may range between the behaviour of one continuous tank reactor ($N = 1$) and that of a tubular reactor ($N \to \infty$).

ILLUSTRATION II. 4a. *Production of ethyl acetate in a cascade of three tank reactors*

In Illustration II.1 a production of 50 tons/day of ester could be obtained by batchwise operation of 3 reaction vessels in parallel having a reaction volume of 18 m³ each. What production can be obtained under the same conditions of feed composition and conversion, when the reactor operation is made continuous with the three vessels in cascade?

For the solution of this problem, a certain value of Φ_m has to be premised, whereupon ξ_{J1}, ξ_{J2} and ξ_{J3} must be calculated by means of Eq. II-16. If ξ_{J3} differs from the desired value, the calculations have to be repeated with a different value of Φ_m until the desired degree of conversion has been obtained. The result of the calculations for this example is that the mass flow must be $\Phi_m = 6.23$ kg/s for the required degree of conversion; this is equivalent to the production of *63.6* tons/day of ethyl acetate, i.e. 27% more than with batchwise operation of these reactor vessels (where $\frac{1}{3}$ of the total time was not used for production). For a production of 50 tons/day in a cascade of three tank reactors of equal size, a volume of $18 \times 50/63.6 = 14.2$ m³ per vessel, or a total volume of *42.6* m³ would be sufficient.

The above examples of the production of ethyl acetate from alcohol and acetic acid in the various reactor systems treated may be summarized as follows:

Illustration	type of operation and reactor	ester production rate tons/day	reaction volume m³
II.2a	continuous, tubular reactor	50	35
II.4a	continuous, cascade of 3 tank reactors	50	43
II.3	continuous, one tank reactor	50	61
II.1	batchwise	50	52
II.3	continuous, one tank reactor	43	52
II.4a	continuous, cascade of 3 tank reactors	64	52
II.2a	continuous, tubular reactor	75	52

It is seen that the tubular reactor has the greatest, and one continuously operated tank reactor the smallest capacity.

Calculation methods for tank reactors in cascade

Even with relatively simple expressions for the conversion rate, the set of equations describing the degree of conversion in a cascade cannot be solved analytically. One of the few exceptions is the case of a first order rate equation, as will be shown below.

We take as an example a reaction A + B → products, for which:

$$|R|_A = kc_A c_B.$$

By introducing the relative degree of conversion ζ_A into Eq. II-16, together with the expressions $c_A = c_{A0}(1 - \zeta_A)$ and $c_B = c_{B0} - c_{A0}\zeta_A$ from Table I-1, we obtain:

$$\zeta_{An} - \zeta_{A(n-1)} = \frac{V_{rn}\varrho_n}{\Phi_m c_{A0}}\,|R|_{An} = c_{A0}k\bar{\tau}_n(1 - \zeta_{An})(1 + e - \zeta_{An}), \quad \text{II-18}$$

where e is the relative excess of B with respect to A; $e = (c_{B0} - c_{A0})/c_{A0}$.

Eq. II-18 can be solved for ζ_{An}, but the form of this solution is rather complicated. The complexity rapidly increases if one makes the next step and tries to express $\zeta_{A(n+1)}$ in terms of $\zeta_{A(n-1)}$. Therefore, a numerical or graphic solution is indicated in this case.

If, however, $e \gg 1$ so that also $e \gg \zeta_A$ (since $0 < \zeta_A < 1$), the factor $(1 + e - \zeta_{An})$ in Eq. II-18 may be regarded as a constant. This means that the reaction has a pseudo first order behaviour with:

$$|R|_A = kc_{B0}c_A = k_1 c_A.$$

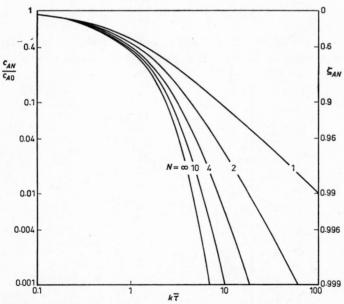

FIG. II-4. Relative degree of conversion ζ_{AN} for an isothermal first order reaction in a cascade of N equal tank reactors.

31

Accordingly, Eq. II-18 becomes:

$$\zeta_{An} - \zeta_{A(n-1)} = k_1 \bar{\tau}_n (1 - \zeta_{An}) ,$$

or

$$\frac{1 - \zeta_{An}}{1 - \zeta_{A(n-1)}} = \frac{1}{1 + k_1 \bar{\tau}_n}. \qquad \text{II-19}$$

If all reactors have the same value of $\bar{\tau}_n = \bar{\tau}/N$, the conversion in N tank reactors in cascade becomes:

$$1 - \zeta_{AN} = \frac{c_{AN}}{c_{A0}} = \left(1 + \frac{k_1 \bar{\tau}}{N}\right)^{-N}. \qquad \text{II-20}$$

This relationship is shown in Fig. II-4, where $1 - \zeta_{AN}$ has been plotted as a function of the total average residence time $\bar{\tau}$. Note that for $N \to \infty$ we have for a finite value of $\bar{\tau}$:

$$\lim_{N\to\infty} (1 - \zeta_{AN}) = \lim_{N\to\infty} \left(1 + \frac{k_1 \bar{\tau}}{N}\right)^{-N} = e^{-k_1 \bar{\tau}},$$

which is the conversion in an ideal tubular reactor with a residence time $\tau_L = \bar{\tau}$.

For somewhat more complicated rate expressions, such as used in Eq. II-18 for a second order reaction between A and B with excess B, a graphic design method was indicated by ELDRIDGE and PIRET [21]. It is, of course, based on the material balance which is now written in the form:

$$\xi_{A(n-1)} = \xi_{An} - \frac{V_{rn}}{\Phi_m} |r|_{An} .$$

Thus, if $|r|_{An}$ is a known function of ξ_{An}, and if V_{rn}/Φ_m has been preselected and is taken to be independent of n, the above expression gives a known re-

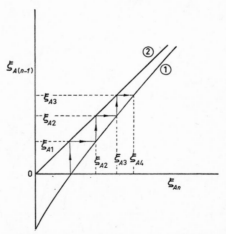

FIG. II-5. Graphic construction for obtaining the conversion in a cascade of equal-size tank reactors; ELDRIDGE and PIRET [21].

lationship between $\xi_{A(n-1)}$ and ξ_{An}. This relationship is then plotted with $\xi_{A(n-1)}$ as ordinate and ξ_{An} as abscissa; it is shown as curve 1 in Fig. II-5. When the auxiliary straight line 2 for which $\xi_{An} = \xi_{A(n-1)}$ is also drawn, the horizontal distance between 1 and 2 is equal to $\xi_{An} - \xi_{A(n-1)}$. A stepwise construction as indicated in Fig. II-5 can then be used in finding the number of tank reactors required for a given conversion.

ELDRIDGE and PIRET [21] have summarized a great number of design equations for various conversion rate expressions which can be solved either by an algebraic stepwise method or by the above graphic method. Their paper contains a number of charts from which the conversion of second-order reactions can be read. JENNEY [22] has published similar data, of which Fig. II-6 is given as an example. It shows the relative conversion ζ_{AN} as a function of $kc_{A0}\bar{\tau}$ (with $\bar{\tau}_n =$ constant) for $e = 0$ and $e = 0.3$ for the reaction system described by Eq. II-18.

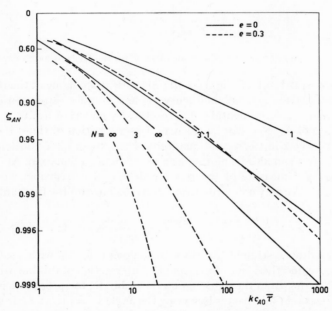

FIG. II-6. Relative degree of conversion ζ_{AN} for second order reactions in a cascade of N equal tank reactors; JENNEY [22].

A more general graphic method for obtaining the conversion in a cascade is given by several authors, among whom JONES [23] and WEBER [24]. It is based on a graphic representation of the conversion rate as a function of the degree of conversion. The conversion rate may be known empirically, e.g. from batch experiments. A construction where a batch experiment is taken as a starting point is shown in Fig. II-7.

33

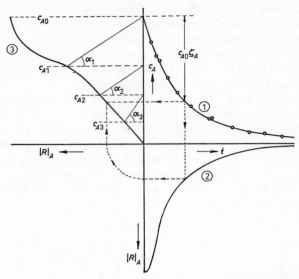

FIG. II-7. Calculation of a cascade of tank reactors on the basis of batch experiments.

In the first quadrant of Fig. II-7 the concentration of one of the reactants A has been plotted against time (curve 1) as a result of an investigation of the system in an experimental batch reactor. By means of Eq. II-3, the conversion rate of A, $|R|_A$, can be calculated as a function of time; it is represented as curve 2 in the second quadrant. Then, by graphic construction as indicated, $|R|_A$ can also be plotted as a function of c_A (curve 3). At constant density, c_A is a measure of the relative degree of conversion, since $c_A = c_{A0}(1 - \zeta_A)$. We may now write the material balance for the first tank reactor as:

$$\frac{c_{A0} - c_{A1}}{|R|_{A1}} = \frac{c_{A0}(\zeta_{A1} - \zeta_{A0})}{|R|_{A1}} = \bar{\tau}_1 .$$

Thus, if we draw a straight line through the point $(0, c_{A0})$ with a slope $\alpha_1 = \arctan \bar{\tau}_1$, we find the value of c_{A1} from the intersection of this line with curve 3. Then, starting from the value c_{A1} on the ordinate, the procedure is repeated for the second tank reactor by taking the angle $\alpha_2 = \arctan \bar{\tau}_2$, from which c_{A2} is found, etc. This method has the advantage over the construction of Fig. II-5 that the average residence times of the various reactors can be varied.

It should be borne in mind that both this procedure and the foregoing one are limited to isothermally operating systems where the conversion rate only depends on the degree of conversion of one of the components.

ILLUSTRATION II. 4b. *Polymerization in a cascade*

In a cascade of tank reactors ($V_{rn} = 26.5$ m³), styrene (A) and butadiene (B) are to be copolymerized at 5°C to a final degree of conversion $\xi_{AN} = 0.0775$. The over-all reaction equation is:

$$A + 3.2B \rightarrow polymer \, ,$$

and the conversion rate is given as:

$$|R|_A = kc_A c_B \, ,$$

with $k = 10^{-5} m^3/kmol \ s$. The inlet concentrations are $c_{A0} = 0.795$ kmol/m³ and $c_{B0} = 3.55$ kmol/m³, while $M_A = 104$ kg/kmol and $M_B = 54$ kg/kmol. The feed rate is 19.7 tons/hr and the density of the reaction mixture is constant at a value $\varrho = 870$ kg/m³. Find the total number N of tank reactors required.

Since all reactors will have the same given residence time, a construction according to Fig. II-5 is advisable. We start from the material balance II-16:

$$\xi_{A(n-1)} = \xi_{An} - \frac{V_{rn} M_A}{\Phi_m} |R|_{An} \, .$$

From Table I-1 we have:

$$c_A = c_{A0} - \varrho \xi_A / M_A \, , \quad \text{and} \quad c_B = c_{B0} - \varrho v_B \xi_A / v_A M_A \, ,$$

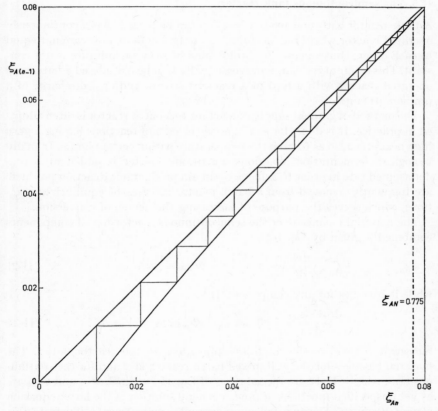

FIG. II-8. Determination of the number of tank reactors for obtaining a degree of conversion $\xi_{AN} = 0.0775$ in a polymerization reaction; Illustration II.5.

so that the material balance becomes:

$$\xi_{A(n-1)} = \xi_{An} - \frac{V_{rn} M_A k c_{A0} c_{B0}}{\Phi_m} \left(1 - \frac{\varrho \xi_{An}}{M_A c_{A0}}\right)\left(1 - \frac{\varrho v_B \xi_{An}}{v_A M_A c_{B0}}\right) =$$

$$= \xi_{An} - 0.0142\,(1 - 10.52\,\xi_{An})\,(1 - 7.54\,\xi_{An}),$$

or:

$$\xi_{A(n-1)} = -1.13\,\xi_{An}^{2} + 1.26\,\xi_{An} - 0.0142 .$$

This relation has been plotted in Fig. II-8 together with the auxiliary line $\xi_{A(n-1)} = \xi_{An}$. From the stepwise construction we find that for obtaining the required value of $\xi_{AN} = 0.0775$ *21* tank reactors in cascade would be needed. It is furthermore seen that in the first reactor $\xi_{A1} = 0.0117$ and in the last $\xi_{A21} - \xi_{A20} = 0.0011$, so that 15% of the total conversion occur in the first reactor and only 1.4% in the last one. Since the reaction is exothermic, this means that much more heat must be removed in the first reactor than in the last.

The high value of N makes that this system has practically the same behaviour as an ideal tubular reactor with the same total residence time. However, the required residence time is so long ($N\tau_n = \bar{\tau} = 24.6$ hrs) that a cascade of reaction vessels is the only economical way of providing for a large reaction volume.

II.5. The semicontinuous tank reactor

A tank reactor with nonsteady operation can be regarded as a continuously operated reactor where the incoming and outgoing mass flows are not equal to each other; consequently, the total mass of reaction mixture is not constant. This reactor type can, however, equally well be considered a batchwise operated reactor with a feed of a reactant stream and/or a discharge of a product stream.

The method of gradual supply of reactant to a batch reactor is often adopted in practice. It is done, for example, in the case of reactions having a very high heat effect, so as to keep the temperature within certain limits. In many biological fermentation reactions nutritious matter is added at a predetermined rate in order to achieve optimum production. Reaction products are frequently removed from a batch reactor in cases of equilibrium reactions, which serves the purpose of increasing the degree of conversion.

The material balance over the semicontinuous reactor for all components combined is given by Eq. I-2:

$$\frac{\mathrm{d}m}{\mathrm{d}t} = \frac{\mathrm{d}(\varrho V_r)}{\mathrm{d}t} = \Phi_{m0} - \Phi_{m1}, \qquad \text{II-21}$$

while it becomes for any component J:

$$\frac{\mathrm{d}(\varrho V_r w_{J1})}{\mathrm{d}t} = \Phi_{m0} w_{J0} - \Phi_{m1} w_{J1} + V_r r_{J1}. \qquad \text{II-22}$$

Subscript 1 refers to the conditions prevailing at the reactor outlet. The material balances for the well-mixed batch reactor II-1 and for the continuous tank reactor II-12 are special cases of Eq. II-22. Since Φ_{m0} and Φ_{m1} are as yet unspecified functions of time, a general solution of the latter equation cannot be given. The two following examples may serve to illustrate this reactor type.

ILLUSTRATION II. 5a. *A semicontinuous (or semi-batch) experiment*

A reaction is to be carried out in a solution which contains a catalytic component. For the determination of the conversion rate, an experimental batch reactor is used which at the start of the experiment ($t = 0$) contains only the solvent and the catalyst; the initial reaction volume is V_{r0}, and the initial density is ϱ_0. The reactants are fed continuously to the reactor at a constant mass rate starting at $t = 0$; they are assumed to be mixed very fast with the reactor contents. The composition and the density of the reaction mixture is then determined as a function of time, and it is asked to find an expression for the conversion rate from these data.

Since no material is removed, $\Phi_{m1} = 0$ and Eq. II-21 becomes:

$$\frac{d(\varrho V_r)}{dt} = \Phi_{m0}, \quad \text{or} \quad \varrho V_r = \varrho_0 V_{r0} + \Phi_{m0}\, t.$$

The material balance for one of the reactants, A, is:

$$\frac{d(\varrho V_r w_{A1})}{dt} = \Phi_{m0} w_{A0} - V_r |r|_{A1}.$$

After elimination of V_r and rearrangement, we have:

$$\frac{|r|_{A1}}{\varrho} = (w_{A0} - w_{A1})\frac{\Phi_{m0}}{\varrho_0 V_{r0} + \Phi_{m0}\, t} - \frac{dw_{A1}}{dt}.$$

The first term on the right-hand side represents the rate at which the mass fraction w_{A1} would increase if the reaction were infinitely slow. Therefore $|r|_{A1}/\varrho$ is equal to the difference between the latter rate and the measured increase of w_{A1} per unit time. If the actual *reaction* velocity were extremely high, we would find that w_{A1} remains practically zero throughout the experiment. The amount of reactant *converted* per unit time then becomes equal to the rate at which reactant is added. Under these circumstances, the assumption of uniformity of the reaction mixture fails and the experiment is meaningless.

ILLUSTRATION II. 5b. *Production of ethyl acetate in a batch reactor with removal of product*

In the system described in Illustration II.1, part of the product P is to be removed during the reaction in order to increase the over-all conversion rate of this equilibrium reaction. The reaction is carried out at 100°C and the contents of the reactor are partly evaporated. The vapour leaving the reactor is concentrated by rectifying distillation, and the top product is an azeotropic mixture with the composition $w_{A1} = 0.084$, $w_{P1} = 0.826$ and $w_{Q1} = 0.090$. The liquid hold-up of the distillation column is assumed to be very small with respect to the reaction volume. The rate of net evaporation from the reactor is chosen in such a way that the mass fraction of P in the reaction mixture does not exceed the value of $w_P = 0.02$. To what extent will the production be increased by these measures if the total reaction time is to remain the same as in Illustration II.1?

With a calculation as shown in Illustration II.1 we find that after $t = 690$ s the mass fraction of P has reached the value $w_P = 0.02$. The composition of the reaction mixture at this moment is given in the table below. At this moment evaporation starts, and with $\Phi_{m1} =$ the rate of removal of the product stream, the material balances are:

total:
$$\varrho\,\frac{dV_r}{dt} = -\Phi_{m1},\qquad\qquad\text{(a)}$$

alcohol (A):
$$\frac{d(V_r c_A)}{dt} = -\Phi_{m1}\frac{w_{A1}}{M_A} - V_r |R|_A,\qquad\qquad\text{(b)}$$

acid (B):
$$\frac{d(V_r c_B)}{dt} = -V_r |R|_B,\qquad\qquad\text{(c)}$$

37

ester (P):
$$c_P \frac{dV_r}{dt} = -\Phi_{m1} \frac{w_{P1}}{M_P} + V_r |R|_P, \qquad (d)$$

water (Q):
$$\frac{d(V_r c_Q)}{dt} = -\Phi_{m1} \frac{w_{Q1}}{M_Q} + V_r |R|_Q. \qquad (e)$$

From the reaction equation we have: $|R|_A = |R|_B = |R|_P = |R|_Q$; ϱ, c_P, w_{A1}, w_{P1} and w_{Q1} are constant. The sum of the four balances for the components is the total material balance. From (a) and (d) we find:

$$\frac{dV_r}{dt} = \frac{V_r |R|_A}{c_P - \varrho w_{P1}/M_P}. \qquad (f)$$

By combining (b), (c) and (e) with (a) and (f), respectively, we get:

$$\frac{dc_A}{dt} = -|R|_A \left[1 + \frac{c_A - \varrho w_{A1}/M_A}{c_P - \varrho w_{P1}/M_P} \right],$$

$$\frac{dc_B}{dt} = -|R|_A \left[1 + \frac{c_{B1}}{c_P - \varrho w_{P1}/M_P} \right],$$

and

$$\frac{dc_Q}{dt} = |R|_A \left[1 - \frac{c_Q - \varrho w_{Q1}/M_Q}{c_P - \varrho w_{P1}/M_P} \right].$$

In the last 4 equations, V_r, c_A, c_B and c_Q vary with time as well as $|R|_A$, which is a given function of the composition (see Illustration II.1). The equations have to be solved by trial and error; some of the results are shown in the following table:

$t(s)$	0	690	4000	7270	7270★
c_A (kmol/m³)	10.20	9.97	9.83	9.76	8.83
c_B (kmol/m³)	3.91	3.68	3.17	2.68	2.54
c_P (kmol/m³)	0	0.23	0.23	0.23	1.37
c_Q (kmol/m³)	17.6	17.8	19.9	21.6	18.9
V_r (m³)	52.0	52.0	47.2	44.2	52.0

Because of the combined effect of the reaction, the reduction of the reaction volume and the partial removal of A, P and Q, the concentrations of A and B decrease more slowly and the concentration of Q increases more quickly than in the batch reactor without product removal. The amount of P produced in 7270 s in this example is:

$$\frac{\varrho w_{P1}}{M_P}[(V_r)_0 - V_r] + V_r c_P = 74.6 + 10.2 = 84.8 \text{ kmol}.$$

In Example II.1, 71.2 kmol of P were produced per batch in the same time, so that the capacity has been increased by 19%.

II.6. The continuous cross-flow reactor system

In the foregoing discussions on continuously operated reactors we assumed that the total feed stream was supplied to the reactor system at one point only, and that the product stream left the system at one outlet point. A distributed feed and/or a distributed take-off along the length of the reactor

---

★ From Illustration II.1

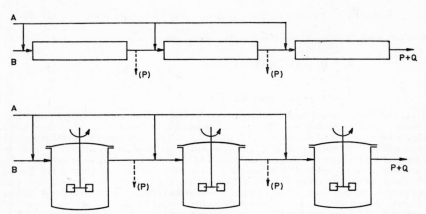

FIG. II-9. Possible cross-flow reactor systems consisting of tubular reactors and of tank reactors.

system (as shown in Fig. II-9) also belongs to the possibilities. We shall call such a system a cross-flow reactor.

There are, of course, many possible variations in the location of the various inlet and outlet points, and also in the distribution of the flow rates over these points. Such applications may be profitable in particular cases, e.g. for the purpose of suppressing undesired side reactions. It will be clear that similar results can be obtained with a programmed feed into or discharge from a semi-continuous batch reactor as considered in the previous section.

For purposes of calculation, material balances have to be applied to appropriate sections of the reactor system. For a tubular reactor, a section between two inlet and/or outlet points can be treated with the theory of Section II.2; for a cross-flow system consisting of tank reactors, the material balance over each reactor is essentially given by Eq. II-12, provided the possibility of more than one feed or discharge stream is taken into account. Solutions for specific problems of this kind can be built up accordingly.

A system which is slightly more accessible to a generalized treatment is the ideal tubular reactor in which the number of side feed points (or discharge points, respectively) is infinite. We call this the idealized cross-flow reactor. Such a gradual distribution of a part of the feed (or of the discharge) over the entire reactor length cannot, of course, be realized in practice, but as an extreme model it may serve to investigate problems of reactor optimization. This has been shown by VAN DE VUSSE and VOETTER [25], and it will be discussed more fully in Section VI.2. This section is concluded with a cross-flow reactor calculation emphasizing the consistent application of material balances. A complex reaction is considered for the first time in this example but the problems arising out of complex reactions will be treated more fully in Section II.7.

ILLUSTRATION II. 6. *Parallel reactions in an idealized cross-flow reactor*

The following two reactions occur simultaneously in a process:

$$A + B \xrightarrow{1} P, \quad \text{with } R_P = k_1 c_A c_B$$
$$A + A \xrightarrow{2} X, \quad \text{with } R_X = \tfrac{1}{2}k_2 c_A^2$$
$$\left. \right\} \quad \begin{aligned} R_A &= -R_P - 2R_X \\ R_B &= -R_P . \end{aligned}$$

P is the desired product and X a waste product, while A is an expensive reactant which cannot be easily removed from the product stream. It is therefore required to obtain a high relative degree of conversion of A (say $\zeta_{AL} = 0.98$) together with a relatively high production, i.e. a high yield of P. The rate equations indicate that the latter may be achieved by keeping the concentration of A in the reactor system relatively low. Accordingly, an idealized cross-flow tubular reactor will be considered where A is fed along the length of the reactor and where B is fed at the inlet end only. We do not as yet wish to optimize the system, but will arbitrarily require an injection distribution of A causing constant concentration $c_A = c_{AL}$ over the entire reactor length. If the total molar feed rates of A and B are equal and $k_1 = k_2$, what is the relative degree of conversion of B to P in this system? How does this result compare with the performance of a batch reactor and a continuous tank reactor under the same conditions?

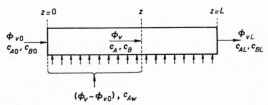

FIG. II-10. The idealized cross-flow tubular reactor.

The diagram of the reactor, together with the symbols to be used, is shown in Fig. II-10. If we assume the density of all streams to be identical, the following set of equations has to be solved:
material balance of A for a section dz:

$$0 = -\mathrm{d}(\Phi_v c_A) + c_{Aw}\mathrm{d}\Phi_v + R_A S \mathrm{d}z ; \tag{a}$$

material balance of B:

$$0 = -\mathrm{d}(\Phi_v v_B) + R_B S \mathrm{d}z . \tag{b}$$

Additional requirements are the constancy of c_A:

$$c_{A0} = c_A = c_{AL} , \tag{c}$$

and the equality of the feed rates of A and B:

$$\Phi_{v0} c_{B0} = \Phi_{v0} c_{A0} + (\Phi_{vL} - \Phi_{v0}) c_{Aw} . \tag{d}$$

If the size of the reactor has to be calculated together with the required distribution of the side injection of A, Eqs. (a) and (b) have to be integrated separately. In this example we shall, however, only work out the relationship between the conversions of A and B for the conditions specified above. To this end, we eliminate $S\mathrm{d}z$ from Eqs. (a) and (b) and substitute (c) and the conversion rate expressions. The resulting differential equation is:

$$(c_{AL} - c_{Aw})\mathrm{d}\Phi_v = \left(1 + \frac{k_2 c_{AL}}{k_1 c_B}\right)\mathrm{d}(\Phi_v c_B) \approx \left\{1 + \Phi_{vL}\frac{k_2 c_{AL}}{k_1(\Phi_v c_B)}\right\}\mathrm{d}(\Phi_v c_B) . \tag{e}$$

The latter approximation is only valid if the variation in Φ_v is small. This would mean that $\Phi_{vL} - \Phi_{v0} \ll \Phi_{v0}$, i.e. the total flow of the side injection is relatively small, but its content in A relatively high. On this assumption Eq. (e) can be integrated between $z = 0$ and $z = L$. Combining the result with Eq. (d), we finally obtain:

$$\ln \frac{\Phi_{vL} c_{BL}}{\Phi_{v0} c_{B0}} = \frac{k_1}{k_2} \left(1 - \frac{c_{BL}}{c_{AL}} \right). \tag{f}$$

We now introduce the relative degrees of conversion of A and B at the reactor outlet. Since the molar feeds of A and B are equal, we have:

$$\zeta_{AL} = 1 - \Phi_{vL} c_{AL}/\Phi_{v0} c_{B0},$$

and

$$\zeta_{BL} = 1 - \Phi_{vL} c_{BL}/\Phi_{v0} c_{B0}.$$

Substitution of these expressions into Eq. (f) leads to the final result:

$$\ln (1 - \zeta_{BL}) = \frac{k_1}{k_2} \frac{\zeta_{BL} - \zeta_{AL}}{1 - \zeta_{AL}}. \tag{g}$$

It is seen that, for this reactor and on the assumptions (c) and (d), a single relationship exists between ζ_{AL} and ζ_{BL}, with the value of k_1/k_2 as a parameter.

If the same reaction is carried out in a *batch reactor*, we may write, with a constant density (see Eq. II-3):

$$\frac{dc_A}{dt} = - k_1 c_A c_B - k_2 c_A^2,$$

and

$$\frac{dc_B}{dt} = - k_1 c_A c_B.$$

In order to obtain a relationship between c_A and c_B, the time is eliminated from these equations:

$$\frac{dc_A}{dc_B} = 1 + \frac{k_2}{k_1} \frac{c_A}{c_B}.$$

With $c_A = c_{A0}$ when $c_B = c_{B0}$, the solution is:

$$\left(\frac{k_2}{k_1} - 1 \right) \ln \frac{c_B}{c_{B0}} = \ln \left[\frac{1 + \left(\dfrac{k_2}{k_1} - 1 \right) \dfrac{c_A}{c_B}}{1 + \left(\dfrac{k_2}{k_1} - 1 \right) \dfrac{c_{A0}}{c_{B0}}} \right],$$

and, in terms of relative conversions, when $c_{A0} = c_{B0}$:

$$\left(\frac{k_2}{k_1} - 1 \right) \ln (1 - \zeta_B) = \ln \left[1 + \left(\frac{k_2}{k_1} - 1 \right) \frac{1 - \zeta_A}{1 - \zeta_B} \right] - \ln \frac{k_2}{k_1}. \tag{h}$$

For $k_1/k_2 = 1$ this expression is reduced to:

$$1 - \zeta_A = (1 - \zeta_B)[1 + \ln(1 - \zeta_B)].$$

For a continuous *tank reactor* the material balances for A and B become:

$$c_{A0} - c_{A1} = k_1 \bar{t} c_{A1} c_{B1} + k_2 \bar{t} c_{A1}^2,$$

and

$$c_{B0} - c_{B1} = k_1 \bar{t} c_{A1} c_{B1}.$$

Division of the first equation by the second yields:

$$\frac{c_{A0} - c_{A1}}{c_{B0} - c_{B1}} = 1 + \frac{k_2}{k_1} \frac{c_{A1}}{c_{B1}},$$

and with $c_{A0} = c_{B0}$:

$$\frac{\zeta_{A1}}{\zeta_{B1}} = 1 + \frac{k_2}{k_1}\frac{1 - \zeta_{A1}}{1 - \zeta_{B1}}. \qquad \text{(k)}$$

We can now compare the solutions (h) and (k) with the result (g) for the idealized cross-flow reactor with uniform concentration of A. With $k_1/k_2 = 1$, stoichiometric feed quantities of A and B, and $\zeta_A = 0.98$, we find:

batch (or tubular) reactor: $\zeta_B = 0.61$
continuous tank reactor: $\zeta_{B1} = 0.86$
idealized cross-flow reactor: $\zeta_{BL} = 0.93$.

It is seen that the continuous tank reactor gives a smaller conversion of B, and consequently a lower yield of P, than the cross-flow reactor. This results from the fact that the ratio c_B/c_A, averaged over the whole reactor content, is highest in the latter case. The higher this ratio, the more the desired reaction is favoured. Since this ratio is lowest in a batch or normal tubular reactor, a relatively large portion of A is here converted to the undesired product.

II.7. Selectivity, yield and reaction path with complex reactions

In Sections II.1 through II.5, elementary reactor calculations for single reactions were discussed with emphasis on the relationship between reaction time or volume and degree of conversion. With more complex reactions, such as parallel and consecutive reactions, several products are obtained; some will be the desired product(s) (symbols : P, Q) and others the undesired ones (symbols: X, Y). Since the reactants in a reactor are meant to be converted to desired product to the greatest possible extent, a reasonably high degree of conversion must not only be obtained, but should be accompanied by a high *selectivity* of the reaction.

The selectivity, σ_P, is the ratio between the amount of a desired product P obtained and the amount of a key reactant A *converted*. When these amounts are expressed in molar units, and the stoichiometry of the reaction equation is taken into account, σ_P ranges between 0 and 1. This definition leads to the equation:

$$\sigma_P \equiv \frac{\xi_P \nu_A M_A}{\xi_A \nu_P M_P}. \qquad \text{II-23}$$

Ultimately, the merits of a complex reaction operation are closely related to the amount of a desired product obtained with respect to the amount of a key reactant A *fed*. This ratio is called the product *yield*, η_P, and it is easily seen from the above that:

$$\eta_P \equiv \sigma_P \zeta_A. \qquad \text{II-24}$$

The yield can likewise vary between 0 and 1; it is high when both the selectivity and the relative degree of conversion are high, but it is low when either of them is small. The definitions II-23 and II-24 are entirely general. They apply equally well to simple reactor systems (Sections II.1 through II.4) as to systems with feed and/or discharge distribution (Sections II.5 and II.6), provided the more general definitions for ξ and ζ are used in the latter cases.

42

Returning to the discussion of complex reactions, we shall mainly consider *parallel* and *consecutive* reactions which exhibit an essentially different behaviour with regard to product distribution. This is qualitatively demonstrated in Fig. II-11 (a and b). For parallel reactions, Fig II-11a indicates that, as soon as reactant is converted, both P and X can form in principle, with a σ_P value anywhere between 0 and 1. The yield of P, of which w_P in Fig. II-11a is a measure, will generally rise as the conversion proceeds. In consecutive reactions, P (in this example assumed to be the desired product) forms first, and is subsequently converted to X. Therefore, initially $\sigma_P = 1$, but in principle it decreases to 0 as the reaction nears its end. Consequently, the yield η_P passes through a maximum value as a function of the degree of conversion.

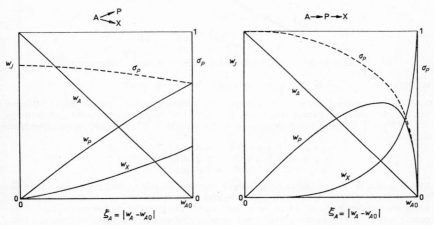

FIG. II-11. Concentrations and selectivity as a function of the degree of conversion for parallel and for consecutive reactions.

The shape of the lines in a diagram like Fig. II-11 depends not only on the type of complex reaction but also on the different rate constants involved (which may greatly depend on temperature) and on the type of reactor in which the reaction is carried out. This was demonstrated for a system of parallel reactions in Illustration II.6. Fig. II-12 summarizes its equations (h), (k) and (g) for the batch reactor, the continuous tank reactor and the idealized cross-flow reactor, respectively. σ_P and η_P have been plotted against the relative degree of conversion of A; since component B can only be converted to the desired product P, we have with the definition II-23 : $\sigma_P = \zeta_B/\zeta_A$, and with II-24: $\eta_P = \zeta_B$.

A similar demonstration can be made for a system of consecutive reactions. To this end, an example of such a system is given below.

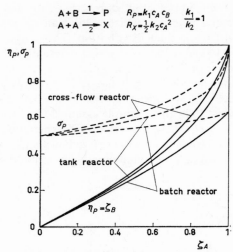

$$A + B \xrightarrow{\ 1\ } P \qquad R_P = k_1 c_A c_B \qquad \frac{k_1}{k_2} = 1$$
$$A + A \xrightarrow{\ 2\ } X \qquad R_X = \tfrac{1}{2} k_2 c_A^2$$

FIG. II-12. Selectivity and yield with parallel reactions; Illustration II.6.

ILLUSTRATION II. 7. *The chlorination of benzene in various reactor systems*

The desired product monochlorobenzene (P) is formed in the chlorination of benzene, but further chlorination resulting in dichloro- and trichloro-benzene (undesired products X and Y, respectively) takes place as well. The equations of the three consecutive reactions are:

$$C_6H_6(A) + Cl_2(B) \rightarrow C_6H_5Cl(P) + HCl \nearrow$$
$$C_6H_5Cl(P) + Cl_2(B) \rightarrow C_6H_4Cl_2(X) + HCl \nearrow$$
$$C_6H_4Cl_2(X) + Cl_2(B) \rightarrow C_6H_3Cl_3(Y) + HCl \nearrow \ .$$

The reaction is carried out in large stirred reaction vessels in which gaseous Cl_2 is dispersed. Hydrochloric acid, some chlorine and a small amount of volatile by-products leave the reactor as gases. In the most favourable temperature range (around 50°C) the reaction is so slow that the conversion rate is determined entirely by the chemical reaction velocity, and that the liquid may be assumed to be saturated with Cl_2 at the prevailing temperature and pressure. Under these circumstances the various net production rates can be written in the following form:

$$R_A = -k_1 c_A c_B , \qquad R_P = k_1 c_A c_B - k_2 c_P c_B ,$$
$$R_X = k_2 c_P c_B - k_3 c_X c_B , \qquad R_Y = k_3 c_X c_B ,$$

where k_1, k_2 and k_3 are functions of temperature. McMULLIN [26] gives for 55°C:

$$\frac{k_1}{k_2} = 8.0 \quad \text{and} \quad \frac{k_2}{k_3} = 30 .$$

As the reaction proceeds, the density of the reaction mixture increases. For the sake of convenience we shall postulate the approximation that the total number of moles per unit volume (disregarding the dissolved chlorine) remains constant:

$$c_A + c_P + c_X + c_Y = c_{A0} .$$

The above data are not sufficient for the calculation of the reaction volume needed for a certain production rate of P. We can, however, calculate the product distribution for various reactor types as a function of the extent of the reaction; for this we may take, either the relative degree of conversion of benzene:

$$\zeta_A = 1 - c_A/c_{A0} ,$$

or the number of moles of Cl_2 used per mole of benzene:

$$\gamma_B = (c_P + 2c_X + 3c_Y)/c_{A0} ;$$

the latter quantity may exceed unity. The reactor types to be discussed are the batch reactor, the continuous tank reactor and a cascade of three tank reactors.

Strictly speaking, the *batch reactor* is here a semi-continuous one since Cl_2 is continuously supplied and HCl is removed; as a result the total mass of the reaction mixture increases. The above assumption that the sum of molar concentrations remains constant, however, involves that the total reaction volume V_r remains constant. Application of the material balance II-22 for benzene (A), which is neither added to nor discharged from the system during the reaction, then yields:

$$\frac{d(\varrho V_r w_A)}{dt} = r_A V_r .$$

With $w_A = M_A c_A/\varrho$ and $r_A = M_A R_A$ we get:

$$\frac{d(V_r c_A)}{dt} = R_A V_r , \quad \text{or} \quad \frac{dc_A}{dt} = R_A .$$

Similarly:

$$\frac{dc_P}{dt} = R_P , \quad \frac{dc_X}{dt} = R_X \quad \text{and} \quad \frac{dc_Y}{dt} = R_Y .$$

This shows that the system may be treated as a normal batch reactor.
After substitution of the rate expressions we form the ratio:

$$\frac{dc_P}{dt} \bigg/ \frac{dc_A}{dt} = \frac{dc_P}{dc_A} = \frac{k_1 c_A - k_2 c_P}{- k_1 c_A} .$$

This differential equation must be solved with the boundary condition: $c_P = 0$ for $c_A = c_{A0}$. Following introduction of c_P/c_A as a new dependent variable, the equation can be integrated:

$$\frac{c_P}{c_{A0}} = \frac{k_1}{k_1 - k_2} \frac{c_A}{c_{A0}} \left[\left(\frac{c_A}{c_{A0}} \right)^{(k_2-k_1)/k_1} - 1 \right]. \tag{a}$$

Similarly, an expression for c_X can be found. Here, however, we shall consider X and Y together the undesired products, with concentration $c_X + c_Y = c_{A0} - c_A - c_P$. Since k_2/k_3 is large, and an excessive degree of chlorination will not be considered ($c_Y \ll c_X$) we have approximately:

$$\gamma_B \approx (c_P + 2c_X + 2c_Y)/c_{A0} = (2c_{A0} - 2c_A - c_P)/c_{A0} .$$

In accordance with the definition II-23, the selectivity is given by:

$$\sigma_P = c_P/(c_{A0} - c_A) = c_P/c_{A0}\zeta_A ,$$

and the yield of monochlorobenzene becomes:

$$\eta_P = c_P/c_{A0} .$$

Some values of the product distribution calculated from Eq. (a) with $k_1/k_2 = 8.0$ are shown in the following table.

Chlorination in a batch reactor

$c_A/c_{A0} = 1 - \zeta_A$	1.0	0.8	0.6	0.4	0.2	0.1	0.05	0.01
$c_P/c_{A0} = \eta_P$	0	0.195	0.384	0.562	0.706	0.745	0.732	0.632
$(c_X + c_Y)/c_{A0}$	0	0.005	0.016	0.038	0.094	0.155	0.218	0.358
γ_B	0	0.21	0.42	0.64	0.89	1.06	1.17	1.35
$c_P/c_{A0} \zeta_A = \sigma_P$	1.0	0.98	0.96	0.94	0.88	0.83	0.77	0.64

The product distribution, σ_P and η_P have been plotted in Fig. II-13 as a function of the degree of chlorination γ_B.

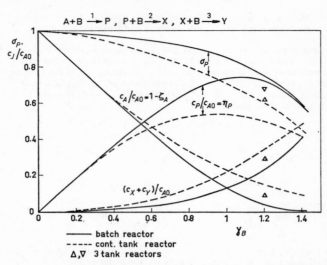

FIG. II-13. Concentrations and selectivity for the chlorination of benzene, $k_1/k_2 = 8.0$; Illustration II.7.

If the reaction is carried out in a single *tank reactor*, the following material balances apply to the liquid phase:

$$0 = \quad \Phi_v(c_{A0} - c_{A1}) - k_1 c_{A1} c_{B1} V_r \,,$$
$$0 = -\Phi_v c_{P1} + (k_1 c_{A1} c_{B1} - k_2 c_{P1} c_{B1}) V_r \,,$$
$$0 = -\Phi_v c_{X1} + (k_2 c_{P1} c_{B1} - k_3 c_{X1} c_{B1}) V_r \,,$$
$$0 = -\Phi_v c_{Y1} + k_3 c_{X1} c_{B1} V_r \,.$$

The ratio of the first two expressions yields the relation between c_{P1} and c_{A1}:

$$\frac{c_{P1}}{c_{A0} - c_{A1}} = 1 - \frac{k_2}{k_1} \frac{c_{P1}}{c_{A1}}. \tag{b}$$

Formulae for c_{X1} and c_{Y1} can similarly be found, but we only use their sum, as before. Some values of the composition calculated from Eq. (b) are given in the following table.

Chlorination in a continuous tank reactor

$c_{A1}/c_{A0} = 1 - \zeta_{A1}$	1.0	0.8	0.6	0.4	0.2	0.1	0.05
$c_{P1}/c_{A0} = \eta_{P1}$	0	0.195	0.369	0.505	0.534	0.425	0.281
$(c_{X1} + c_{Y1})/c_{A0}$	0	0.005	0.031	0.095	0.266	0.475	0.669
γ_{B1}	0	0.21	0.43	0.70	1.07	1.38	1.62
$c_{P1}/c_{A0}\zeta_{A1} = \sigma_{P1}$	1.0	0.98	0.92	0.84	0.67	0.47	0.30

The composition according to Eq. (b) has also been plotted in Fig. II-13. It is seen that in this case the maximum yield of monochlorobenzene (P) is much smaller than in the case of the batch reactor and that the selectivity rapidly diminishes as a function of increasing conversion.

The maximum yield of monochlorobenzene (P) can be increased with respect to the above process by carrying out the reaction in a cascade of tank reactors instead of in one tank reactor. We select as an example a cascade of *three tank reactors*. From the many possible distributions of the total reaction volume and the chlorine feed over the three tanks we arbitrarily select a system where the chlorine consumption in each tank reactor has the same value.

The material balances for A and P over the n-th tank reactor give the relationship:

$$\frac{c_{Pn} - c_{P(n-1)}}{c_{A(n-1)} - c_{An}} = 1 - \frac{k_2}{k_1} \frac{c_{Pn}}{c_{An}}.$$

In view of the requirement of equal chlorine consumption we eliminate c_{Pn} and $c_{P(n-1)}$ by introducing the relative degrees of chlorination:

$$\gamma_{Bn} \approx (2c_{A0} - 2c_{An} - c_{Pn})/c_{A0},$$

and

$$\gamma_{B(n-1)} \approx (2c_{A0} - 2c_{A(n-1)} - c_{P(n-1)})/c_{A0},$$

after which the above formula becomes:

$$\frac{\gamma_{Bn} - \gamma_{B(n-1)}}{c_{A(n-1)} - c_{An}} c_{A0} = 1 - \frac{k_2}{k_1}\left[2 - (2 - \gamma_{Bn})\frac{c_{A0}}{c_{An}}\right]. \tag{c}$$

It has to be applied to the three successive reactors; the following table gives the results for $k_1/k_2 = 8.0$ and $\gamma_{B1} = \gamma_{B2} - \gamma_{B1} = \gamma_{B3} - \gamma_{B2} = 0.4$.

Chlorination in a cascade of three tank reactors

	$n = 0$	$n = 1$	$n = 2$	$n = 3$
γ_{Bn}	0	0.4	0.8	1.2
$c_{An}/c_{A0} = 1 - \zeta_{An}$	1	0.627	0.305	0.090
$c_{Pn}/c_{A0} = \eta_{Pn}$	0	0.346	0.590	0.620
$(c_{Xn} + c_{Yn})/c_{A0}$	0	0.027	0.105	0.290
$c_{Pn}/c_{A0}\zeta_{An} = \sigma_{Pn}$	1.0	0.93	0.85	0.68

The result for $n = 3$ is represented by one point in Fig. II-13. It is seen that the performance of the cascade lies between that of the single tank reactor and the batch reactor.

It is a general feature of consecutive reactions that — if an intermediate product is the one desired — a batch or tubular reactor, or a cascade approaching its behaviour, gives the highest conversion to the desired product. It is clear from Fig. II-13 that the reaction should be stopped when the concentration of the desired product has reached its maximum value. For continuous operation this means that the maximum yield of P is obtained only at one particular value of the throughput. Any departure from this value involves a decrease in the yield.

The fact that the selectivity is still large at a small degree of conversion can be used in principle if the non-converted reactant can be separated in an auxiliary unit from the products and recirculated to the reactor. In this way, both the selectivity and the degree of conversion (calculated over the combination of reactor and separating unit) can be kept at a high value. The proper selection of the conditions to be used is governed entirely by economic considerations.

The reaction path

Since three kinds of substances are distinguished in complex reactions: reactant(s), desired and undesired products, it is frequently convenient to represent the composition of the reaction mixture in a triangular composition diagram. The concentration of these substances should then be expressed in such units that their sum is constant all over the composition triangle. The line giving the course of composition as the degree of conversion increases will

47

be called the reaction path. We shall adopt the convention that the left-hand corner of the triangle represents 100% of reactant, the top corner 100% of desired product and the right-hand corner 100% of waste product. Hence, the nearer the reaction path approaches the left-hand side AP, the higher the selectivity σ_P is; furthermore, the smaller the vertical distance between a point of the reaction path and the top corner P, the higher the corresponding value of the yield η_P is.

The reaction path is primarily determined by the type of complex reaction; its shape is further influenced by the ratio of the reaction velocity constants involved (i.e., by the temperature), by the type of reactor in which the reaction is carried out, and by the operating conditions, such as feed composition, supply or removal of components during the reaction, etc. In the following we shall mainly discuss the influence of the reaction type and of the reactor system. For the sake of simplicity, we shall use molar concentrations, assuming that the sum of the three concentrations involved is constant.

Of *parallel* reactions, the simplest case is that of two competing reactions which are of the same order with respect to the reactants. The isothermal reaction path is a straight line as shown in Fig. II-14 with a slope depending on the ratio of the reaction velocity constants k_1 and k_2. The reaction path in this exceptional case does not depend on whether the reaction is carried out in a batch or tubular reactor, or in a continuous tank reactor. The ratio of P and X obtained upon complete conversion, i.e. the maximum yield η_P, can only be influenced by temperature. It should be borne in mind, however, that the capacity of the tank reactor is always lower than that of the tubular reactor.

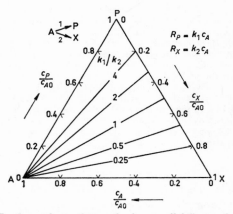

FIG. II-14. Isothermal reaction paths for parallel first order reactions.

If the parallel reactions are of different order with respect to the reactant concentration, the reaction path is curved. As an example, the results of

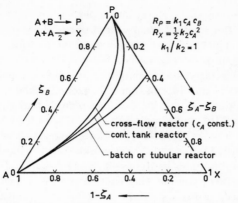

FIG. II-15. Isothermal reaction paths for parallel reactions of different order with respect to one of the reactants; Illustration II.6. Stoichiometric quantities of A and B fed.

Illustration II.6 and of Fig. II-12 are shown in Fig. II-15. With isothermal operation in a batch reactor or a continuous tubular reactor, it is seen that the rate of the undesired reaction decreases relatively as the conversion increases in consequence of the decrease of c_A. With the use of a continuous tank reactor or a properly operated cross-flow reactor, the concentration of A is intentionally kept relatively low so that the desired reaction which is only first order in A, is favoured. Here, with an extremely low value of c_A, practically pure P can be produced; this would, however, require an extremely large reaction volume. If, on the other hand, the desired reaction is of a higher order in A than the undesired one, it is advantageous to keep the aver-

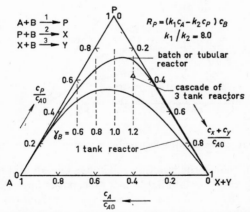

FIG. II-16. Isothermal reaction paths for the chlorination of benzene; Illustration II.7.

age value of c_A over the entire reactor as high as possible; a batch or tubular reactor is to be preferred for carrying out such a reaction.

With *consecutive* reactions, the reaction path always ends in the final product(s) of the reaction chain. In many cases one of the intermediate products is the one desired. The maximum yield depends on the rates of formation and consumption of P, respectively, and on the way in which the reaction is carried out. This is illustrated in the triangular diagram of Fig. II-16 which summarizes the results of the chlorination of benzene treated in Illustration II.7. As before, the products di- and trichlorobenzene (X and Y, respectively) are together considered the undesired product. It is seen from this way of representation, as well as from Fig. II-13, that batch operation is most favourable. CHERMIN and VAN KREVELEN [27] have worked out the batch reaction paths for all possible combinations of 2 consecutive reactions of zero, first and second order. As another example, the reaction path is shown in Fig. II-17 for a reaction where the primary product P reacts further with reactant. If it is carried out in a batch reactor, only the first reaction occurs initially since only a small amount of P is present. At the end of the reaction, more P is present than A so that dc_P/dt is negative; however, depending on the value of k_1/k_2 more or less of P may be left after A has been completely converted, so that the reaction path does not necessarily end in the right-hand corner of the diagram. In a continuous tank reactor the composition is equal to that at the outlet; even at a relatively small degree of conversion of A, the composition of the reaction mixture favours the conversion of A and P to X.

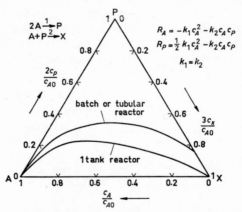

FIG. II-17. Isothermal reaction paths for combined consecutive and parallel reactions.

It has been shown that if the reaction scheme is known and the expressions for the conversion rates are available, reaction paths for batch (or tubular) and tank reactors can, in principle, be predicted; for the former reactor types this entails the solution of differential equations, and for the latter algebraic equations only. Now it may occur that the reaction path for a batch or a tubular reactor is known as a result of a number of laboratory experiments, but that no corresponding rate expressions are available. In such a case it is possible to find the reaction path for a tank reactor by a graphic construction. The method can only be used for reactions where at least one of the products, P or X, does not take part in the reaction and is a true final product.

If we consider a point 1 on an empirical batch reaction path, then we have (in molar units):

$$\left(\frac{dc_A}{dt}\right)_1 = R_{A1} \text{ and } \left(\frac{dc_P}{dt}\right)_1 = R_{P1}, \quad ^\star$$

so that:

$$\left(\frac{dc_A}{dc_P}\right)_1 = \left(\frac{R_A}{R_P}\right)_1.$$ II-25a

If the same point in the triangular diagram represents the composition at which a continuous tank reactor operates, we have (with $\varrho = $ constant):

$$\Phi_v(c_{A1} - c_{A0}) = R_{A1}V_r \text{ and } \Phi_v(c_{P1} - c_{P0}) = R_{P1}V_r,$$

so that:

$$\frac{c_{A1} - c_{A0}}{c_{P1} - c_{P0}} = \left(\frac{R_A}{R_P}\right)_1.$$ II-25b

A comparison of Eqs. II-25a and II-25b shows that the feed composition (c_{A0}, c_{P0}) of a tank reactor operating in point 1 must lie on the tangent to the batch reaction path at point 1 (see Fig. II-18). Conversely, one point of

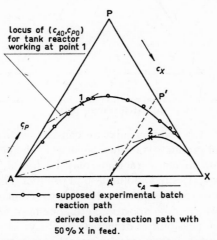

FIG. II-18. Principle of the method for finding the reaction path in a tank reactor from an empirical batch reaction path.

the reaction path for a tank reactor is found by drawing the tangent from the point (c_{A0}, c_{P0}) to a batch reaction path. Evidently, in order to construct

---

$\star$ We do not need to consider c_X since $c_A + c_P + c_X$ is assumed to be constant.

a number of such points, more than one batch reactor path must be available. They can be found by considering that, if the initial reaction mixture of the batch experiment already contained some of the final product (not taking part in the reaction), the batch reaction path would be entirely similar. In Fig. II-18, for example, there is complete similarity between the reaction path starting from point A′ (50% A and 50% X) in the secondary triangle A′P′X and the one starting with pure A. Point 2 in this diagram is one of the possible working points of a tank reactor with a feed containing component A only because the tangent in point 2 passes through the left-hand corner. Thus, after construction of a number of "secondary" batch reaction paths it is possible to construct the reaction path for a tank reactor by the method of tangents described above. Fig. II-19 shows another illustration of this procedure, which naturally can be applied equally well when the composition is given in mass units. In principle, the method can be extended to a cascade of tank reactors.

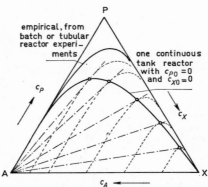

FIG. II-19. Construction of isothermal reaction path for one tank reactor from an empirical batch reactor path.

For processes where the reaction mixture consists of different components and a whole range of products is formed (such as in the petroleum industry), a triangular diagram in mass fractions may be useful, provided suitable discrimination between desired and undesired products is possible. By carrying out such reactions to different degrees of conversion and by variation of temperature, catalyst, feed composition, etc., one may readily see from the reaction paths which possibilities of increasing the yield of the desired product(s) exist. For a proper interpretation of such experiments it is essential, however, that the reaction paths obtained are isothermal. This technique has been extensively used by WEBER [28] and HUIBERS [29], and it was described in a recent book by WATERMAN, BOELHOUWER and HUIBERS [30]. These authors frequently approximate the reaction path by means of a hyperbola which passes through points A and X. For consecutive reactions, where X stands for the final product(s), such a mathematical description is always possible by proper selection of the constants involved. In principle, such a description does not apply to reactions where the end of the reaction path lies anywhere between the corners P and X.

II.8. A comparison between the different model reactors

The reactor models discussed in the foregoing sections are the well-mixed batch reactor, the continuously operated ideal tubular reactor, the continuously operated tank reactor and the cascade of tank reactors. The semi-continuous batch reactor and the cross-flow tubular reactor are not essentially different from the batch and tubular reactor, respectively. A comparison between the four basic reactor types mentioned above can be divided into two parts:

i. a comparison between batch and continuous operation, and

ii. a comparison between the tubular reactor and the tank reactor.

Batch versus continuous operation

In the design of a reactor for chemical production, the question must in principle be raised as to whether the process should be operated batchwise or continuously. Under the influence of recent developments, especially in the large chemical industries, there is a tendency towards making new processes continuous. There are, however, many processes for which continuous operation would be unprofitable or even impossible. General rules for the selection of either way of operation cannot be given, but some indications are summarized below.

Batch reactors are often used for small production rates and long reaction times. They are flexible and the reaction conditions can be adjusted; they are useful in plants where they serve for the production of various different chemicals (e.g., in the pharmaceutical industry). Batch operation is often preferred for reactions where rapid fouling occurs or contamination is feared (e.g., in biological fermentations). The investment costs of a batch reactor including auxiliary equipment generally are relatively low; on the other hand, relatively extensive manual operation and supervision are required, while automation is often difficult and costly.

Continuously operated reactors are capable of turning out a product of more constant quality; they require little supervision and they are well suited for the application of automatic control. Continuous reactors are especially applied at high production rates and high conversion rates. Gasphase reactions are almost exclusively carried out in a continuous process*.

An important factor in the decision of whether a batch or continuous process is to be preferred is the economic flexibility of the installation. For

---

* The internal-combustion engine is one of the exceptions, but its primary purpose is to produce mechanical power and not chemicals.

purposes of illustration, the economic diagrams are shown schematically for a certain process in Fig. II-20 (a and b), for batch and continuous operation, respectively. These diagrams give the production costs in MU (monetary units) per unit time as a function of the production rate Φ_P. The various lines are explained below.

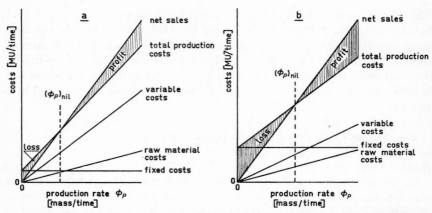

FIG. II-20. Economic diagrams typical of batch operation (a — low absolute production rate) and of continuous operation (b — high absolute production rate).

a. The *fixed costs* (depreciation, maintenance, supervision, etc.) are independent of Φ_P. They are mostly expressed as a certain percentage of these total investment costs, and they are relatively higher for continuous operation. Wages of operating personnel for the continuous plant are included in the fixed costs since it is assumed that the number of operators in this case does not depend on the production level.
b. The *variable costs* (electric power, steam, cooling water and other utilities, laboratory service, etc.) are approximately proportional to the production rate. They are generally much higher for a batch process because of starting and stopping operations, alternate heating and cooling of the installation and the difficulty of heat recovery by heat exchange; in this case, the wages of operating personnel are included in the variable costs.
c. The *raw material costs* are assumed to be proportional to the production rate and equal for the two ways of operation.
d. The *total production costs* are the sum of (a), (b) and (c).
e. The *net sales* of the product(s) (= sales revenues — sales expenses) are assumed to be the same in both cases.

The difference between (e) and (d) is equal to the loss or profit of the plant. The intersection of the lines (e) and (d) determines the break-even point $(\Phi_P)_{\text{nil}}$ below which the process is no longer profitable. Fig. II-20 (a and b) indicates that $(\Phi_P)_{\text{nil}}$ is smallest for batch operation, which means that it has greater economic flexibility*. On the other hand, with a relatively high value of Φ_P the profit is largest with continuous operation.

Tubular reactor versus tank reactor

In the ideal tubular reactor, all elements of volume entering the system have passed through the same history when arriving at the outlet. In the ideally mixed tank reactor, on the other hand, a fluid element entering the system immediately loses its identity since it is mixed with the whole reactor contents having the composition of the outlet stream. Consequently, the reaction course in a batch reactor is imitated in an ideal tubular reactor, whereas it is essentially different in a continuous tank reactor.

This difference is above all reflected in a difference in the quality of the product obtainable in the two types of reactors. It has already been shown in Section II.7 that, in cases of complex reactions, product distribution may greatly depend on the type of reactor used. As a general rule, a tubular reactor is to be preferred if the undesired reaction predominates at a high degree of conversion. Conversely, a tank reactor should be used whenever the desired reaction is stimulated at a high degree of conversion. In addition, a tank reactor may be useful if it is desired to "skip" a certain composition range.

Also, with reactions involving the growth of a certain species (such as polymerization, crystallization), the tubular reactor and the tank reactor will yield entirely different products. These products will be relatively more uniform (e.g., in the degree of polymerization or in the size distribution of crystal particles, respectively) when produced in a tubular reactor rather than in a tank reactor.

With regard to reactor capacity, the composition of the reaction mixture in a tank reactor is equal to the outlet composition; it has been already demonstrated in the preceding sections that, for this reason the capacity of a tank reactor is always smaller than that of a tubular reactor, if the reaction volume and the conditions are identical in both cases. This is also demonstrated in Fig. II-21, which shows the ratio between the volume of a tubular reactor and that of a tank reactor needed to obtain a certain relative degree of conversion for first and second order rate expressions. It is seen that the production capacity of a tank reactor is relatively small, especially at high degrees of conversion.

If a long residence time of the reaction mixture is required, a reactor consisting of a tube or tube bundle has technical and economical disadvantages. In such a case a cascade of tank reactors should be used instead. A cascade of only three reactors is in many instances considered a fair approximation of the tubular reactor (see also Fig. II-21), although in practice cascades of 10 to 20 reactors are encountered for special purposes.

---

* The economic result of a manufacturing process is less sensitive to an increase in production and raw materials costs, and to a decrease of the market value of its products, as its economic flexibility becomes greater.

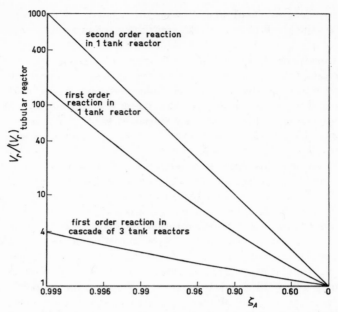

FIG. II-21. Comparison of required reactor volumes for isothermal first and second order reactions as a function of ζ_A.

In conclusion, it should be mentioned that we have used the concepts of tubular reactor and tank reactor in an abstract sense. They do not necessarily have the shape of a tube or a tank, respectively, although in practice this is mostly so. More essential, however, is the fact that a continuously operated reactor — in which mixing in the direction of main flow is negligible — has the characteristics of an ideal tubular reactor. If, on the other hand, mixing in the direction of flow is intensive, the properties of the tank reactor are approached. In this respect, the distribution of residence times is a characteristic feature of continuously operated reactors; this subject will be treated in Chapter III.

II.9. Some examples of the influence of reactor design and operation on the economics of the process

A detailed discussion of the economics of a chemical plant is beyond the scope of this book. As far as economical operation of a reactor is concerned, it will generally be sound policy to waste as little raw material and product as possible, especially when they are valuable, and to design and operate a reactor system the fixed and variable costs of which are reasonably low. In the preceding sections we have seen that in the case of a simple reactor design the reaction conditions (such as temperature, pressure and concentration)

56

and the reactor type already permit a certain amount of variation which will eventually influence the profitability of the installation. Apart from these there are a number of possibilities of variation which can be used either in the design stage or during operation in order to improve or adjust the plant economics. In this section mention will be made of only three of these possibilities which are frequently encountered in practice, i.e.:

i. the use of one of the reactants in excess;

ii. the recirculation of unconverted reactant;

iii. the policy of operation under non-steady process conditions.

The use of one of the reactants in excess

From the point of view of *capacity* it is always advantageous to feed the reactants in their stoichiometric ratio and at maximum concentrations. If, however, one of the reactants is relatively expensive it is sometimes rewarding to use the other, less expensive, reactant in excess so as to obtain a higher *yield* with respect to the former reactant. This is especially true if the recovery of the more expensive reactant from the product stream is difficult.

In practice, reactants frequently must be diluted, e.g. in order to suppress undesired side reactions or temperature changes occasioned by a large heat of reaction and a limited heat exchange capacity. Supposing the more expensive reactant, A, to have a fixed feed concentration c_{A0}, the use of the other reactant, B, in excess allows the reactor to be made smaller at the cost of extra expenses for B.

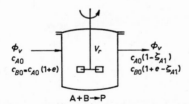

FIG. II-22. Continuous tank reactor with relative excess e of reactant B.

By way of illustration, let us consider the simple reaction $A + B \rightarrow P$ being carried out in a continuous tank reactor (Fig. II-22). We assume the density of the reaction mixture to be constant and the conversion rate to be determined by $|R|_A = kc_A c_B$. Using the relative excess of B with respect to A (e, as defined in Section II.4), the concentration at the inlet and at the outlet of the reactor can be expressed in terms of c_{A0}, e and the relative degree of conversion ζ_{A1}. According to Eq. II-11, the reaction volume is:

$$V_r = \frac{\Phi_v \zeta_{A1}}{kc_{A0}(1 - \zeta_{A1})(1 + e - \zeta_{A1})} .$$

At constant values of Φ_v, k, c_{A0} and ζ_{A1}, the reaction volume decreases as e increases. At the same time, however, the costs connected with the extra

57

feed of B rise. Hence, there is the possibility of an optimum value of e where the total production costs pass through a minimum as a function of e.

A slightly different problem is encountered if V_r, Φ_v and c_{A0} are given quantities and an increase in conversion is considered by using B in excess. In that case, the gain obtained by a greater degree of conversion of A is to be balanced against the extra costs of reactant B.

Excess of one of the reactants is also applied in reactions where the equilibrium does not lie entirely on the product side. This likewise results in a higher degree of conversion of a possibly expensive reactant. If this reactant can be separated from the product, its recirculation to the reactor has the same effect.

Recirculation of unconverted reactant

As an example let us consider an equilibrium reaction A → P carried out in a tubular reactor (cf. Fig. II-23). The product stream leaving the reactor is fed to a separation unit (e.g., a distillation column) where A and P are separated practically completely. Φ_m is the mass flow of feed consisting only of A ($w_A = 1$); the degree of conversion of A in the reactor is $\xi_{AL}(= 1 - w_{AL})$, and Φ_{mr} is the mass flow which is recirculated.

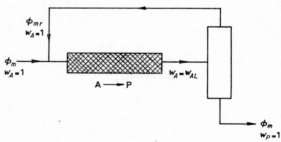

FIG. II-23. Tubular reactor with recirculation of nonconverted reactant A.

From a material balance for A over the separation unit we have:

$$\Phi_{mr} = (\Phi_m + \Phi_{mr})(1 - \xi_{AL}) .$$

The reaction volume is found from Eq. II-10:

$$V_r = (\Phi_m + \Phi_{mr}) \int_0^{\xi_{AL}} \frac{\mathrm{d}\xi_A}{|r|_A} .$$

Suppose the conversion rate can be approximated by:

$$|r|_A = k\varrho \, (w_A - w_P/K) ,$$

where K is the equilibrium constant of the reaction and the product $k\varrho$ is constant. With the use of the last three equations we then find for the reaction

58

volume:

$$\frac{\varrho V_r k}{\varPhi_m} = \frac{-K}{(K+1)\xi_{AL}} \ln \left(1 - \frac{K+1}{K} \xi_{AL}\right).$$

This quantity has been plotted in Fig. II-24 as a function of ξ_{AL} for $K = 1$ and for $K \gg 1$, together with the recirculation ratio $\varPhi_{mr}/\varPhi_m$. Since the total production costs will rise when $\varrho V_r k/\varPhi_m$ and $\varPhi_{mr}/\varPhi_m$ increase, it is clear that an optimum value of ξ_{AL} exists. The position of this economic optimum can, of course, be determined only on the basis of detailed cost calculations.

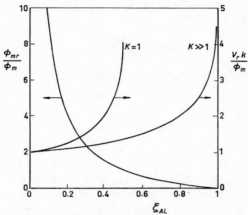

FIG. II-24. Recirculation ratio and reactor volume for a first order equilibrium reaction in the installation shown in Fig. II-23.

Maximum production rate and optimum load with intermittent operation

The operation of batch reactors or of continuous catalytic processes in which the activity of the catalyst decreases as a function of time frequently poses the following two problems:

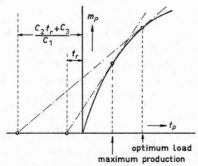

FIG. II-25. Production times t_p for a maximum average production rate and for optimum load, respectively.

a. What reaction or production time should be selected for obtaining maximum production with the installation?

b. What policy should be adopted for minimizing production costs (optimum load)?

In these installations, the cumulative mass m_P of P produced is a function of the production time, t_p, in such a way that the instantaneous production rate, $\Phi_P = dm_P/dt_p$, decreases with increasing t_p (see Fig. II-25). The relation between m_P and t_p may be either theoretical or empirical. If t_r is the period of time during which the reactor is out of operation for purposes of emptying, cleaning and charging, or of replacing or regenerating catalyst, the average production rate is:

$$\overline{\Phi}_P = \frac{m_P}{t_p + t_r}.$$

Maximum average production rate is governed by the condition:

$$d\overline{\Phi}_P/dt_p = 0 ,$$

which yields:

$$\frac{dm_P}{dt_p} = \frac{m_P}{t_p + t_r}.$$

It is seen from Fig. II-25 that the corresponding value of t_p can be obtained by drawing the tangent to the $m_P - t_p$ curve from the point $(-t_r, 0)$.

The operating costs must be available for the calculating of the *optimum load* of the installation. Suppose that:

$C_1 =$ the costs per unit time during production,
$C_2 =$ the costs per unit time when the reactor does not produce, and
$C_3 =$ the additional expenses per period (e.g. extra manpower, special facilities or new catalyst),

then the average total costs per unit mass of product equal $(C_1 t_p + C_2 t_r + C_3)/m_P$. For optimum load this expression must be a minimum, from which condition we find that:

$$\frac{dm_P}{dt_p} = \frac{m_P}{t_p + (C_2 t_r + C_3)/C_1}.$$

The corresponding value is obtained from the point of contact of a tangent to the m_P-curve going through the point $(-(C_2 t_r + C_3)/C_1, 0)$, as shown in Fig. II-25. It will be clear from this that the conditions for maximum capacity and optimum load do not, in principle, coincide.

ILLUSTRATION II. 9. *Maximum production and optimum load in a batch process*

Determination of the above two quantities is required for the batch reactor treated in Illustration II.1. The pertinent production costs are:

During operation,	27.60 MU/hr★	(C_1)
During down-period,	8.40 MU/hr	(C_2)
Additional per period,	104.00 MU	(C_3); the down-period t_r is 1 hour.

Fig. II-26 shows the relative degree of conversion ζ_B of acid B as a function of reaction time, which can be calculated from the data given in Illustration II.1. Since the amount of ethyl acetate produced is directly proportional to ζ_B, it is not necessary to convert the ordinate in Fig. II-26 to m_P.

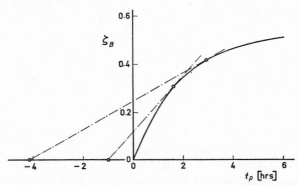

FIG. II-26. Construction of reaction times t_p for maximum production rate and for optimum load, respectively, in a batch process; Illustration II.10.

The tangent to the ζ_B-curve through the point (-1 hr) on the abscissa gives a point of contact at $\zeta_B = 0.31$ and $t_p = 1.6$ hr. Hence, the maximum average production rate of ethyl acetate (P) is:

$$\frac{24}{t_p + 1.0} \times c_{B0}\, \zeta_B M_P = 985 \text{ kg/day m}^3 .$$

For finding the optimum load, a tangent has to be drawn through the point on the abscissa:

$$t_p = -\frac{8.40\, t_r + 104.00}{27.60} = -4.1 \text{ hr} ,$$

which yields: $\zeta_B = 0.42$ and $t_p = 2.9$ hr. A comparison of the two policies of operation is given in the following table:

condition	maximum production	optimum load
relative degree of acid conversion ζ_B	0.31	0.42
reaction time t_p(hr)	1.6	2.9
ester production (kg/batch)	5560	7530
ester production rate (kg/m³ day)	985	660
production costs (10^{-3} MU/kg ester)	28.1	25.5

It is seen that the reaction costs per unit mass of product are 10% higher at maximum production rate than under conditions of optimum load. It furthermore appears that the design requirement in Illustration II.1 ($\zeta_B = 0.35$) does not represent an economic optimum. Finally, it is to be noted that the above calculation only gives production costs for the reactor itself. The total production costs are higher by an amount which is determined by the losses of raw materials and product, and the expenses incurred in other parts of the plant (feed preparation, product separation, product storage and delivery).

★ MU = monetary unit, approximately equal to one Dutch guilder.

CHAPTER III

RESIDENCE TIME DISTRIBUTION AND MIXING IN CONTINUOUS FLOW REACTORS

The purpose of this chapter is to discuss to what extent continuous reactor systems used in practice are different from the models treated in the previous chapter. As a starting point of this discussion we take the residence time distribution, which is largely characteristic of the reactor type and on the basis of which a comparison with the model reactors is possible. Next, the influence of the residence time distribution on the chemical conversion in a reactor is treated. It appears that in case of a large spread in residence times and for reactions which are not of the first order with respect to the reactants the knowledge of the residence time distribution is not sufficient for predicting the degree of conversion. Additional information on the degree of mixing between elements of different history is needed.

III.1. The residence time distribution function $F(\tau)$

By the residence time distribution function $F(\tau)$ of a continuous flow system we understand the volume fraction of the fluid at the outlet which has resided in the system during a time less than τ. In other words, if we assign to an element of volume leaving the system after a residence time τ the "age" τ, $F(\tau)$ is the volume fraction in the outlet stream having an age lower than τ.

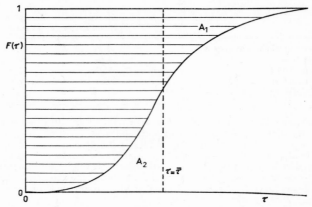

FIG. III-1. A residence time distribution curve; $A_1 = A_2$.

Clearly, we have for $\tau = 0 : F(0) = 0$, and for $\tau = \infty : F(\infty) = 1$.

According to the above definition, the differential of $F(\tau)$, $\mathrm{d}F(\tau)$, is the volume fraction of the outgoing stream which has a residence time between τ and $\tau + \mathrm{d}\tau$. After multiplication of $\mathrm{d}F(\tau)$ by τ and integration between $\tau = 0$ and $\tau = \infty$ we find the average residence time $\bar{\tau}$ of the fluid in the system:

$$\bar{\tau} = \int_0^{\infty} \tau \, \mathrm{d}F(\tau) \,. \qquad \qquad \text{III-1}$$

Fig. III-1 shows an arbitrary residence time distribution function. As a consequence of Eq. III-1, the shaded area is equal to $\bar{\tau}$; this also means that the areas A_1 and A_2 must be equal.

For a few idealized systems the function $F(\tau)$ can be calculated beforehand. As will be shown in the next section, the $F(\tau)$ curve for an ideally mixed continuous tank reactor is a simple exponential function. For an ideal tubular reactor the $F(\tau)$ curve can be described by:

$$F(\tau) = 0 \qquad \text{for} \qquad 0 < \tau < \tau_L \,,$$

and

$$F(\tau) = 1 \qquad \text{for} \qquad \tau > \tau_L \,,$$

since in this case all elements of volume leaving the system have the same age τ_L.

In accordance with the above definition of $F(\tau)$, the probability that an element of volume, which has entered the system at $t = 0$, has left it within a period of time t is given by $F(t)$. The probability that it will leave at a moment later than t is $[1 - F(t)]$.

From the latter interpretation of the residence time distribution function it follows that its shape can be experimentally determined by changing some property of the fluid entering the system as a function of time and by investigating the resulting change at the outlet. As the property to be measured, use is generally made of the concentration of some tracer substance. The only requirements are that such a substance must not disappear during the experiment (e.g., by chemical reaction, adsorption or settling) and that its concentration can be conveniently and accurately measured (e.g., by electrical conductivity, light absorption or nuclear radiation).

We shall call the varying inlet concentration w_0 the *incoming signal* and the outlet concentration w_1 the *outgoing signal* in such an experiment. The outgoing signal is then called the *response* of the system to the incoming signal. Both in theoretical and experimental studies, three forms of incoming signals are mostly used:

i. a step-function, where at $t = 0$ the incoming concentration changes from one steady value to a different one;

ii. a sharp pulse, where at $t = 0$ a certain amount of tracer is injected into the inlet in the shortest possible time;

iii. a steady sinusoidal variation of the incoming signal; here the response signal is likewise sinusoidal with the same frequency. By plotting the amplitude attenuation and the phase shift of the outgoing signal with respect to the incoming one as a function of the applied frequency ω, the so-called frequency-response diagram of the system is obtained. This way of presentation is customary in the theory of automatic control and servomechanisms for characterizing the dynamic behaviour of the various elements in a control circuit.

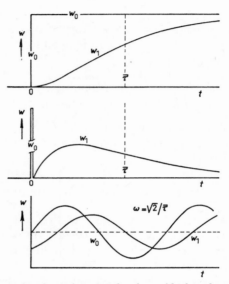

FIG. III-2. The response signal w, of a cascade of two ideal tank reactors to a varying incoming signal w_0, when this is a step-function, a pulse or a sinusoidal function, respectively.

Fig. III-2 shows as an example the response of two equal tank reactors in cascade to the three types of input signals mentioned above. The curves of response to a stepwise and a pulse signal and the frequency-response diagram essentially contain the same information and each of them can, in principle, be transformed into one of the others. For example, a pulse signal is the derivative with respect to time of a step-function, and consequently the response of a certain system to a pulse signal is equal to the derivative of its response to a stepwise input signal*. The translation of the frequency-response diagram into a step-function or pulse response curve and vice versa is somewhat more complicated; it will not be treated here.

In practice it is often difficult to produce signals which approach the mathematical forms mentioned under *i* and *ii*; therefore, they only give good

---

* This statement is generally valid for linear systems; the continuous flow systems with inert concentration signals belong to this group.

results in experiments with systems having a relatively long average residence time and a rather large spread in the residence time distribution. If the latter is not present, frequency-response measurements may have to be applied; they are time-consuming and require special equipment for the production of sinusoidal signals in a wide frequency range.

With regard to the relationship between the residence time distribution function and the response of a system to an input signal it appears that the relative signal of response to a step-function is identical with the $F(\tau)$ curve. This can be shown in the following manner.

Suppose that, at $t = 0$ at the inlet of the system, w_0 is changed from w_0^- to w_0^+. Then, at a time t, the fraction $F(t)$ of the fluid leaving the system (which has an age smaller than t) has the composition w_0^+, whereas the fraction $[1 - F(t)]$ has the original inlet composition w_0^-. Hence, the mass fraction w_1 at the outlet is given by:

$$w_1 = F(t)\, w_0^+ + [1 - F(t)]w_0^- .$$

From this we find for the relative response to a step-function:

$$\frac{w_1 - w_0^-}{w_0^+ - w_0^-} = F(t) . \qquad\qquad \text{III-2}$$

Regarding the relative response to a pulse input signal, it can easily be shown that it is equal to the derivative of $F(t)$:

$$\frac{w_1 \Phi_m}{m_T} = \frac{\mathrm{d}F(t)}{\mathrm{d}t} , \qquad\qquad \text{III-3}$$

where w_1 is the response signal due to the pulse injection, Φ_m the mass flow rate through the system and m_T the amount of tracer injected at $t = 0$ into the inlet stream.

For a general discussion on the $F(t)$ curve and the application of the incoming signals of types i and ii, reference is made to a paper by DANCKWERTS [31]. The relation between the residence time distribution and the frequency-response characteristics was discussed by KRAMERS and ALBERDA [32].

III.2. Residence time distribution in a continuous tank reactor

The residence time distribution function of an ideally mixed tank reactor can be calculated by several methods as shown below.

Direct derivation
Due to the ideal mixing, an element of volume immediately upon entering the mixed volume may occur at any place in the system. It is not possible, therefore, to derive its previous history from its position. Hence, the chance

that it leaves the system within a specified time is entirely independent of this previous history. As a consequence, the probability that it stays in the system longer than, say, $(t + \Delta t)$ is composed of the two independent probabilities of its staying longer than t and Δt, respectively:

$$1 - F(t + \Delta t) = [1 - F(t)][1 - F(\Delta t)] .$$

Now, for an ideally mixed vessel we have:

$$F(\Delta t) = \frac{\Phi_m}{\varrho V_r} \Delta t = \Delta t / \bar{\tau} ,$$

since all elements of volume have an equal chance of leaving the system. By substitution of the latter equation in the former, and by letting Δt approach an infinitely small increment dt, we obtain the differential equation for $F(t)$:

$$\frac{dF(t)}{dt} + \frac{1}{\bar{\tau}} F(t) = \frac{1}{\bar{\tau}} .$$

With the boundary condition $F(0) = 0$ its solution is:

$$F(t) = 1 - e^{-t/\bar{\tau}} . \qquad\qquad \text{III-4}$$

Circulation model (BROTHMAN, WEBER and BARISH [33])

We consider an agitated vessel with a well-defined internal circulation flow (Fig. III-3a) or a loop in which fluid circulates (Fig. III-3b) as an approximation of a well-mixed tank reactor. The volumetric circulation flow rate Φ_{vc} is assumed to be much greater than the steady flow Φ_v through the system.

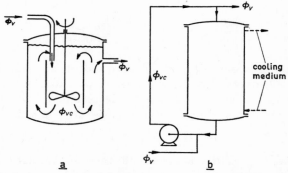

FIG. III-3. Circulation systems as an approximation to a continuous tank reactor; a — tank with internal circulation, b — reactor (e.g., heat exchanger) with external circulation.

The probability p of an element of volume leaving the system after one cycle is assumed to be equal to $\Phi_v / (\Phi_{vc} + \Phi_v)$. With $\bar{\tau} = V_r / \Phi_v$ and the time for one circulation $t_c = V_r / (\Phi_{vc} + \Phi_v)$ we get:

$$p = t_c / \bar{\tau} .$$

Consequently, the probability that an element of volume which entered the system at $t = 0$ is still present in the system after one cycle is given by:

$$1 - F(t_c) = 1 - p \, .$$

Actually, after each cycle the probability of staying in the system is $(1 - p)$. Since these probabilities are independent in successive circulation periods, we may write:

$$1 - F(mt_c) = (1 - p)^m \, ,$$

or:

$$F(mt_c) = 1 - (1 - p)^m \, . \qquad\qquad \text{III-5}$$

If plotted as a function of the integer m, $F(mt_c)$ would be a discontinuous line consisting of horizontal line segments at a level $F(mt_c)$ between m and $m + 1$. As the ideally mixed tank reactor is approached, Φ_{vc}/Φ_v goes to infinity, or $t_c/\bar{t} = p$ approaches zero, and the $F(mt_c)$ curve becomes a continuous function of time $t = mt_c$:

$$\lim_{t_c \to 0} F(mt_c) = F(t) = \lim_{p \to 0} [1 - (1 - p)^m] =$$

$$= \lim_{p \to 0} [1 - (1 - p)^{t/p\bar{t}}] = 1 - e^{-t/\bar{t}} \, .$$

It is seen that this result is identical with Eq. III-4.

Response to a step-function

If the mass fraction w_0 of a tracer material in the inlet stream of an ideally mixed tank reactor is changed from a value 0 to w_0^+ at the moment $t = 0$, the material balance for $t > 0$ becomes:

$$\frac{\mathrm{d}(\varrho V_r w_1)}{\mathrm{d}t} = \Phi_{m0} w_0^+ - \Phi_{m1} w_1 \, .$$

Under the initial conditions that $w_1 = 0$ at $t = 0$, and on the assumption that the total mass in the reactor remains constant ($\Phi_{m0} = \Phi_{m1}$) during such an experiment, the solution is:

$$\frac{w_1}{w_0^+} = 1 - e^{-t/\bar{t}} \, .$$

According to Eq. III-2, this expression is identical with $F(t)$, and this also results from comparison with III-4.

It is seen from Fig. III-4, which contains the $F(t)$ curve for the ideally mixed tank reactor, that the spread in the residence time distribution is very great. It is also to be noted that, with such a system, a change in inlet conditions immediately manifests itself at the outlet; in view of the automatic control of a continuous tank reactor this is an extremely favourable feature.

The question arises to what extent a real continuous tank reactor approaches the ideal tank reactor. In actual practice the feed stream entering into

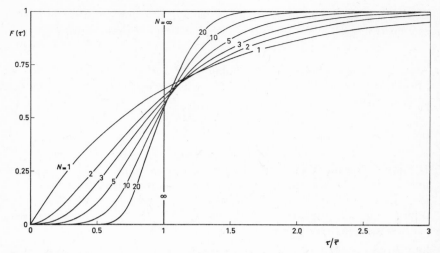

FIG. III-4. Residence time distribution curves for several cascades of N equal tank reactors.

the agitated fluid is not immediately dispersed over the whole contents. It will take some time for this to happen to a sufficient extent, and this time will be of the order of magnitude of the mixing time. As a consequence, the response to a step-function in the inlet concentration will be initially delayed with respect to the ideal response curve Eq. III-4, but at the same time little lumps of the feed stream, which have not yet sufficiently disintegrated, may pass through the outlet. They then cause irregular peaks in the beginning of the response curve. These effects are very hard to describe in a quantitative manner and they depend for a great deal on the locations of the inlet and the outlet with respect to the agitator and to each other.

The smaller the ratio of mixing time and average residence time $\bar{\tau}$, the better is the residence time distribution of an ideal tank reactor approached. For most practical purposes, a ratio smaller than 1/10 gives a sufficient approximation to an ideal tank reactor. Rules for estimating mixing times in agitated liquids are given by, e.g., VAN DE VUSSE [34]. It appears from his paper that the mixing time is of the same order of magnitude as the time required for once pumping around the contents of the tank. In this connection, the above criterion is equivalent to the condition $p < 1/10$ in Eq. III-5 for an adequate approach to ideal mixing.

III.3. Residence time distribution in a cascade of tank reactors

We consider a cascade of N ideally mixed tank reactors with equal volumes V_{rn}. For finding the residence time distribution function we calculate the response w_N to a stepwise change of a tracer concentration at the inlet from a value 0 to w_0^+ at $t = 0$. For tank reactor No. n, the material balance (non-steady operation, no chemical reaction and constant total mass flow through the system) is:

$$\varrho V_{rn} \frac{\mathrm{d}w_n}{\mathrm{d}t} = \Phi_m(w_{n-1} - w_n) .$$

After introduction of the total average residence time in the system, $\bar{\tau} = \varrho N V_{rn}/\Phi_m$, we obtain:

$$\frac{\mathrm{d}w_n}{\mathrm{d}t} + \frac{N}{\bar{\tau}} w_n = \frac{N}{\bar{\tau}} w_{n-1} . \qquad \text{III-6}$$

With the initial condition $w_n = 0$ for $t = 0$, the solution becomes:

$$w_n = \mathrm{e}^{-Nt/\bar{\tau}} \int_0^t \frac{N}{\bar{\tau}} w_{n-1} \, \mathrm{e}^{Nt/\bar{\tau}} \, \mathrm{d}t .$$

Calculation of the integral for the first tank reactor (where $w_0 = w_0^+ = $ constant) and then for the successive ones yields the final result:

$$\frac{w_N}{w_0^+} = F(t) = 1 - \mathrm{e}^{-Nt/\bar{\tau}} \times$$

$$\times \left[1 + \frac{Nt}{\bar{\tau}} + \frac{1}{2!}\left(\frac{Nt}{\bar{\tau}}\right)^2 + \cdots + \frac{1}{(N-1)!}\left(\frac{Nt}{\bar{\tau}}\right)^{N-1} \right] . \qquad \text{III-7}$$

As required, this function is zero for $t = 0$ and unity for $t \to \infty$. In Fig. III-4 a number of $F(\tau)$ curves according to Eq. III-7 are shown as a function of $\tau/\bar{\tau}$. It is seen that as N increases the spread in distribution becomes smaller and that as $N \to \infty$ the $F(\tau)$ curve for the ideal tubular reactor is approached.

If the slope of the $F(\tau)$ curves is calculated from Eq. III-7 we find that it is given by the Poisson distribution function:

$$\frac{\mathrm{d}F(\tau)}{\mathrm{d}(\tau/\bar{\tau})} = N \, \mathrm{e}^{-N\tau/\bar{\tau}} \frac{1}{(N-1)!} \left(\frac{N\tau}{\bar{\tau}}\right)^{N-1} .$$

The value of the slope near the inflection point of the S-shaped $F(\tau)$ curves is found by putting $\tau/\bar{\tau} = 1$, so that we obtain:

$$\left(\frac{\mathrm{d}F(\tau)}{\mathrm{d}(\tau/\bar{\tau})}\right)_{\tau/\bar{\tau}=1} = \frac{N\mathrm{e}^{-N}N^{N-1}}{(N-1)!} = \frac{N^{N+1}\mathrm{e}^{-N}}{N!} .$$

Now, according to Stirling's rule we have for $N > 5$ within 2%:

$$N! \approx N^N \mathrm{e}^{-N}\sqrt{2\pi N} .$$

Introduction of this approximation into the former equation yields:

$$\left(\frac{\mathrm{d}F(\tau)}{\mathrm{d}(\tau/\bar{\tau})}\right)_{\tau/\bar{\tau}=1} \approx \sqrt{\frac{N}{2\pi}}, \quad N > 5 . \qquad \text{III-8}$$

This result also illustrates the fact that the $F(\tau)$ curve becomes steeper as N increases. The above calculations can be extended to a cascade where the reactors do not have equal volumes; this was shown by MASON and PIRET [35].

It would be extremely difficult to take into account the non-ideal mixing in actual tank reactors. In general, however, it can be said that such an effect would tend to increase somewhat the effective value of N of a cascade. Since the shape of the $F(\tau)$ curve is rather insensitive to N with large values of N, the non-ideal mixing may be disregarded in that case.

III.4. Residence time distribution in a tubular reactor with longitudinal dispersion; analogy with a cascade

Whereas the $F(\tau)$ curve of an ideal tubular reactor has the shape of a retarded step-function (compare Section III.1), the $F(\tau)$ curve for an actual reactor of the tubular type is not sharp but S-shaped (Fig. III-5). The cor-

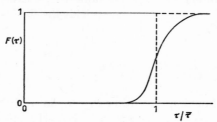

FIG. III-5. Residence time distribution curves of an ideal (...) and a real (—) tubular reactor.

responding spread in residence times is due to the phenomenon of *longitudinal dispersion*, to which the following effects may contribute:

i. Vortices and turbulent eddies may produce convective mixing in the direction of flow (longitudinal mixing);

ii. The velocity distribution over a cross-section is not generally uniform, and consequently the residence times of particles travelling along different streamlines will be different;

iii. In principle, molecular diffusion always takes place.

In the majority of practical cases, the effects of *i* and *ii* are much greater than the effect of *iii*. Furthermore, there is an essential difference between *i* and *ii* in the sense that phenomenon *i* can give rise to "back-mixing", i.e. upstream transport of material under the influence of a concentration gradient, whereas in case *ii* back-mixing is, in principle, impossible.

When the spread in the residence times is relatively small, it generally appears that the $F(\tau)$ curve is highly similar to a curve obtained by integrating the normal error or Gaussian distribution curve. This suggests that the residence time distribution of a non-ideal tubular reactor may be considered approximately the result of piston flow (as in the ideal case) combined with a diffusion-like longitudinal dispersion. The latter is taken into account by means of a constant effective longitudinal dispersion coefficient D_l; it has the same dimension as the molecular diffusivity but may be much greater than this due to effects i and ii. We shall derive the residence time distribution function of such a system by calculating its response to a stepwise change in tracer concentration at $t = 0$ at the inlet $z = 0$.

The tracer concentration w is a function of the position z and of time. A material balance over a section dz of the tube yields for the unsteady state and in the absence of chemical reaction:

$$\frac{\partial w}{\partial t} = D_l \frac{\partial^2 w}{\partial z^2} - \frac{\Phi_m}{S\varrho} \frac{\partial w}{\partial z},$$

$\qquad$ III-9

where $\Phi_m/S\varrho$ may be put equal to the flow velocity $\langle v \rangle$ averaged over the cross section; it is constant when $S\varrho$ is independent of z. We use the initial condition:

$$\left. \begin{array}{ll} w = 0 & \text{for} \quad z > 0 \\ w = w_0^+ & \text{for} \quad z < 0 \end{array} \right\} \text{ at } t = 0,$$

and the boundary conditions for $t \geqslant 0$:

$$\begin{array}{ll} w = 0 & \text{for} \quad z = \infty \\ w = w_0^+ & \text{for} \quad z = -\infty. \end{array}$$

It appears that a solution can be found where w/w_0^+ is a function of the following single variable:

$$\frac{z - \langle v \rangle t}{\sqrt{4D_l t}} = \zeta.$$

This new variable is introduced into Eq. III-9 by means of the substitutions:

$$\frac{\partial w}{\partial z} = \frac{dw}{d\zeta} \frac{\partial \zeta}{\partial z}, \qquad \frac{\partial^2 w}{\partial z^2} = \frac{d^2 w}{d\zeta^2} \left(\frac{\partial \zeta}{\partial z} \right)^2 + \frac{dw}{d\zeta} \frac{\partial^2 \zeta}{\partial z^2},$$

and

$$\frac{\partial w}{\partial t} = \frac{dw}{d\zeta} \frac{\partial \zeta}{\partial t}.$$

The differential equation then becomes:

$$\frac{d^2(w/w_0^+)}{d\zeta^2} + 2\zeta \frac{d(w/w_0^+)}{d\zeta} = 0,$$

$\qquad$ III-10

with the boundary conditions:

$$w/w_0^+ = 0 \text{ for } \zeta = \infty,$$

and

$$w/w_0^+ = 1 \text{ for } \zeta = -\infty.$$

The solution to Eq. III-10 with its boundary conditions is:

$$\frac{w}{w_0^+} = \tfrac{1}{2}\left[1 - \frac{2}{\sqrt{\pi}}\int_0^{(z-\langle v \rangle t)/\sqrt{4D_l t}} \exp(-\zeta^2)\,d\zeta\right] =$$

$$= \tfrac{1}{2}\left[1 - \mathrm{erf}\left(\frac{z-\langle v \rangle t}{\sqrt{4D_l t}}\right)\right]^{\!\star}. \qquad \text{III-11}$$

The relative response, w_L/w_0^+, at the end of the tube ($z = L$) is equal to $F(t)$ (see Eq. III-2), so that with $L/\langle v \rangle = \bar{\tau}$ we obtain:

$$F(t) = \frac{w_L}{w_0^+} = \tfrac{1}{2}\left[1 - \mathrm{erf}\left(\tfrac{1}{2}\sqrt{\frac{\langle v \rangle L}{D_l}} \times \frac{1 - t/\bar{\tau}}{\sqrt{t/\bar{\tau}}}\right)\right]. \qquad \text{III-12}$$

The residence time distribution function $F(\tau)$ follows from Eq. III-12 when t is replaced by τ. For the slope of this function at the value $\tau = \bar{\tau}$ we find:

$$\left[\frac{dF(\tau)}{d(\tau/\bar{\tau})}\right]_{\tau/\bar{\tau}=1} = \tfrac{1}{2}\sqrt{\frac{\langle v \rangle L}{\pi D_l}}, \qquad \text{III-13}$$

which shows that this slope approaches infinity as D_l becomes zero (ideal tubular reactor).

Now, a cascade consisting of a large number of ideally mixed tank reactors and a tubular reactor with a relatively small longitudinal dispersion have $F(\tau)$ curves which are very similar to each other. They may be said to be approximately identical when their slopes at $\tau = \bar{\tau}$ are equal. By comparing Eqs. III-8 and III-13 we see that this is so when:

$$N = \frac{\langle v \rangle L}{2D_l} \equiv N'. \qquad \text{III-14}$$

This correspondence between a tubular system with dispersion and a cascade is only exact for $N = \infty$, but for practical purposes it can be used for $N > 10$. Since the dimensionless group $\langle v \rangle L/2D_l$ is indicative of the number of mixers in a cascade with which it is equivalent, we shall denote it by the symbol N'.

The analogy $N' \triangleq N$ fails for $N < 10$ for various reasons. Firstly the shapes of the corresponding $F(\tau)$ curves become different as N' and N decrease; furthermore, the result III-8 is restricted to $N > 5$ and the derivation of Eq. III-11 is restricted to relatively small dispersions (i.e., N' large). Actually, the proper boundary conditions to be used in solving Eq. III-9 are (also see Eqs. III-17 and 18):

$\star$ The error function is defined as:

$$\mathrm{erf}\, y = \frac{2}{\sqrt{\pi}}\int_0^y e^{-\zeta^2}\,d\zeta;\ \mathrm{erf}(\pm\,\infty) = \pm 1,\ \mathrm{erf}(0) = 0.$$

and

$$\langle v \rangle w_0^+ = \langle v \rangle w - D_l \frac{\partial w}{\partial z} \quad \text{for } z = 0$$

$$\frac{\partial w}{\partial z} = 0 \qquad\qquad\qquad \text{for } z = L$$

$$\left. \right\} \; t \geqslant 0 .$$

The solution with these boundary conditions was recently calculated by HIBY and SCHÜMMER [36]. Fig. III-6 shows some of their results for $N' = 2$ and $N' = 5$ in comparison to the $F(\tau)$ curves of 2 and 5 tank reactors in cascade, respectively. It is seen that the discrepancy between the corresponding $F(\tau)$ curves is appreciable. In the limiting case $N' = 0$, Eq. III-9 with these boundary conditions yields the response curve of an ideally mixed tank reactor ($N = 1$).

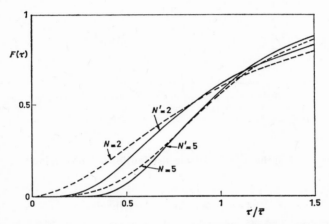

FIG. III-6. $F(\tau)$ curves for $N' = 2$ and $N' = 5$ according to HIBY and SCHÜMMER (see [36]) in comparison to those for a cascade with $N = 2$ and $N = 5$ equal tank reactors.

ILLUSTRATION III.4. *Blending in pipeline transport*

In order to illustrate the use of Eq. III-11 we shall discuss the following problem. Two different liquids A and B are transported in succession over a distance of 1 km through a pipeline with an internal diameter d_t of 10 cm at an average velocity of 1 m/s. The two liquids have approximately the same density and viscosity; $\nu = 5 \times 10^{-6}$ m²/s. If the transition from A to B is sharp at the inlet of the pipeline, during what period should a mixture of A and B be discharged separately at the end in order not to let contamination of A by B exceed 4%, and that of B by A 1%? D_l in this case is given by the relationship:

$$\frac{\langle v \rangle d_t}{D_l} = \frac{0.283}{\sqrt{f}} ,$$

where f is the Fanning friction factor (see Section III.9).

If we denote the mass fraction of B by w, w_0 changes from 0 to 1 at $t = 0$ at the inlet of the tube; the problem to be solved is to find the times at which w_L has the values 0.04 and 0.99, respectively, at the end of the tube.

From the above data we find $Re = 2 \times 10^4$, and the corresponding value of f for smooth pipes is 0.0062. Hence:

$$\frac{\langle v \rangle L}{D_l} = \frac{L}{d_t} \times \frac{\langle v \rangle d_t}{D_l} = 10^4 \times \frac{0.283}{\sqrt{0.0062}} = 3.74 \times 10^4 ,$$

which indicates that the dispersion is relatively small. The average residence time $\bar{\tau} = L/\langle v \rangle = 1000$ s. Application of Eq. III-11 to this problem gives the following results:

w_L (mass fraction of B at the outlet)	0.04	0.99
$\operatorname{erf}\left(\frac{1}{2}\sqrt{\frac{\langle v \rangle L}{D_l}} \times \frac{1 - t/\bar{\tau}}{\sqrt{t/\bar{\tau}}}\right)$	0.92	-0.98
$\frac{1}{2}\sqrt{\frac{\langle v \rangle L}{D_l}} \times \frac{1 - t/\bar{\tau}}{\sqrt{t/\bar{\tau}}}$	1.24	-1.65
$\frac{1 - t/\bar{\tau}}{\sqrt{t/\bar{\tau}}} \approx 1 - t/\bar{\tau}$	-1.28×10^{-2}	1.70×10^{-2}
$t - \bar{\tau}$ (s)	-12.8	17.0

It is seen that the discharge of undesired mixture should start about 13 seconds before $t = \bar{\tau}$, and continue until 17 seconds after this moment. The amount discharged is the fraction $(13 + 17)/1000$ of the pipe volume, i.e. 0.24 m³, corresponding to a length of 30 m pipe.

III.5. Influence of the residence time distribution on conversion in a continuous flow reactor

In previous sections the residence time distribution was discussed for a few model reactor systems: the tank reactor, a cascade of tank reactors and a tubular reactor with longitudinal dispersion. Combination of this information with the results of the reactor calculations in Chapter II indicates that, in general, a large spread in residence time distribution will involve a relatively small reactor capacity. A closer analysis of the possible causes of a spread in residence times is needed for a more quantitative study of this influence.

A measure of the spread in residence times is the *hold-back*, a quantity defined by DANCKWERTS [31] as:

$$H = \int_0^1 F(\tau)\, \mathrm{d}(\tau/\bar{\tau}) . \qquad \text{III-15}$$

While the value of $F(\tau)$ at $\tau = \bar{\tau}$ is the fraction in the outlet with an age lower than $\bar{\tau}$, the hold-back is the fraction of the feed which has entered the system during $0 < t < \bar{\tau}$ and has left it within the same period of time. Consequently, it also represents the fraction of the contents of the system at $t = 0$ which is held back in it during the period $0 < t < \bar{\tau}$. For an ideal tubular reactor, $H = 0$; and for an ideally mixed tank reactor, $H = 1/e$ (see Fig. III-7).

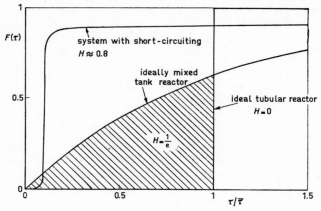

FIG. III-7. Illustration of hold-back H and short-circuiting.

It may be said that the degree of conversion obtainable in a continuous reactor generally decreases as the value of H becomes higher, if the average residence time $\bar{\tau}$ and the reaction conditions are not changed. Clearly, the ideal tubular reactor with $H = 0$ is the extreme case with the maximum possible capacity. If $H > 0$, the capacity is reduced but the extent of this reduction is not solely dependent on the magnitude of H; as was pointed out in Section III.4, there are two essentially different effects which may contribute to a positive value of H (disregarding molecular diffusion):

i. Mixing on a microscopic scale between elements of different age;

ii. A flow pattern where the fluid particles follow different paths without mutual mixing on a microscopic scale.

We shall refer to a *mixed system* when the hold-back is entirely determined by the effect *i*, and to a *segregated system* when the effect *ii* is the origin of the spread in residence times. In practice, all possible combinations of *i* and *ii* may be encountered.

A *mixed system* can be described by means of the longitudinal dispersion model characterized by the value of N' (see Section III.4) or by a cascade of N tank reactors (see Section III.3), depending on whether or not the flow pattern gives rise to back-mixing. For N' and $N > 10$, the two models give approximately the same results. The maximum amount of mixing, i.e. the extreme case of effect *i*, is obtained in the ideally mixed tank reactor ($N' = 0$ and $N = 1$); the maximum value of H due to this effect is $1/e$. The tank reactor provides for a very effective dilution of the reactants entering the reactor, and a relatively small average conversion rate is its result.

In a *segregated system* the elements of volume do not interact upon entering the reactor; they still retain their identity on leaving the reactor. A pure form of segregation is encountered in reactors with laminar flow under conditions where interaction by molecular diffusion between the different stream-

75

lines is negligible. Other systems, where segregated flow largely contributes to the spread in residence time distribution, are those where a certain amount of short-circuiting of the flow between the inlet and the outlet occurs. Here, a part of the contents is present in "dead" spaces which contribute to the total reaction volume but are not effectively purged by the main flow. In these dead spaces the reaction would be near completion, which involves a very small conversion rate. At the same time, the main stream would hardly contribute to conversion because of its relatively short residence time. Fig. III-7 shows as an example the $F(\tau)$ curve of a system with short-circuiting. Roughly 90% of the feed pass through the system in one tenth of the average residence time, while 10% have an average residence time of about $9\,\bar{\tau}$ (note that Eq. III-1 must always be obeyed). The value of H in this example is about 0.8. CHOLETTE and CLOUTIER [37] have discussed what conclusions bearing upon short-circuiting in a reaction vessel can be drawn from an experimentally determined $F(\tau)$ curve. It will be evident, however, that this phenomenon should be avoided as much as possible in chemical reactors.

Both for mixed systems and for completely segregated systems, methods are available for calculating the conversion on the basis of known conversion rate expressions. These methods will be discussed in Sections III.6 and III.7, respectively. For an intermediate system between a mixed and a segregated one, dependable calculations are only possible when the observed residence time distribution is properly interpreted, i.e. when a model is available which is in agreement with the flow phenomena in the reactor. In general, when H

TABLE III-1

Characterization of continuous flow systems for conversion calculations.

System:	i. mixed	intermediate	ii. segregated
$H = 0$	ideal tubular reactor (II.2)		
$H > 0$	longitudinal dispersion (back-mixing) (III.6) cascade (no back-mixing) (II.4)	segregated flow with interaction by diffusion and mixing, e.g., viscous flow reactor (III.7)	completely segregated flow (III.7)
$H = 1/e$	ideally mixed tank reactor (II.3)	e.g., poorly mixed tank reactor	segregated tank reactor (III.8)
$H \rightarrow 1$	non-existent		complete bypassing

is relatively large, the calculated conversion will depend on the model adopted (see Section III.7). When the spread in residence times is relatively small ($H \ll 1$), the longitudinal dispersion model (and the cascade model as well) is suitable for estimating the deviation from the performance of an ideal tubular reactor, even when the flow is segregated.

As a summary of the above considerations, Table III-1 shows a classification of continuous flow systems according to the spread in residence time distribution and to the degree of interaction between the different elements of volume in the system. The sections in which the chemical conversion in these systems is treated have been indicated between brackets.

III.6. Conversion in mixed systems; the longitudinal dispersion model

The gap between the ideal tubular reactor and the ideally mixed tank reactor can be bridged both by the longitudinal dispersion model and by the cascade of tank reactors. As will be discussed in III.9, the residence time distribution in tubular reactor types can, in general, be approximated by either of these models. If severe back-mixing occurs, the longitudinal dispersion model is more appropriate than the cascade model.

Isothermal reactor calculations in a cascade of tank reactors have already been treated in Section II.4. In the following, therefore, we shall only deal with the conversion in a tubular reactor with piston flow and a superimposed effect of longitudinal dispersion characterized by the longitudinal dispersion coefficient D_l.

Suppose that D_l and the average fluid velocity $\langle v \rangle$ are constant over the length of the reactor and that molar concentrations can be used. The concentration distribution of, say, a reactant A is obtained from a material balance over a differential volume $S \mathrm{d}z$. In comparison with the steady state balance for the ideal tubular reactor, Eq. II-7, it is now complicated by the presence of a term describing the net transport by longitudinal diffusion:

$$0 = S D_l \frac{\mathrm{d}^2 c_A}{\mathrm{d}z^2}\,\mathrm{d}z - \langle v \rangle\, S\, \frac{\mathrm{d}c_A}{\mathrm{d}z}\,\mathrm{d}z + R_A S\,\mathrm{d}z\,. \qquad \text{III-16}$$

If no longitudinal dispersion occurs in the inlet and outlet connections ($z < 0$ and $z > L$, respectively) we have the following boundary conditions. At $z = 0$, the continuity of transport of A must be obeyed, so that:

$$\langle v \rangle\, c_{A0} = \langle v \rangle\, c_A - D_l \frac{\mathrm{d}c_A}{\mathrm{d}z}\,, \quad \text{at} \quad z = 0\,; \qquad \text{III-17}$$

for a finite value of D_l this condition involves a discontinuous decrease in c_A at $z = 0$. A similar relationship should apply for $z = L$:

$$\langle v \rangle\, c_A - D_l \frac{\mathrm{d}c_A}{\mathrm{d}z} = \langle v \rangle\, c_{AL}\,, \quad \text{at} \quad z = L\,.$$

However, when D_l is finite and $\mathrm{d}c_A/\mathrm{d}z$ is negative because of chemical conversion, this equation would mean that the outlet concentration c_{AL} is higher than the value of c_A *in* the reactor at $z = L$. As DANCKWERTS [31] pointed out, this is against physical intuition so that the proper boundary condition must be:

$$\frac{dc_A}{dz} = 0 \quad \text{at} \quad z = L \, . \qquad \qquad \text{III-18}$$

WEHNER and WILHELM [38] proved that Eq. III-18 is correct when there is no dispersion at $z < 0$ and $z > L$; VAN DER LAAN [39] discussed the boundary conditions in the more general case where dispersion occurs outside the region $0 < z < L$ as well.

The solution of Eqs. III-16, 17 and 18 is rather simple if the conversion rate is of the first order, $R_A = -kc_A$. With the latter substitution, and after the introduction of $z' = z/L$, $\bar{\tau} = L/\langle v \rangle$ and $N' = \langle v \rangle L/2D_l$, the system to be solved becomes:

with

$$\left. \begin{array}{c} \dfrac{d^2c_A}{dz'^2} - 2N'\dfrac{dc_A}{dz'} - 2N'\,k\bar{\tau}c_A = 0 \, , \\[2ex] 2N'(c_A - c_{A0}) - \dfrac{dc_A}{dz} = 0 \quad \text{at} \quad z' = 0 \, , \\[2ex] \dfrac{dc_A}{dz} = 0 \quad \text{at} \quad z' = 1 \, . \end{array} \right\} \qquad \text{III-19}$$

Its solution is:

$$\frac{c_{AL}}{c_{A0}} = \frac{4q}{(1+q)^2 e^{-N'(1-q)} - (1-q)^2 e^{-N'(1+q)}} \, , \qquad \text{III-20}$$

where

$$q = \sqrt{1 + 2k\bar{\tau}/N'} \, .$$

This result is valid for all values of N' between 0 and ∞. If $N' \gg 1$ and $\gg k\bar{\tau}$, we have:

$$q \approx 1 + \frac{1}{2}\left(\frac{2k\bar{\tau}}{N'}\right) - \frac{1}{8}\left(\frac{2k\bar{\tau}}{N'}\right)^2 + \cdots \, ,$$

and Eq. III-20 becomes:

$$\frac{c_{AL}}{c_{A0}} \approx \left[1 + \frac{(k\bar{\tau})^2}{2N'}\right] e^{-k\bar{\tau}} \, . \qquad \text{III-21}$$

In the limit $N' \to \infty$ the outlet concentration of an isothermal ideal tubular reactor is obtained.

If both N' and $k\bar{\tau}N'$ are smaller than one, the exponential forms in the denominator can be expanded in series, with the result:

$$\frac{c_{AL}}{c_{A0}} \approx \left[1 + k\bar{\tau} + \tfrac{1}{3} N' k^2\bar{\tau}^2(1 - \tfrac{1}{2} N')\right]^{-1} \, .$$

For $N' \to 0$ the corresponding expression for an ideal tank reactor is obtained. From these extreme results it is seen that Eq. III-20 applies to all cases between the ideal tubular reactor and the tank reactor where mixing on microscale takes place and segregation is absent.

In view of Eq. III-21 it is of interest to determine the value of N' above which the difference in performance between a reactor with longitudinal dispersion and an ideal tubular reactor remains within a prescribed limit. It may, e.g., be required that the relative deviation in the *outlet concentration*, $\Delta c_{AL}/c_{AL}$, is less than a small fraction f; it is seen from Eq. III-21 that this produces the requirement:

$$f \geqslant \frac{(k\bar{t})^2}{2N'} \approx \frac{\ln^2(c_{AL}/c_{A0})}{2N'},$$

or

$$N' \geqslant \frac{\ln^2(c_{AL}/c_{A0})}{2f}.$$

Fig. III-8 shows the limiting value of N' for a first order reaction when $f = 0.01$; the smaller the value of c_{AL}/c_{A0}, the higher N' should be in order to obtain the result of an ideal tubular reactor within 1%. This must be borne in mind when kinetic measurements in a real isothermal tubular reactor are to be interpreted.

For purposes of production, on the other hand, it may be of importance that the *relative degree of conversion* ζ_{AL} does not deviate more than a frac-

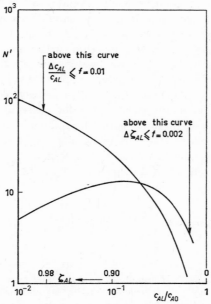

FIG. III-8. Influence of longitudinal dispersion on departure from the performance of an ideal tubular reactor $(N' = \infty)$; first order reaction.

tion f from the ζ_{AL} value for an ideal tubular reactor ($\Delta\zeta_{AL} \leqslant f$). Since in our example $\zeta_{AL} = 1 - c_{AL}/c_{A0}$, this means that:

$$f \geqslant \frac{(k\bar{\tau})^2}{2N'}\,\mathrm{e}^{-k\bar{\tau}} \approx \frac{(c_{AL}/c_{A0})\,\ln^2(c_{AL}/c_{A0})}{2N'},$$

or:

$$N' \geqslant \frac{(c_{AL}/c_{A0})\,\ln^2(c_{AL}/c_{A0})}{2f}.$$

Fig. III-8 shows the minimum value of N' according to this requirement with $f = 0.002$. This curve passes through a maximum at $\zeta_{AL} = 0.865$ with $N' = 135$. If $N' > 135$ (or, in general, $N' > 0.27/f$) the conversion is affected by less than 0.2% (or $100\,f\%$, respectively) with respect to an ideal tubular reactor.

For reactions which are higher than first order, the minimum allowable values of N' are higher since the conversion with reactions of higher order is more affected by a spread in residence time distribution than with first order reactions. A further quantitative treatment along these lines was given by FAN and BAILIE [40] and by LEVENSPIEL and BISCHOFF [41, 42]. LEVENSPIEL [43] also discussed the limitations of the analogy Eq. III-14 with reference to the conversion of first and second order reactions.

When the hold-back in a reactor of the tubular type has such a value that an appreciable decrease in reactor capacity would result, a larger reaction volume will be needed than that of an ideal tubular reactor for obtaining the same degree of conversion of the reactants. Although this statement is true in general, it should be borne in mind that, with certain types of complex reactions, it is not only the conversion but also the selectivity which depends on the residence time distribution; see, e.g., Section II.7, where the performances of a tubular reactor and of a tank reactor were compared for several complex reactions. This is especially true for consecutive reactions where one of the intermediate products is the desired one. In such case, the yield of desired product passes through a maximum as a function of the reactor load. Both the maximum yield and the corresponding reactor load are adversely affected by longitudinal dispersion, as will be shown in the following illustration.

ILLUSTRATION III. 6. *Consecutive reactions in a tubular reactor with longitudinal dispersion*

We consider the reactions $A \overset{1}{\rightarrow} P \overset{2}{\rightarrow} X$ with the rate equations:

$$R_A = -k_1 c_A \quad \text{and} \quad R_P = k_1 c_A - k_2 c_P.$$

The reaction is carried out isothermally in a tubular reactor with longitudinal dispersion. The influence of longitudinal dispersion on the maximum yield of P is to be studied.

At constant density, the concentration distribution along the reactor length z is given by the set of equations III-19 (where k has to be replaced by k_1) and a similar set for species P:

$$\frac{d^2 c_P}{dz'^2} - 2N' \frac{dc_P}{dz'} + 2N'(k_1 \bar{\tau} c_A - k_2 \bar{\tau} c_P) = 0,$$

with

$$2N' c_P - \frac{dc_P}{dz'} = 0 \quad \text{at} \quad z' = 0,$$

$$\frac{dc_P}{dz'} = 0 \quad \text{at} \quad z' = 1.$$

Solution of these equations for the yield at the end of the reactor ($z' = z/L = 1$) results in:

$$\eta_P = \frac{c_{PL}}{c_{A0}} = \frac{4s}{s-1} \left(\frac{-q}{(1+q)^2 e^{-N'(1-q)} - (1-q)^2 e^{-N'(1+q)}} + \right.$$

$$\left. + \frac{r}{(1+r)^2 e^{-N'(1-r)} - (1-r)^2 e^{-N'(1+r)}} \right),$$

where:

$$s = k_1/k_2, \quad N' = \langle v \rangle L/2 D_l,$$

$$q = \sqrt{1 + 2k_1 \bar{\tau}/N'}, \quad r = \sqrt{1 + 2k_1 \bar{\tau}/sN'}.$$

The solution for η_P corresponds to Eq. III-20 when the second reaction does not occur ($s = \infty$), since then $c_{PL} = c_{A0} - c_{AL}$. If the second reaction is much faster than the first ($s \to 0$), the value of η_P tends towards zero, as expected.

When the ideal tubular reactor is approached, we have

$$\lim_{N' \to \infty} \eta_P = \frac{s}{1-s} \left(e^{-k_1 \bar{\tau}} - e^{-k_1 \bar{\tau}/s} \right),$$

while in the extreme case of an ideal tank reactor, η_P becomes:

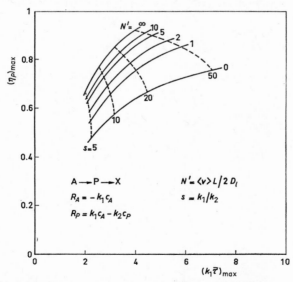

FIG. III-9. Influence of longitudinal dispersion and the selectivity parameter s on the maximum yield and the corresponding residence time for consecutive first order reactions.

$$\lim_{N' \to 0} \eta_P = k_1\bar{\tau}/(1 + k_1\bar{\tau})(1 + k_1\bar{\tau}/s) .$$

Both expressions can be verified by applying the elementary isothermal reactor calculations of Chapter II to these two reactor types.

Now, the yield η_P has a maximum value $(\eta_P)_{max}$ as a function of $k_1\bar{\tau}$; $(\eta_P)_{max}$ and the corresponding value of $(k_1\bar{\tau})_{max}$ at which the maximum yield is reached can be numerically calculated as a function of the parameters s and N'. Some results are shown in Fig. III-9. For a constant value of $k_1/k_2 = s$, the ideal tubular reactor gives the highest maximum yield. The maximum yield is decreased by longitudinal dispersion, and $(k_1\bar{\tau})_{max}$ increases at the same time, which means that the reactor load has to be reduced. This effect of the spread in residence times can only be counteracted by increasing s, i.e. by a change in reaction temperature, since k_1 and k_2 will generally be different functions of temperature.

III.7. Conversion in reactors with segregated flow, and possible approximations for intermediate systems

Suppose that the $F(\tau)$ curve of a reactor is known and that the conversion rate as a function of the composition of the reaction mixture is also available. It then appears that the conversion in this reactor can be predicted, provided the assumption be made that the flow through the reactor is completely segregated. Under these conditions, the degree of conversion of a reactant A, $\xi_A(\tau)$, in the fraction $dF(\tau)$ of the outlet stream (having an age between τ and $\tau + d\tau$) is equal to that in an ideal tubular reactor with a total residence time τ (or in a batch reactor with a reaction time $t = \tau$). At the outlet of the reactor, the different streams having different residence times are combined, so that the average degree of conversion at the outlet will be:

$$\langle \xi_A \rangle = \int_{\tau=0}^{\tau=\infty} \xi_A(\tau)\, dF(\tau) . \qquad \text{III-22}$$

It was shown by SCHOENEMANN [44] and HOFMANN [45] that this calcula-

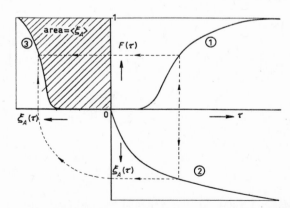

FIG. III-10. Construction according to SCHOENEMANN [44] for determining the conversion from the residence time distribution and an empirical conversion-time relation.

tion can be carried out graphically as illustrated in Fig. III-10. Here, Curve 1 is the experimentally determined function $F(\tau)$, and Curve 2 the calculated or experimental relation between the degree of conversion and reaction time in a batch or ideal tubular reactor. Curve 3 is then constructed; it gives the degree of conversion as a function of $F(\tau)$. According to Eq. III-22, the shaded area is equal to the conversion $\langle \xi_A \rangle$ obtained with this reactor.

It should be borne in mind that this procedure is only justified if the system is completely segregated. However, for small degrees of conversion and/or relatively small values of the hold-back it provides a good approximation, even if the observed residence time distribution is caused by mixing on a molecular scale. SCHOENEMANN'S method is exact when the conversion rate is of the first order with respect to one of the reactants, irrespective of the fact whether or not mixing between elements of different age takes place. This can be explained as follows.

Suppose we have two equal volumes V with different reactant concentrations c'_A and c''_A and assume that the reaction is of the order n with respect to A. If these streams do not mix, the conversion rate is $Vk[(c'_A)^n + (c''_A)^n] = 2Vk\langle c_A^n \rangle$. If they are mixed prior to reaction, the concentration in boht volumes will be $(c'_A + c''_A)/2 = \langle c_A \rangle$, and the conversion rate will be $2Vk\langle c_A \rangle^n$. Since:

$$\langle c_A^n \rangle = \langle c_A \rangle^n \quad \text{when} \quad n = 1 \, ,$$

it is only for a first order reaction that it makes no difference in the conversion rate whether the elements having different concentrations remain segregated or are mixed prior to or during the reaction. Because in general:

$$\langle c_A^n \rangle > \langle c_A \rangle^n \quad \text{when} \quad n > 1 \, ,$$

and

$$\langle c_A^n \rangle < \langle c_A \rangle^n \quad \text{when} \quad n < 1 \, ,$$

mixing between elements of different concentrations during the reaction will decrease the conversion rate when the order of the reaction is higher than unity; it will increase the conversion rate when $n < 1$. Consequently, when Eq. III-22 is applied to a system which is not segregated, the calculated degree of conversion will be too high when $n > 1$ and too low when $n < 1$. This problem was discussed in greater detail by DANCKWERTS [46] and by ZWIETERING [47].

From these considerations it may be concluded that for high degrees of conversion, for relatively large values of the hold-back and for reactions which are not of the first order, the $F(\tau)$ curve alone does not contain enough information for predicting the degree of conversion. This will be demonstrated by means of the following example [48].

Let a second order reaction ($|R|_A = kc_A^2$) be carried out in a reactor having a residence time distribution as given by Fig. III-11. There are three ways of interpreting this $F(\tau)$ curve, which permit a rather simple calculation of the relative conversion ζ_A of the system:

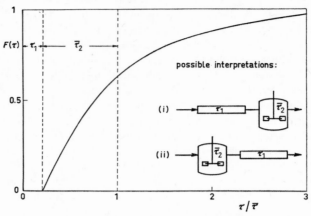

FIG. III-11. $F(\tau)$ curve of a cascade consisting of a tubular reactor and a tank reactor.

i. The system having the observed $F(\tau)$ curve may consist of a tubular reactor with residence time τ_1 followed by a tank reactor with an average residence time $\bar{\tau}_2$.

For ζ_A we find:

$$\zeta_A = 1 + \frac{1}{2kc_{A0}\bar{\tau}_2}\left(1 - \sqrt{1 + 4\frac{kc_{A0}\bar{\tau}_2}{1 + kc_{A0}\tau_1}}\right).$$

ii. The system is identical to *i* but the flow is reversed, so that the reaction mixture passes first through the tank reactor and then through the tubular reactor. In this case ζ_A becomes:

$$\zeta_A = 1 + \frac{1 - \sqrt{1 + 4kc_{A0}\bar{\tau}_2}}{2kc_{A0}\bar{\tau}_2 - kc_{A0}\tau_1(1 - \sqrt{1 + 4kc_{A0}\bar{\tau}_2})}.$$

iii. Assuming completely segregated flow, we find with Eq. III-22:

$$\zeta_A = \frac{kc_{A0}\tau_1}{1 + kc_{A0}\tau_1} + \int_{\tau_1}^{\infty}\frac{kc_{A0}\tau}{1 + kc_{A0}\tau} \times \frac{e^{-(\tau-\tau_1)/\bar{\tau}_2}}{\bar{\tau}_2}\,d\tau.$$

These three formulae give different values of ζ_A with the same set of parameters. E.g., with $kc_{A0}\tau_1 = 1$ and $\bar{\tau}_2/\tau_1 = 4$ we find:

Case *i* $\zeta_A = 0.750$,

Case *ii* $\zeta_A = 0.719$,

and Case *iii* $\zeta_A = 0.771$.

The latter interpretation of $F(\tau)$ gives the highest possible degree of conversion because no mixing has been assumed to occur. In Case *ii* ζ_A is lower than in Case *i* since mixing at a high concentration level causes the greatest reduction in the average conversion rate. It can be demonstrated that the three formulae given above approach each other when $kc_{A0}(\tau_1 + \bar\tau_2) \ll 1$ (small degree of conversion) or when $\tau_1/\bar\tau_2 \gg 1$ (small hold-back).

It must be concluded that for systems with a relatively large hold-back, of which the $F(\tau)$ curve shows that it is not a typically mixed system and of which it cannot be said either that it is entirely segregated, the degree of conversion cannot be accurately calculated unless the reaction is of the first order. It is, however, quite possible to obtain a good approximation to such a problem if it can be roughly estimated to what extent mixing effects and segregated flow contribute to the observed residence time distribution. The solution can be narrowed down between that for complete segregation and a number of solutions obtained with models consisting of such a combination of elementary systems of the mixed type that the $F(\tau)$ curve and the flow phenomena in the reactor are properly accounted for.

Only rarely does it occur that the flow pattern in a system to be used as a reactor is so well known that an exact calculation of the conversion can be carried out. One of these exceptional cases is the viscous flow reactor with constant viscosity of which a few aspects will be discussed in the next illustration.

ILLUSTRATION III. 7. *A tubular reactor with viscous flow*

If the density is constant and the viscosity does not depend on the radial position in the tube, the fluid velocity for established laminar flow is given by:

$$v = 2\langle v\rangle\,(1 - r^2/R^2)\,.$$

The equation of continuity for a reactant A with a conversion rate $|R|_A = kc_A{}^n$ then becomes for the steady state:

$$D_A\frac{\partial^2 c_A}{\partial z^2} - 2\langle v\rangle\left(1 - \frac{r^2}{R^2}\right)\frac{\partial c_A}{\partial z} + D_A\left(\frac{\partial^2 c_A}{\partial r^2} + \frac{1}{r}\frac{\partial c_A}{\partial r}\right) - kc_A{}^n = 0, \qquad \text{(a)}$$

where D_A is the molecular diffusivity of A. The boundary conditions are:

$$\left.\begin{array}{lll} z = 0 & c_A = c_{A0} \\ r = 0 & \partial c_A/\partial r = 0 \\ r = R & \partial c_A/\partial r = 0\,. \end{array}\right\} \qquad \text{(b)}$$

A boundary condition for $z = L$ is not given, since for all practical purposes the molecular diffusion of A in the direction of flow [the first term of Eq. (a)] can be neglected with respect to the convective transport [second term in (a)]. Therefore we shall omit the first term in Eq. (a) assuming that the condition $\langle v\rangle L/D_A \gg 1$ is obeyed correspondingly.

The third term in Eq. (a) accounts for molecular diffusion in the radial direction. As to the relative importance of this term, two extreme cases may be considered:

i. The effect of radial diffusion is negligible; this means that during the passage of the reaction mixture through the tube the molecular diffusion has no opportunity to level out radial concentration gradients, or $D_A\bar\tau/R^2 \to 0$. In this case the flow is completely segregated and in Eq. (a) only the second and fourth term are of importance. The relative conversion ζ_{AL} can be obtained by direct integration along a streamline and by then averaging the result over the cross section of the tube. We can, of course, equally well calculate first the residence time distribution function, for which we find:

$$F(\tau) = 0 \quad \text{for} \quad 0 < \tau/\bar{\tau} < \tfrac{1}{2},$$
$$F(\tau) = 1 - (\bar{\tau}/2\tau)^2 \quad \text{for} \quad \tau/\bar{\tau} \geqslant \tfrac{1}{2},$$

and then apply Eq. III-22 for calculating ζ_{AL}. Some results of such calculations, which were first discussed by DENBIGH [49], are shown in Fig. III-12.

ii. The radial diffusion is so effective that the concentration over a cross section is virtually constant $(D_A \bar{\tau}/R^2 \to \infty)$. If the influence of diffusion in the direction of flow is nevertheless negligible, the ideal tubular reactor is approached since the longitudinal dispersion is then reduced by radial diffusion (also see Section III.9).

For the region intermediate between i and ii and for a first order reaction rate $(n = 1)$, CLELAND and WILHELM [50] solved Eq. (a) (neglecting the first term). Fig. III-12 shows such a solution for $D_A/kR^2 = 0.1$. They also verified their calculations by studying the isothermal decomposition of acetic anhydride in water in a tube with viscous flow. The region of variables in which verification was possible proved rather narrow. Particularly at too large tube diameters, internal circulation caused by density differences over the cross section was observed. As a result, longitudinal dispersion diminished and the behaviour of the ideal tubular reactor was approached. Similar calculations and experiments were recently carried out for second order reactions by VIGNES and TRAMBOUZE [51].

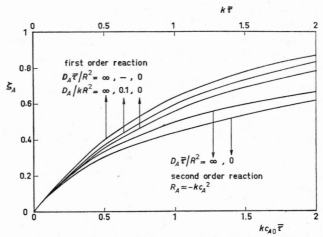

FIG. III-12. Conversion in an isothermal viscous flow reactor; first and second order reactions with influence of radial molecular diffusion.

The behaviour of an ideal tubular reactor will be approached in a viscous flow reactor if there is also radial transport by flow. This occurs, for example, with laminar flow through curved tubes (see Section III.9). Similarly, HOVARKA and KENDALL [52] showed that, by putting baffles inside a laminar flow tubular reactor, the conversion of a second order reaction was increased.

Extremely complicated problems are encountered in tubular reactors where highly viscous materials are processed and where the viscosity may depend extensively on the degree of conversion. When the circumstances are such that the viscosity near the tube wall becomes very high, most of the feed as a result of a high degree of conversion will pass through the central part of the tube and severe shortcircuiting may occur.

III.8. Mixing versus segregation in a tank reactor

The differences between mixing on a molecular scale and complete segregation can be well demonstrated for a system having the $F(\tau)$ curve of the ideally mixed tank reactor (Eq. III-4). These two extremes can be encountered if the reaction proceeds in the dispersed phase of an emulsion in a stirred tank reactor. The emulsion droplets in such a system will show the residence time distribution of a tank reactor, as can be shown by the same reasoning as used for the derivation of Eq. III-4.

Now, during their passage through the reactor the drops may collide with each other and even coalesce. As a result of the coalescence of two drops an intimate mixing of their contents takes place and after some time a large drop formed by coalescence may be broken up into two or more smaller drops. If this coalescence occurs with a low frequency, i.e. when the average lifetime of a drop between two such events is much longer than their average residence time in the reactor, each drop virtually leads its own life and the system is a segregated one. On the other hand, if each drop can coalesce many times during its presence in the reactor, all drops will have practically the same composition; in the extreme case of infinite frequency of coalescence, the dispersed phase would behave like the contents of an ideally mixed tank reactor.

It is of interest to compare reactor capacities and yields for both extreme cases. Studies on this subject have been published by RIETEMA [53], HORN and KÜCHLER [54] and GREENHALGH, JOHNSON and NOTT [55].

Suppose that a reaction with a conversion rate $|R|_A = kc_A{}^n$ is carried out in a tank reactor with complete segregation. For the calculation of the relative conversion of A, ζ_{A1}, Eq. III-22 has to be used:

$$\zeta_{A1} = \int_{\tau=0}^{\tau=\infty} \zeta_A(\tau) e^{-\tau/\bar{\tau}} \, d\,(\tau/\bar{\tau}) \,,$$

where $\bar{\tau}$ is the average residence time of the reacting mixture in the reaction volume, i.e. in the dispersed phase. $\zeta_A(\tau)$ is the relative conversion which would be obtained in an isothermal ideal tubular reactor or in a batch reactor in a time τ:

$$\zeta_A(\tau) = 1 - \frac{c_A(\tau)}{c_{A0}} \,,$$

where $c_A(\tau)$ is the solution to the material balance equations for such a system:

$$\frac{dc_A}{c_A{}^n} = -k d\tau \,, \quad \text{with} \quad c_A = c_{A0} \quad \text{for} \quad \tau = 0 \,.$$

The solutions for $n = \frac{1}{2}$ and 2 are shown in Table III-2, together with the corresponding solutions for the case where the reaction mixture is mixed on a molecular scale (tank reactor model). For $n = 1$, the segregated and the completely mixed case give the same result:

$$\zeta_{A1} = 1 - (1 + k\bar{\tau})^{-1} \,.$$

In Fig. III-13, ζ_{A1} has been plotted against $kc_{A0}{}^{n-1}\bar{\tau}$ for $n = \frac{1}{2}$, 1 and 2. It is

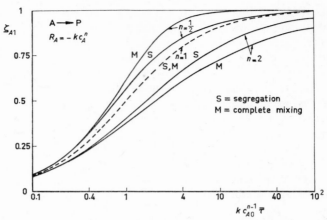

FIG. III-13. Relative conversion in a reactor with the residence time distribution of a tank reactor; a comparison between segregated flow (S) and complete mixing (M).

seen that for a reaction order higher than 1 the highest conversion is obtained with segregated flow. If $n < 1$ the degree of conversion is higher when the contents of the reactor are mixed on a molecular scale.

TABLE III-2

Conversion formulae with $|R|_A = kc_A^n$ in tank reactor with segregation and complete mixing, respectively.

$n = \frac{1}{2}$	$n = 2$
Segregation:	*Segregation:*
$\zeta_A(\tau) = 1 - \left(1 - \dfrac{k\tau}{2\sqrt{c_{A0}}}\right)^2 ; 0 < \tau \leqslant \dfrac{2\sqrt{c_{A0}}}{k}$.	$\zeta_A(\tau) = 1 - \dfrac{1}{1 + kc_{A0}\tau} ; 0 < \tau < \infty$
$\zeta_{A1} = \dfrac{k\bar\tau}{\sqrt{c_{A0}}}\left[1 - \dfrac{k\bar\tau}{2\sqrt{c_{A0}}}\left(1 - e^{-2\sqrt{c_{A0}}/k\bar\tau}\right)\right]^{\star}$.	$\zeta_{A1} = 1 - \displaystyle\int_0^\infty \dfrac{e^{-\tau/\bar\tau}}{1 + kc_{A0}\bar\tau(\tau/\bar\tau)}\,\mathrm{d}(\tau/\bar\tau) =$
	$= 1 + \dfrac{1}{kc_{A0}\bar\tau}e^{1/kc_{A0}\bar\tau}\,\mathrm{Ei}\left(-\dfrac{1}{kc_{A0}\bar\tau}\right)^{\dagger}$
Complete mixing:	*Complete mixing:*
$\zeta_{A1} = \dfrac{(k\bar\tau)^2}{2c_{A0}}\left(-1 + \sqrt{1 + \dfrac{4c_{A0}}{(k\bar\tau)^2}}\right)$.	$\zeta_{A1} = 1 + \dfrac{1}{2kc_{A0}\bar\tau}\left(1 - \sqrt{1 + 4kc_{A0}\bar\tau}\right)$

★ The integration for obtaining ζ_{A1} must be carried out between $\tau = 0$ and $\tau = 2\sqrt{c_{A0}}/k$.

† Ei is the Eulerian integral defined by $\mathrm{Ei}\,(-x) = \displaystyle\int_x^\infty \dfrac{e^{-y}}{y}\,\mathrm{d}y$; tabulated values are found in JAHNKE and EMBDE [56].

88

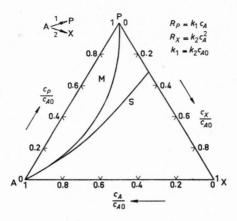

FIG. III-14. Reaction path for parallel reactions of different order in a tank reactor with segregated flow (S) and with complete mixing (M).

With complex reactions the yield of a desired product may also be affected by the degree of segregation. Fig. III-14 shows as an example the reaction paths for a set of parallel reactions which are of different order in reactant A. In the case of complete mixing and at a high degree of conversion the production of P is favoured because the concentration of A is then low in the entire reactor volume; when $\bar{\tau} \to \infty$, even pure P can be produced, although at an infinitely slow rate. In the case of segregation, each element of volume (or each droplet) is essentially a small batch reactor in which the concentration of A diminishes with time. In the initial stage, the undesired product X is formed as well as P so that the product stream consisting of drops of various ages will contain both species.

We have discussed here only the extreme cases of complete mixing and segregation, respectively. Recently, calculations for the intermediate region were made by CURL [57], who showed that, for $0 < n < 1$ and a high degree of conversion, even a relatively small degree of segregation may cause a sensible reduction of the conversion. MADDEN and DAMERELL [58] and MILLER, RALPH, CURL and TOWELL [59] published measurements on the frequency of coalescence in oil-in-water and water-in-oil emulsions, respectively, in different agitated vessels. The average time between two coalescenses decreases as a function of increasing volume fraction of the dispersed phase and of increasing stirrer speed. The order of magnitude of this time lies between 5 and 500 s; it may be greatly influenced by mass transfer with chemical reaction and by heat effects, and surface-active materials are very effective in inhibiting coalescence.

To conclude this section, an illustration will be given of a polymerization reaction in an emulsion in a continuously operated tank reactor.

ILLUSTRATION III. 8. *Emulsion polymerization in a continuous tank reactor*

A reactant $A(M_A = 104$ kg/kmol) is to be polymerized in the dispersed phase in a stirred tank reactor. The results of batch experiments are available for the reaction conditions to be used. The following wholly empirical conversion rate formula has been derived from these results (compare, e.g., Eq. I-20):

$$|R|_A = kc_A^{3/2}, \text{ with } k = 2.5 \times 10^{-4} \text{s}^{-1}\left(\frac{\text{kmol}}{\text{m}^3}\right)^{-1/2}.$$

These experiments furthermore yielded the information that the spread in the degree of polymerization, p (molecules of monomer per molecule of polymer), is rather small and that the average degree of polymerization can be approximated by:

$$p(t) = 14.1\sqrt{t},$$

where t is the reaction time in the batch reactor in seconds.

It is requested to calculate the size of the tank reactor, the average degree of polymerization and the distribution of p for a production of 10 tons of polymer per day with a relative degree of conversion $\zeta_{A1} = 0.9$, under the assumption that coalescence between the drops does not occur. The feed of the dispersed phase consists of pure A, and the density of this phase during the reaction remains constant at a value of 832 kg/m³. The volume fraction of the dispersed phase in the reactor will be 0.165.

The material balance for a batch or an ideal tubular reactor together with the given rate equation yields for the relative degree of conversion $\zeta_A(\tau)$ after a reaction time τ:

$$\zeta_A(\tau) = 1 - \left(\frac{2}{2 + k\tau\sqrt{c_{A0}}}\right)^2.$$

On the basis of Eq. III-22 the average conversion ζ_{A1} in the stream leaving the reactor becomes:

$$\zeta_{A1} = \int_0^\infty \left[1 - \left(\frac{2}{2 + k\tau\sqrt{c_{A0}}}\right)^2\right] e^{-\tau/\bar{\tau}} \mathrm{d}(\tau/\bar{\tau}).$$

From this equation it is found that for $\zeta_{A1} = 0.9$: $k\bar{\tau}\sqrt{c_{A0}} = 15.4$, from which it follows that $\bar{\tau} = 21\,600$ s $= 6$ hours. The required production of polymer is 0.116 kg/s and equal to $0.9 \times \varrho_A V_r/\bar{\tau}$; it follows that the volume of the dispersed phase $V_r = 3.34$ m³, and that the total liquid volume in the reactor has to be $3.34/0.165 = 20.2$ m³.

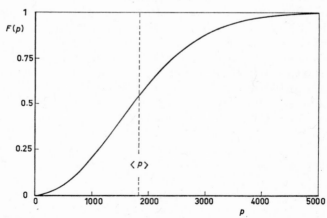

FIG. III-15. Distribution function of the degree of polymerization p; Illustration III.8.

A drop leaving the reactor after a residence time τ has an average degree of polymerization $p(\tau) = 14.1\sqrt{\tau} = 2070\sqrt{\tau/\bar{\tau}}$. The fraction $(1 - e^{-\tau/\bar{\tau}})$ of the product stream contains the drops for which $p \leqslant p(\tau)$. Since $\tau/\bar{\tau}$ can be directly expressed in terms of p, we can also denote this fraction by

$$F(p) = 1 - \exp\left[-(p/2070)^2\right],$$

where $F(p)$ is the fraction at the outlet with a degree of polymerization smaller than p. This distribution is shown in Fig. III-15; it is only approximative since the degree of polymerization in the batch experiment may have had a relatively wide spread itself. This effect, however, is to some extent obliterated by the very large spread in residence times of the tank reactor. The average degree of polymerization at the outlet of the reactor, $\langle p \rangle$, follows from:

$$\langle p \rangle = \int_{p=0}^{p=\infty} p\, \mathrm{d}F(p) = 2070 \sqrt{\frac{\pi}{2}} = 1830.$$

It is questionable whether the assumption that no coalescence between different emulsion drops occurs would be valid, particularly in view of the long average residence time in this system. However, it is not possible to make a parallel calculation for a tank reactor in which the reaction mixture is completely mixed. The basic data were obtained in a batch reactor and exactly the same type of reaction operation is used as a basis of the above calculations. It is known, however, that in polymerization reactions the conversion rate and the growth of polymer depend not only on the reactant concentration but also on the product distribution itself. Since the latter will be entirely different in a completely mixed tank reactor, the batch experiments do not contain sufficient information for the design of such a reactor system.

III.9. Some data on the longitudinal dispersion in continuous flow systems

Only in the case of the more or less "mixed" systems is it possible to characterize the spread in residence time distribution by means of a single quantity. Depending on whether back-mixing occurs or not, this quantity is $N' = \langle v \rangle L/2D_l$ or, respectively, the number N of ideal mixers in a cascade to which the system is equivalent. If the longitudinal dispersion is relatively small, either of these two quantities may adequately describe the residence time distribution because of the correspondence between N' and N (Eq. III-14).

In flow systems which do not evidently contain a cascade of well-agitated volumes it is customary to ascribe the spread in residence times to an apparent value of the longitudinal dispersion coefficient D_l. The Péclet number for longitudinal dispersion is frequently used in relating this quantity to the various flow parameters. It is defined as:

$$Pé_l \equiv \langle v \rangle\, d/D_l , \qquad\qquad \text{III-23}$$

where d is a characteristic length which is significant in view of the mechanism causing the dispersion (e.g. a tube diameter of a particle diameter). Thus we also have the relation:

$$N' = Pé_l L/2d . \qquad\qquad \text{III-24}$$

Some theoretical and experimental data on the longitudinal dispersion in continuous flow systems will be summarized below*.

With *laminar flow* in a straight tube, a considerable spread in residence time distribution is to be expected as a consequence of the velocity profile. With a parabolic velocity profile, the residence time distribution would be (DENBIGH [49]):

$$F(\tau) = 0 \qquad \text{for } \tau < \tfrac{1}{2}\bar{\tau}\,,$$
$$F(\tau) = 1 - (\bar{\tau}/2\tau)^2 \text{ for } \tau \geqslant \tfrac{1}{2}\bar{\tau}\,.$$

Now, this distribution can be modified as a result of molecular diffusion. Whereas diffusion in the direction of flow is generally negligible, transverse molecular diffusion may cause an appreciable reduction in dispersion because it provides for an exchange of material between different streamlines (also see Illustration III.7). In case this radial diffusion is sufficiently established during passage through the tube, the residence time distribution can be approximately described with a coefficient of longitudinal dispersion D_l; the corresponding value of the effective Péclet number in Poiseuille flow becomes, according to TAYLOR [61] and VAN DEEMTER, BROEDER and LAUWERIER [62]:

$$P\acute{e}_l = \frac{\langle v \rangle d_t}{D_l} \approx 192 D/d_t\langle v \rangle = 192(ReSc)^{-1}\,.$$

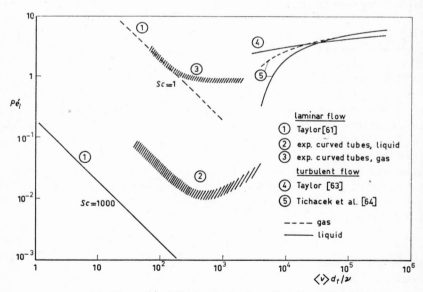

FIG. III-16. $P\acute{e}_l = \langle v \rangle d_t/D_l$ for single phase flow through tubes.

---

* Some material was taken from an excellent survey by HOFMANN [60], to which the reader is referred for further study and literature references.

Note that D_l will decrease as the molecular diffusivity increases. The above formula will only apply if the time constant for transverse molecular diffusion ($\approx d_t^2/D$) is not much longer than the average residence time $\bar{\tau}$; this leads to the condition $L/d_t > \langle v \rangle d_t/D$, or in view of the above result to $P\acute{e}_l \times L/d_t > 200$. As can be seen from the $P\acute{e}_l$ values in Fig. III-16, this condition is obtainable in practice for gases ($Sc \approx 1$), but it would lead to excessively high values of L/d_t for liquids.

If viscous flow of a reaction mixture in a straight tube would produce too great a dispersion, it can be considerably reduced by spiralling the tube. It appears that due to the secondary flow in a curved pipe the spread in retention times of the (now spiralling) streamlines is $\frac{1}{2}$ to $\frac{1}{3}$ of that in a straight tube with Poiseuille flow. Moreover, the influence of radial diffusion is increased since the distances over which the diffusion has to take place have been reduced by the secondary flow. As a consequence, the apparent longitudinal dispersion coefficient for laminar flow in curved tubes is surprisingly small, especially for gases. Some experimental results have been shown in Fig. III-16*.

For *turbulent flow* in tubes, the Péclet number for longitudinal dispersion is much higher than for laminar flow. Owing to turbulence, the transverse transport of momentum and of matter is facilitated so that the velocity profile is flattened out and radial mixing is improved.

TAYLOR [63] made an estimate of D_l in the region $10^4 < \langle v \rangle d_t/\nu < 10^6$, with the result:

$$P\acute{e}_l = \frac{\langle v \rangle d_t}{D_l} \approx 0.28 f^{-1/2} \,,$$

where f is the Fanning friction factor. A more precise analysis along the same lines was published by TICHACEK, BARKELEW and BARON [64]; the results of their calculations are shown in Fig. III-16, which also contains TAYLOR's relationship for turbulent flow. The available data from laboratory experiments confirm the above theories within a factor of 2. SJENITZER [65] correlated a great number of measurements, some of which were performed with commercial pipelines; on the basis of these data he proposed the empirical relationship:

$$P\acute{e}_l = 7.6 \times 10^{-8} f^{-3.6} \left(\frac{d_t}{L}\right)^{0.141}.$$

This formula predicts more longitudinal dispersion than the above theoretical results.

On the whole, the Péclet number for turbulent flow in pipes at $Re > 10^4$ is so large that with an L/d_t ratio of, e.g., 50 the value of N' already becomes 50 or higher and the ideal tubular reactor is approached.

---

* Unpublished results, Laboratory of Physical Technology, Technical University, Delft.

Some information is available on the longitudinal dispersion of single phase flow in *tubular systems with mechanical agitation*. A special feature of these is that the longitudinal dispersion can be greatly influenced by the angular velocity ω of the agitator. For the flow through the annulus between a rotating cylinder (radius R_1) and a stationary outer cylinder (radius R_2), CROOCKEWIT, HONIG and KRAMERS [66] established that:

$$Pé_l = \frac{\langle v \rangle (R_2 - R_1)}{D_l} \approx 38 \frac{\langle v \rangle}{\omega R_1},$$

in the range of speeds where the flow exhibits laminar toroidal vortices. These vortices break down into general turbulence at higher angular speeds and $Pé_l$ becomes rather independent of ω.

For a "rotating disc contactor", a tube divided into compartments by stator rings with a central rotating disc in each compartment, STEMERDING [67] and also WESTERTERP and LANDSMAN [36] found that the coefficient of longitudinal dispersion is composed of two parts. One contribution is the same as that for a cascade of mixers; the other one is entirely due to agitation and proportional to ω. Consequently, for a rotating disc contactor consisting of N compartments and having a disc radius R, the value of $N' = \langle v \rangle L/2D_l$ can be written as:

$$N' = \frac{N}{1 + C\omega R/\langle v \rangle};$$

the constant C was equal to 2×10^{-3} in the latter investigation. WESTERTERP and MEYBERG [68] demonstrated in separate experiments that the second contribution to D_l is a true back-mixing phenomenon.

When a fluid is flowing through a *packed bed* of solid particles, the variations in the local velocity cause a dispersion in the direction of flow. In not overly short beds this dispersion can be described by means of a longitudinal dispersion coefficient, although no real back-mixing takes place. McHENRY and WILHELM [69] found from frequency response measurements with a gas flow through a bed of spherical particles that $Pé_l = \langle v \rangle d_p/D_l$ varied from 1.6 to 2.3 in the range $20 < Re_p < 400$. According to Eq. III-24 this would mean that:

$$N' \approx L/d_p.$$

In view of the correspondence $N' \triangleq N$ (see Section III.4), a packed bed having a length L would give the same residence time distribution as L/d_p mixers in cascade. This suggests that the voids in a packed bed can be considered a cascade of well-mixed volumes which are a distance d_p apart. This picture is convenient for estimating the longitudinal dispersion in a gas flowing through a packed bed, although the actual mechanism of the dispersion is probably different.

It appears from dispersion measurements with liquids that $Pé_l$ is smaller

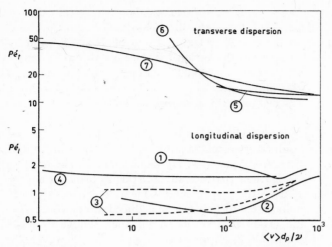

FIG. III-17. Various experimental results for longitudinal and transverse dispersion of single phase flow through a bed of packed spheres;
Longitudinal dispersion:
1 — Mc Henry and Wilhelm, gas [69]; 2 — Cairns and Prausnitz, liquid [70]; 3 — Hiby, liquid [71]; 4 — Hiby, liquid, wall effect excluded [71];
Transverse dispersion:
5 — Bernard and Wilhelm [72]; 6 — Latinen [73]; 7 — Hiby [71].

than it is in the case of gases (Curve 2 and Region 3 in Fig. III-17). This is presumably due to the fact that, in the case of liquids, the exchange of matter between more or less stagnant regions and the main stream is inhibited by the small diffusivity; accordingly, there is slightly more "by-passing" than with gases. Data 1, 2 and 3 in Fig. III-17 refer to longitudinal dispersion averaged over the whole cross section of the packed tube; they also contain, therefore, the effects of the non-uniform velocity distribution near the tube wall. Measurements by Hiby [71] without wall-effects (Curve 4 in Fig. III-17) indicate that they may have a considerable influence on the longitudinal dispersion. This influence seems to diminish as Re_p increases from 100 to 1000.

It is seen from the order of magnitude of $Pé_l$ that the longitudinal dispersion in packed beds can be so small that the ideal tubular reactor is closely approached for $L/d_p > 100$. The value of $Pé_l$ may become lower than indicated in Fig. III-17 when there is a large wall effect ($d_p/d_t > 0.1$), when the packing of the particles is non-uniform or when the flow entering the bed is not properly distributed. In shallow beds containing not more than about 10 layers of particles, as used for extremely rapid, catalysed gas reactions or solid-gas reactions, the spread in the residence time distribution may be considerable.

As a complement to $Pé_l$, some data are shown in Fig. III-17 on the Péclet number for *transverse* dispersion in a fixed bed. It appears that for $Re_p > 100$

95

the value of $Pé_t = \langle v \rangle d_p / D_t$ approaches about 12, so that the coefficient of transverse dispersion D_t is roughly 10 times smaller than D_l. This also follows from a theoretical analysis by DE JOSSELIN DE JONG [74] and by SAFFMAN [75], who calculated the dispersion for the flow through a random array of capillaries which served as a model for a bed of solid particles. The radial transport of heat and matter due to this phenomenon is of importance for catalytic tubular reactors; this problem will be the subject of Section V.6.

Regarding longitudinal dispersion in *liquid flow through a fluidized bed* of solids, some results were recently published by CAIRNS and PRAUSNITZ [76] and by KRAMERS, WESTERMANN, DE GROOT and DUPONT [77]. It appears from these investigations that, for an undisturbed bed, D_l increases from the packed bed value to the empty tube value as the porosity ε of the bed is increased from about 0.4 to 1. It can be deduced from a comparison between Figs. III-16 and III-17 that $\langle v \rangle d_p / D_l$ will then change from about 1 to a value of the order of d_t / d_p. In practical applications, however, the flow in a liquid fluidized bed may be greatly disturbed by an uneven flow distribution at the bottom of the bed and by particular shapes of, or inserts in, the space available for fluidization. Such disturbances will considerably increase mixing in the direction of flow.

With *gas flow through fluidized beds*, the model of piston flow with superimposed longitudinal dispersion would merely be a very rough approximation of what is actually happening. The excess of fluidizing gas is rapidly segregated from the rather dense particle phase and ascends quickly through the bed in the form of bubbles, which may become very large. As a consequence, there is rather good top-to-bottom mixing of the solids together with the interstitial and possibly adsorbed gas. If a residence time distribution experiment is performed or if a chemical reaction occurs in the gas phase, the compositions of the bubbles and of the interstitial gas will be different and material will be exchanged between the two. The rates of by-passing of large bubbles, of longitudinal mixing in the dense phase and of mass transfer between these phases are very sensitive to the density of the particles, their average size and especially their size distribution. It will be clear that with rapid reactions the conditions in the dense particle phase will be near equilibrium, resulting in a relatively small capacity of the bed as a whole; with slow reactions the short-circuiting effect by the large bubbles will cause a much lower conversion than in the case of a uniform solid-gas distribution. VAN DEEMTER [78] mathematically formulated the above model; his theory allows estimating the degree of conversion for a gas reaction with a known conversion rate on the basis of an experimental residence time distribution function.

For the order of magnitude of the spread in the residence time distribution in a gas fluidized bed, reference is made to a survey by REMAN [79] of results obtained with commerical cracking catalyst (d_p = 50–150 μm). It appears that, for this particle size distribution, the ratio $D_l/\langle v\rangle$ is rather independent of the fluidizing velocity but that it is roughly proportional to the squared bed diameter. Values for $D_l/\langle v\rangle$ were reported to vary between 0.1 and 2 m. The corresponding values of $Pé_l$, based on the particle diameter, are 10^{-3} and 5×10^{-5}, respectively. A comparison with fixed beds and liquid fluidized beds shows that the spread in residence times in a gas fluidized bed is greater by several orders of magnitude.

Not much information is as yet available on the residence time distribution in equipment where *two fluid phases* are brought into contact. In packed columns with concurrent upward gas-liquid flow, $Pé_l$ values were found to range from 100 to 5% of the corresponding value for single phase flow, depending on the liquid and gas load [60, 80]. For countercurrent flow of liquid and gas in a submerged packing of Raschig rings, $Pé_l$ for the liquid phase was found to be of the order of 0.1 [81]. For countercurrent flow of two immiscible liquids in a packed column, $Pé_l$ values lie in the same range [60]. Less mixing occurs in liquids flowing downwards over a packing material. KRAMERS and ALBERDA [32] found for a 0.7 m high packing of 10 mm Raschig rings that N' ranged from 10 to 20. The longitudinal dispersion increased with decreasing liquid load, but the gas velocity had little influence below the loading point.

When gas and liquid are brought into contact in a bubble column, a considerable spread in residence times is to be expected in both phases because of the violent mixing action exerted by the gas. This spread can be reduced only by introducing devices for "staging" the flows, e.g. trays for contacting the two phases. JARDINE [82] found the residence time distribution of a gas flowing through a layer of liquid on a sieve tray to be similar to that of 2 to 4 mixers in cascade.

HANHART [83] concluded from measurements performed in a mechanically agitated gas-liquid contactor that, at a high speed of agitation, the residence time distribution of the gas very nearly approached the distribution of one mixing vessel.

Many data given here and elsewhere in the literature relate to laboratory experiments. The rules for scaling-up to industrial dimensions are very uncertain particularly as regards two-phase flow, so that more information on the residence time distribution in full-scale equipment for the continuous treatment of gases, liquids and solids is badly needed.

CHAPTER IV

THE ROLE OF THE HEAT EFFECT IN CHEMICAL REACTORS

All chemical reactions are in principle accompanied by evolution or absorption of heat. In practice, therefore, a reaction hardly ever proceeds entirely under isothermal conditions, as was assumed in Chapters II and III. A certain temperature level and a certain temperature range at which the reaction must be carried out will generally be specified. Consequently, the heat effects must be taken into account when removing or supplying heat during the reaction.

The choice of the desired temperature level and temperature range is determined by one or more of the following factors:
– The chemical and physical properties of the reaction mixture, such as the position of the chemical equilibrium, the conversion rate of the main reaction, the occurrence of undesired reactions, the dewpoint of a gaseous reaction mixture, the boiling point and the solidification point of a liquid reaction mixture, etc.
– The properties of any catalyst used, such as sintering of solid catalyst, decomposition, aging, etc.
– The properties of the constructional materials, such as strength, thermal stability, corrosion, etc.
– The cost of bringing the reactants to the reaction temperature and of keeping the reaction mixture at the desired temperature level.

Several means are available for keeping a reaction mixture between prescribed temperature limits:
– Adjustment of the initial or entry temperature of the reaction mixture, e.g. in case of adiabatic operation.
– Addition of an inert compound for reducing temperature changes.
– Division of a reactor into adiabatic sections with intermediate cooling or heating of the mixture.
– Supply or withdrawal of heat during the reaction, e.g. by heat transfer from or to another medium or by evaporation of a volatile compound of the reaction mixture.
– Circulation through an external heat exchanger of a separate heat carrier, e.g. a solid catalyst.

In the study of these many possible alternatives it is essential that the energy balance be properly applied in conjunction with the material balance.

98

This is the main theme of this chapter, which deals with applications to the more current types of reactors.

IV. 1. The energy balance and the heat of reaction

As mentioned in Section I.2, Eq. I-3 conveniently formulates the principle of conservation of energy for a finite mass m with volume V_r of a reaction mixture:

$$\frac{d(\langle u \rangle m)}{dt} = -\Delta(h\Phi_m) + \dot{Q} - \dot{W}, \qquad \text{IV-1}$$

where u and h represent the internal energy and the enthalpy, respectively, per unit mass of the reaction mixture. They are interrelated according to:

$$h = u + p/\varrho. \qquad \text{IV-2}$$

If we denote the internal energy and the enthalpy per unit mass of species J by u_J and h_J, we can write for u and h, respectively:

$$u = \sum_J u_J w_J, \quad \text{and} \quad h = \sum_J h_J w_J.$$

For additional use of Eq. IV-1 it is important to relate a change in u or h to a change in the physical conditions and composition of the reaction mixture. We shall do this below for the enthalphy h, which is a function of pressure, temperature and composition:

$$dh(p,T,w_J) = \sum_J w_J \frac{\partial h_J}{\partial p} dp + \sum_J w_J \frac{\partial h_J}{\partial T} dT + \sum_J d(h_J w_J)_{p,T}. \quad \text{IV-3}$$

For the first two sums we may write:

$$\sum_J w_J \frac{\partial h_J}{\partial p} dp = \frac{1}{\varrho} dp,$$

and:

$$\sum_J w_J \frac{\partial h_J}{\partial T} dT = c_p dT,$$

where c_p is the specific heat at constant pressure of the reaction mixture. The last term of Eq. IV-3 represents the enthalpy change at constant temperature and pressure due to a change in the degree of conversion. In order to relate this term to the heat of reaction, we first consider, as an example, the reaction equation:

$$\nu_A A + \nu_B B \rightarrow \nu_P P + \nu_Q Q,$$

with which a heat effect ΔH_r is associated when the reaction moves completely from the left side to the right side at constant temperature and pressure (see Section I.3). For ΔH_r we have in this case, according to Eq. I-4:

$$\Delta H_r = \nu_P H_P + \nu_Q H_Q - \nu_A H_A - \nu_B H_B.$$

A small change in composition due to conversion can be characterized by a change in one of the mass fractions, say w_A. The changes in the other mass fractions are related to dw_A (see Eq. I-25) by:

$$\frac{dw_A}{\nu_A M_A} = \frac{dw_B}{\nu_B M_B} = -\frac{dw_P}{\nu_P M_P} = -\frac{dw_Q}{\nu_Q M_Q} .$$

If we assume the h_J's to be independent of composition*, the last term of Eq. IV-3 can now be written as:

$$\sum_J d(h_J w_J)_{p,T} = \sum_J (h_J dw_J)_{p,T} =$$

$$= (\nu_A M_A h_A + \nu_B M_B h_B - \nu_P M_P h_P - \nu_Q M_Q h_Q) \frac{dw_A}{\nu_A M_A} =$$

$$= (\nu_A H_A + \nu_B H_B - \nu_P H_P - \nu_Q H_Q) \frac{dw_A}{\nu_A M_A} =$$

$$= -\Delta H_r \frac{-d\xi_J}{\nu_J M_J} \equiv \frac{(\Delta H_r)_J}{M_J} d\xi_J \equiv (\Delta h_r)_J d\xi_J . \qquad \text{IV-4}$$

Therefore, while ΔH_r is the heat of reaction associated with the stoichiometric formula, $(\Delta H_r)_J$ is the heat of reaction per mole of J converted, and $(\Delta h_r)_J$ the heat of reaction per unit mass of J converted. The sign of ΔH_r, $(\Delta H_r)_J$ and $(\Delta h_r)_J$ [$= (\Delta H_r)_J/M_J$] is always the same; it is negative for exothermic reactions and positive for endothermic reactions.

As a result of the above considerations, we shall use the following relation in applying Eq. IV-1 to single reactions:

$$dh = \frac{1}{\varrho} dp + c_p dT + (\Delta h_r)_J d\xi_J , \qquad \text{IV-5}$$

and, similarly, for the internal energy per unit mass:

$$du = -pd\left(\frac{1}{\varrho}\right) + c_v dT + (\Delta u_r)_J d\xi_J . \qquad \text{IV-6}$$

$(\Delta u_r)_J$ is the heat of reaction at constant temperature and density, per unit mass of J converted or formed; it is related to the molar heat of reaction $(\Delta U_r)_J$ and the integral heat effect ΔU_r according to:

$$(\Delta u_r)_J = \frac{(\Delta U_r)_J}{M_J} = \frac{\Delta U_r}{\nu_J M_J} .$$

The last two terms of Eq. IV-1 are still to be discussed. If the reaction volume V_r is increased by an amount dV_r during the reaction, $\dot{W}$ is represented by:

$$\dot{W} = p\,dV_r/dt , \qquad \text{IV-7}$$

where p is the absolute pressure of the system. For the rate of heat supply to the reaction mixture, $\dot{Q}$, several expressions can be used, depending on the

---

* This means that heats of mixing are disregarded in this derivation.

method by which heat is supplied or removed. For example, if heat is withdrawn through a heat exchange surface with an area A by means of a coolant having the temperature T_c, we can write for $\dot{Q}$:

$$\dot{Q} = -UA\,(T - T_c)\,. \qquad\qquad \text{IV-8}$$

U is the over-all heat transfer coefficient and T the temperature of the reaction mixture.

IV. 2. The well-mixed batch reactor

Since the total mass of the reaction remains constant and the conditions are uniform over the entire contents of the reactor, Eq. IV-1 becomes:

$$m\,\frac{\mathrm{d}u}{\mathrm{d}t} + p\,\frac{\mathrm{d}V_r}{\mathrm{d}t} = \dot{Q}\,. \qquad\qquad \text{IV-9}$$

For reactor calculations this equation must be considered in conjunction with the material balance for the batch reactor (see Eq. II-1):

$$m\,\frac{\mathrm{d}\xi_J}{\mathrm{d}t} = |r|_J V_r\,. \qquad\qquad \text{IV-10}$$

In accordance with normal operating procedures, a distinction can be made between operation at constant pressure (e.g., in an open vessel) and at constant volume and density (e.g., in an autoclave).

At *constant pressure*, we can combine Eqs. IV-2 and IV-5 with Eq. IV-9 to yield:

$$m\,\frac{\mathrm{d}}{\mathrm{d}t}(u + \frac{p}{\varrho}) = m\,\frac{\mathrm{d}h}{\mathrm{d}t} = mc_p\,\frac{\mathrm{d}T}{\mathrm{d}t} + m(\Delta h_r)_J\,\frac{\mathrm{d}\xi_J}{\mathrm{d}t} = \dot{Q}\,. \qquad \text{IV-11}$$

It is seen from this equation that, if the reaction proceeds at constant temperature and pressure, the amount of heat to be supplied per unit mass of species J converted, $\dot{Q}\mathrm{d}t/m\mathrm{d}\xi_J$, is equal to $(\Delta h_r)_J$; this is in agreement with the definition IV-4. Furthermore, it should be borne in mind that the enthalpy is a point property so that the heat supply per unit mass of mixture necessary for a change in temperature from T_a to T_b and in conversion from ξ_{Ja} to ξ_{Jb},

$$\int\limits_{T_a,\xi_{Ja}}^{T_b,\xi_{Jb}} [c_p\mathrm{d}T + (\Delta h_r)_J\mathrm{d}\xi_J] = \int\limits_a^b \frac{\dot{Q}}{m}\,\mathrm{d}t\,,$$

is independent of the path of integration. This is illustrated in Fig. IV-1, which shows two particular paths of integration. In Path 1 the reaction mixture is supposed to be heated from T_a to T_b at a degree of conversion ξ_{Ja} whereupon it reacts at T_b with a change of conversion from ξ_{Ja} to ξ_{Jb}; according to Path 2 the conversion takes place entirely at T_a and it is followed by the temperature rise of a mixture having the final composition

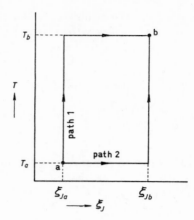

FIG. IV-1. Two paths for integrating Eq. IV-11.

characterized by ξ_{Jb}.

With a *constant volume* of the reaction mixture, its density remains constant as well, so that Eq. IV-9 becomes:

$$m\frac{\mathrm{d}u}{\mathrm{d}t} = mc_v\frac{\mathrm{d}T}{\mathrm{d}t} + m(\Delta u_r)_J\frac{\mathrm{d}\xi_J}{\mathrm{d}t} = \dot{Q}.$$
IV-12

The heat supply per unit mass of J converted, $\dot{Q}\,\mathrm{d}t/m\,\mathrm{d}\xi_J$, is equal to the heat of reaction $(\Delta u_r)_J$ if temperature and density remain constant. For the integration of Eq. IV-12 we can take advantage of the fact that the internal energy — at constant density only a function of temperature and composition — is a point property.

In general, when dealing with a batch reactor, it will be required to calculate the reaction temperature and the degree of conversion as a function of time under prescribed conditions of heat supply or removal, or to calculate the heating or cooling requirements for obtaining a desired temperature range and reactor capacity. To this end, the material balance IV-10 has to be used together with the energy balance IV-9 or one of its derived forms such as IV-11 or IV-12. A straightforward simultaneous solution will generally not be feasible since the conversion rate depends both on temperature and on the degree of conversion itself. Accordingly, numerical methods of solution have to be used which are often combined with a trial-and-error procedure. We shall give below two illustrative examples from the many possible problems in this field.

ILLUSTRATION IV. 2a. *Influence of the policy of operation on the reaction time*

In a batch reactor having a volume $V_r = 5$ m³, an exothermic reaction A → P is carried out in the liquid phase. For the conversion rate we have:

$$|R|_A = kc_A \, [\text{kmol/m}^3\text{s}] \, ,$$

with:

$$k = 4 \times 10^6 \exp(-7900/T)\,\text{s}^{-1} \, .$$

Further data are:
$(\Delta h_r)_A = -1.67 \times 10^6 \, \text{J/kg} \, ,$
$\varrho c_p = 4.2 \times 10^6 \, \text{J/m}^3 \, {}^\circ\text{C} \, ,$
$M_A = 100 \, \text{kg/kmol, and}$
$c_{A0} = 1 \, \text{kmol/m}^3 \, .$

The initial temperature T_0 of the reaction mixture is 20°C and the maximum allow-able reaction temperature is 95°C. The reactor contains a spiral for heat exchange purposes; its surface area A is 3.3 m² and it can be operated with steam ($T_s = 120°C$, $U = 1360 \, \text{W/m}^2 \, °\text{C}$) and with cooling water ($T_c = 15°C$, $U = 1180 \, \text{W/m}^2°\text{C}$). The times required for filling and emptying the reactor are 600 and 900 s, respectively.

The problem to be solved is to calculate the duration of one reaction cycle and the steam consumption for a relative conversion $\zeta_A \geqslant 0.90$ and for the following policies of operation:

I. Preheat to 55°C, let the reaction proceed adiabatically, start cooling when 95°C or $\zeta_A = 0.90$ is reached, cool down to 45°C.

II. Heat up to 95 °C, let the reaction proceed isothermally until $\zeta_A = 0.90$, cool down to 45°C.

We shall use the energy balance in the form IV-11 for this problem. It appears that for the calculation of the *heating-up period* the chemical conversion and its heat effect can be neglected. For this period, therefore, Eq. IV-11 becomes:

$$\varrho c_p V_r \frac{\mathrm{d}T}{\mathrm{d}t} = UA\,(T_s - T) \, .$$

After integration between $T = 20°C$ and $T = 55°C$ it is found that the latter temper-ature is reached after 2030 seconds.

For the *adiabatic* reaction operation (Case I), the material and heat balances become in terms of the relative degree of conversion, $\zeta_A = 1 - c_A/c_{A0} = \varrho \xi_A/c_{A0} M_A$:

$$\frac{\mathrm{d}\zeta_A}{\mathrm{d}t} = k\,(1 - \zeta_A) \, ,$$

and:

$$\varrho c_p \frac{\mathrm{d}T}{\mathrm{d}t} + (\Delta h_r)_A c_{A0} M_A \frac{\mathrm{d}\zeta_A}{\mathrm{d}t} = 0 \, .$$

The latter equation constitutes a linear relation between T and ζ_A. In this example, $\zeta_A = 0$ at $T = 55°C$ so that integration yields:

$$T = 55 + \frac{(\Delta h_r)_A c_{A0} M_A}{\varrho c_p} \zeta_A \; °\text{C} \, .$$

Hence it follows that at $\zeta_A = 0.9$ the temperature will be 90.8°C, i.e., below the maxi-mum value of 95°C. Moreover, the reaction velocity constant k can now be expressed as a function of c_A only. Hence, the material balance can be integrated, preferably by means of a graphic procedure. The results are shown in Fig. IV-2. Both the $\zeta_A - t$ and the $T - t$ curves have an inflection point. The slope of the curves [proportional to $k\,(1 - \zeta_A)$] is relatively small in the initial stage of the reaction because of the low temperature (k small) and in the final stage because of the high degree of conversion.

For Case II, *simultaneous heating and reaction*, the equations to be solved are:

$$\frac{\mathrm{d}\zeta_A}{\mathrm{d}t} = k\,(1 - \zeta_A) \, ,$$

103

and:

$$\varrho c_p \frac{\mathrm{d}T}{\mathrm{d}t} + (\Delta h_r)_A c_{A0} M_A \frac{\mathrm{d}\zeta_A}{\mathrm{d}t} = \frac{UA}{V_r} (T_s - T) \, .$$

In this case the solution has to be arrived at with the aid of a step-by-step method. Starting from the initial concentration and temperature, a small temperature interval ΔT is selected. The equations are then solved for Δt with the average values of T and k and the initial value of ζ_A for that interval. The value of Δt thus estimated is then to calculate $\Delta \zeta_A$ from the first equation, so that a better approximation of the average concentration in the interval becomes available. A second approximation for Δt is then found and the procedure is repeated until the solution is consistent within the desired limits. In the present example, this calculation was carried out with temperature intervals of 5°C until the maximum temperature of 95°C was reached; the results are shown in Fig. IV-2. For the subsequent completion of the reaction under isothermal conditions, only the material balance is needed with the value of k at 95°C.

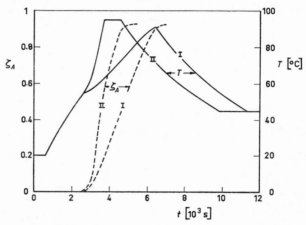

FIG. IV-2. Conversion and temperature in a batch reactor; Illustration IV.2a, Cases I and II.

The time required for cooling down the reaction mixture to 45°C can be calculated in a similar manner as the heating-up period, if the effects of the small amount of additional conversion are neglected.

The period of a complete reaction cycle, as obtained from the above calculations, is given below:

		Case I	Case II
seconds for:	filling	600	600
	preheating	2030	2030
	reaction	3590	1930
	cooling	5100	5300
	emptying	900	900
	total	12220 s	10760 s
	or	3.4 hrs	3.0 hrs.

It can be calculated that the steam consumption per cycle will be 330 and 510 kg for Cases I and II, respectively. Consequently, an extra steam consumption of 180 kg involves a gain in time of 24 minutes. Apart from this, it is evident that the production capacity is greatly limited by the long cooling period in this installation. If, for example, the reaction product were discharged through a separate cooler immediately after the desired conversion was reached, the capacity could be almost doubled.

104

ILLUSTRATION IV. 2b. *An explosion*

A closed spherical tank with a volume of 250 m³ contains air with 4% by volume of *n*-butane vapour at $T_0 = 18°C$ and a pressure p_0 of 1 atm. The mixture is ignited due to the presence of pyrophoric iron sulphide. The combustion of butane (B) follows the equation:

$$C_4H_{10} + 6\tfrac{1}{2}O_2 \rightarrow 4CO_2 + 5H_2O .$$

The standard heat of combustion (18°C, 1 atm.) of butane according to this reaction equation is equal to $\Delta H_r = -688,000 \text{ kcal} = -2.88 \times 10^6 \text{ kJ}$. What will be the maximum pressure in the tank after the explosion, if the gas mixture is assumed to follow the ideal gas law?

Since the reaction proceeds adiabatically and at constant volume, according to Eq. IV-9 the total internal energy of the reaction mixture does not change upon conversion. The temperature rise due to the explosion can best be calculated from Eq. IV-12 with $\dot{Q} = 0$:

$$\int_{T_0}^{T} c_v dT + \int_{\xi_{B0}}^{\xi_B} (\Delta u_r)_B d\xi_B = 0 . \qquad (a)$$

Since the internal energy is a point property, the second integral can be calculated under standard conditions, and consequently the specific heat for the composition of the final reaction mixture has to be taken for c_v in the first integral.

In calculating $(\Delta u_r)_B$, we recall that the difference between ΔH_r for the above reaction (p and T constant) and ΔU_r (V and T constant) is the work needed for expansion of the gas mixture at standard temperature and pressure when the reaction goes to completion:

$$\Delta H_r = \Delta U_r + p\Delta V .$$

Since the number of moles increases by 3/2 in the above reaction equation and the ideal gas law has been assumed to apply, we have:

$$p\Delta V = \frac{3}{2} RT = 3.56 \times 10^3 \text{ kJ} .$$

Hence, the correction to be applied is only of the order of 0.1% so that we may write:

$$(\Delta u_r)_B = \frac{(\Delta U_r)_B}{M_B} \approx \frac{(\Delta H_r)_B}{M_B} = \frac{\Delta H_r}{M_B} = 49.7 \times 10^3 \text{ kJ/kg} .$$

The initial and final gas compositions can be easily calculated; they are listed in the table below:

	M_J (kg/kmol)	before explosion		after explosion	
		mole fraction	w_{J0}	kmol/kmol of original mixture	w_J
C_4H_{10} (B)	58	0.040	0.077	0.0089	0.017
N_2	28	0.758	0.708	0.758	0.708
O_2	32	0.202	0.215	–	–
CO_2	44	–	–	0.124	0.182
H_2O	18	–	–	0.155	0.093
total		1.000	1.000	1.046	1.000

Since $\xi_B = 0.077 - 0.017 = 0.06$, the second term of Eq. (a) is now calculated as:

$$-49.7 \times 10^3 \times 0.06 = -2980 \text{ kJ/kg mixture.}$$

The specific heat at constant volume of the product mixture must be calculated as a function of temperature. After some trials it appears that the average value of c_v over the temperature range to be considered is 1.06 kJ/kg°C, so that Eq. (a) indicates that:

$$2980 = 1.06\,(T - T_0)\,, \quad \text{or} \quad T = 2830\ °C\,.$$

Assuming the ideal gas law to apply, the explosion pressure can be calculated as a result of the temperature rise and the relative increase of the number of moles in the mixture:

$$p = p_0 \times \frac{291 + 2810}{291} \times 1.046 = 11.1\ \text{atm}.$$

IV. 3. The continuous tank reactor with heat exchange

For the steady operation of a continuous tank reactor provided with a heat exchange area A, the energy balance IV-1 becomes:

$$0 = -\Phi_m(h_1 - h_0) + UA\,(T_c - T_1)\,. \qquad \text{IV-13}$$

The difference in enthalpy between the outgoing and the incoming stream can be obtained by integration of Eq. (IV-5). Assuming the pressure difference between inlet and outlet to be negligible, we arrive at:

$$h_1 - h_0 = \int_{T_0,0}^{T_1,\xi_{J1}} [c_p \mathrm{d}T + (\Delta h_r)_J \mathrm{d}\xi_J]\,.$$

The value of $h_1 - h_0$ is independent of the path of integration. We may therefore choose a path where the reactor feed is heated from T_0 to T_1 and the heat of reaction is absorbed or liberated at the outlet conditions $(T = T_1)$; this integration path is the same as Path 1 in Fig. IV-1. Accordingly, we find for Eq. IV-13:

$$0 = -\int_{T_0}^{T_1} [c_p]_{\xi_{j}=0}\,\mathrm{d}T - [(\Delta h_r)_J]_{T=T_1}\xi_{J1} + \frac{UA}{\Phi_m}(T_c - T_1)\,. \qquad \text{IV-14}$$

This relation can be used in conjunction with the isothermal material balance II-12 for calculating the reaction temperature and the degree of conversion in tank reactors where the heat effect and the external supply or removal of heat are taken into account. Some aspects of the stability of such a reactor with exothermic reactions will be discussed in Section IV.5.

Extension of the theory to a cascade of tank reactors does not involve essential difficulties. A simple illustration is given below.

ILLUSTRATION IV. 3. *Heat transfer requirements in a cascade of tank reactors*

The reaction of Illustration IV. 2a is to be carried out continuously in a cascade of 3 tank reactors of equal size at 95 °C; the feed conditions and the required relative conversion ζ_{A3} are the same as in Illustration IV.2a and the production of the installation should be that of Case I, i.e. $0.9 \times 5/12{,}220 = 0.375 \times 10^{-3}$ kmol/s of A converted. Calculate the reactor volume and the heat exchange requirements.

With constant density, temperature and reaction volumes we have:

$$1 - \zeta_{A1} = \left(1 + \frac{k\bar{\tau}}{3}\right)^{-1}$$

$$1 - \zeta_{A2} = (1 - \zeta_{A1})\left(1 + \frac{k\bar{\tau}}{3}\right)^{-1} = \left(1 + \frac{k\bar{\tau}}{3}\right)^{-2}$$

$$1 - \zeta_{A3} = (1 - \zeta_{A2})\left(1 + \frac{k\bar{\tau}}{3}\right)^{-1} = \left(1 + \frac{k\bar{\tau}}{3}\right)^{-3}.$$

With $\zeta_{A3} = 0.9$ we find $\zeta_{A1} = 0.538$, $\zeta_{A2} = 0.785$ and $k\bar{\tau}/3 = 1.15$. The value of k at 95°C is $1.92 \times 10^{-3}\,\mathrm{s}^{-1}$, so that the average residence time $\bar{\tau}$ in the whole system must be 1800 s. The volumetric rate of flow through the system is determined by the required degree of conversion and the production rate; it is equal to $0.375 \times 10^{-3}/0.9 = 0.416 \times 10^{-3}\,\mathrm{m}^3/\mathrm{s}$. Hence, the total reaction volume is $0.416 \times 10^{-3} \times 1800 = 0.75\,\mathrm{m}^3$, distributed over three reactors of equal size.

With regard to the heat exchange requirements, it is decided to operate the first reactor adiabatically and to provide cooling coils for the two other tanks. For calculating the required inlet temperature of the first reactor, we use Eq. IV-14 without the last term:

$$0 = -c_p(T_1 - T_0) - (\Delta h_r)_A \frac{c_{A0}M_A}{\varrho}\zeta_{A1},$$

or:

$$T_0 = 95 + \frac{-1.67 \times 10^6 \times 1 \times 100 \times 0.538}{4.2 \times 10^6} = 73.6°C.$$

For the second reactor, we calculate the required heat transfer area A_2 from Eq. IV-12 omitting the second term ($T_1 = T_2$):

$$0 = -(\Delta h_r)_A \frac{c_{A0}M_A}{\varrho}(\zeta_{A2} - \zeta_{A1}) + \frac{UA_2}{\Phi_m}(T_c - T_2).$$

Values of $T_c = 20°C$ and $U = 1180\,\mathrm{W/m^2\,°C}$ result in $A_2 = 0.19\,\mathrm{m}^2$, and, after a similar calculation for the third tank, $A_3 = 0.09\,\mathrm{m}^3$. These cooling surfaces can be easily installed.

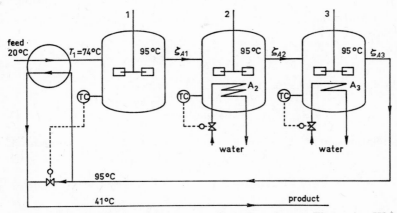

FIG. IV-3. Cascade of three tank reactors with heat exchange; Illustration IV.3.

Fig. IV-3 shows a possible flow sheet for this continuous process. It has several advantages over the batch process treated in Illustration IV.2a:
– No steam is consumed and the heat of reaction is completely utilized in the first reactor.

107

− The heat transfer requirements are not excessive.
− The total reaction volume is only 0.75 m³, vs. 5 m³ for batch operation.
− The reaction temperature can be kept within the desired limits by simple automatic control.

The stability of these reactors will be discussed in Illustration IV.5.

IV. 4. The tubular reactor with external heat exchange

In this section we shall assume that the temperature and the composition of the reaction mixture are uniform over the cross section of the reactor tube and depend only on the distance z from the feed point. The complications arising from a radial temperature gradient and a radial change of composition — frequently encountered in fixed bed catalytic reactors — will not be considered here but in Section V.6.

According to Eq. IV-1 the steady state energy balance over a differential volume of the reactor becomes:

$$0 = -\Phi_m \mathrm{d}h + \mathrm{d}\dot{Q} . \qquad \text{IV-15}$$

If the pressure changes relatively little over the reactor, the enthalpy change $\mathrm{d}h$ is made up of two contributions: one due to a temperature change $\mathrm{d}T$, and one due to a conversion characterized by the change in degree of conversion of one of the components. We thus have according to Eq. IV-5:

$$\mathrm{d}h = c_p \mathrm{d}T + (\Delta h_r)_J \mathrm{d}\xi_J .$$

The heat supply (which may be positive or negative) is assumed to be provided by heat transfer from a medium flowing outside the tube with a temperature T_c. The over-all heat transfer coefficient U is supposed to be localized at the tube wall. By introducing the hydraulic radius of the tube, R_h, which is the ratio between the cross-sectional area S and the circumference, we obtain for $\mathrm{d}\dot{Q}$:

$$\mathrm{d}\dot{Q} = \frac{U(T_c - T)}{R_h} S \, \mathrm{d}z .$$

Following the above substitutions, Eq. IV-15 becomes:

$$0 = \Phi_m c_p \mathrm{d}T + \Phi_m (\Delta h_r)_J \mathrm{d}\xi_J + \frac{U(T - T_c)}{R_h} S \, \mathrm{d}z . \qquad \text{IV-16}$$

This relationship must be used in conjunction with the material balance II-9:

$$0 = -\Phi_m \mathrm{d}\xi_J + |r|_J S \, \mathrm{d}z ,$$

for the calculation of the temperature and the degree of conversion along the reactor.★

★ In some cases the flow through a tubular reactor is associated with a considerable pressure drop due to frictional losses and to the acceleration of the reaction mixture (e.g. in a cracking furnace); under such circumstances the equations of motion or the momentum balance have to be taken into account also, as well as the influence of pressure on the enthalpy of the mixture.

A straightforward solution of the last two equations is only possible in a few special cases. For instance, if the reactor runs under adiabatic conditions, the last term in Eq. IV-16 vanishes and a single relation is left between the temperature and the degree of conversion. The conversion rate can hence be expressed as a function of the degree of conversion only, so that the material balance can be directly integrated.

Another case where the reactor calculation does not present special difficulties is the rather trivial one where the heat effect is small and the heat transfer with the surrounding medium is extremely good. Under such conditions the reactor works isothermally at $T \approx T_c$ and eq. IV-16 can further be disregarded.

In general, however, the calculation of a non-isothermal cooled or heated tubular reactor requires the simultaneous solution of IV-16 and II-9, e.g. by means of the step-by-step method indicated in Illustration IV. 2a, which is also employed in the following illustration where an endothermic catalytic reaction is dealt with.

ILLUSTRATION IV. 4a. *A catalytic dehydrogenation reaction in a tubular reactor*

It is required to calculate a tubular reactor for the production of methyl-ethyl ketone (P) from 2-butanol (A) according to the endothermic reaction:

$$CH_3CHOHC_2H_5 \rightarrow CH_3COC_2H_5 + H_2$$

$$\qquad\qquad (A) \qquad\qquad\qquad (P) \qquad\quad (Q)$$

The reaction is to be carried out in 25 parallel tubes (internal diameter 0.10 m) filled with brass spheres (having a diameter of 3.43 mm) as a catalyst. PERONA and THODOS [84] studied the conversion rate for this catalytic material between 350 and 400°C at atmospheric pressure. They arrived at the expression:

$$|R'|_A = \frac{k'(p_A - p_P p_Q / K)}{p_P(1 + K_A p_A + K_{AP} p_A / p_P)},$$

where the conversion rate is given on the basis of the external surface of the catalytic spheres; k', K_A and K_{AP}, and K represent the reaction velocity constant, the adsorption equilibrium constants, and the reaction equilibrium constant, respectively; these quantities are given as a function of temperature. The feed is 100 tons/day of butanol which has to attain a degree of conversion ξ_{AL} of 0.95.

Further data are:
$(\Delta H_r)_A = +59 \times 10^6$ J/kmol , or
$(\Delta h_r)_A = +0.80 \times 10^6$ J/kg ,
$C_p = 178 \times 10^3$ kJ/kmol mixture, assumed constant,
p = average pressure in reactor = 5 atm,
$T_0 = 450°C$,
$T_h = 800°C$ (heating medium),
$U = 200$ W/m² °C.

It is assumed that temperature and composition are uniform over the cross section of the tube and that the kinetic data referred to above may be extrapolated to higher temperatures and pressures.

The rate equation is first rewritten in terms of the degree of conversion of A, $\xi_A = 1 - w_A$, by means of the procedure indicated in Section I.5. Then, since the amount of catalyst per tube is to be calculated, the conversion rate is based on the unit mass of catalyst; this amounts to a division of $|R'|_A$ by the ratio mass/surface area of the catalyst which can

109

be calculated from the sphere diameter and the density ϱ_s of brass; this ratio is 4.8 kg/m². Finally, the conversion rate is expressed in mass units of A so that an expression for $|r_s|_A$ is obtained:

$$|r_s|_A = 0.0209 \, |R'|_A \quad \text{[kg A converted/s kg cat.]},$$

in which the partial pressures are given in terms of the total pressure and ξ_A. For further calculations it is convenient to have $|r_s|_A$ as a function of ξ_A and T in graphic form. It is shown in Fig. IV-4.

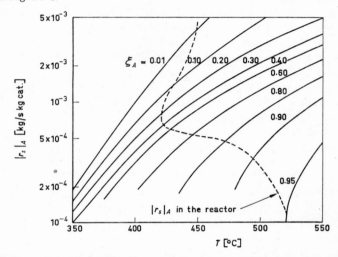

FIG. IV-4. The conversion rate for the catalytic dehydrogenation of 2-butanol (component A) at 5 atm., calculated and extrapolated from data of PERONA and THODOS [84]; Illustration IV.4a.

Instead of the distance z from the reactor inlet, we now take as a variable the mass of catalyst m_s between the inlet and the point under consideration. The equations to be solved then become Eq. (II-11):

$$0 = \mathrm{d}\xi_A - |r_s|_A \mathrm{d}(m_s/\varPhi_m),\tag{a}$$

and from Eq. IV-16 with $m_s = \varrho_s(1 - \varepsilon)Sz$:

$$0 = c_p\mathrm{d}T + (\Delta h_r)_A\mathrm{d}\xi_A - \frac{U(T_h - T)}{\varrho_s(1 - \varepsilon)R_h}\,\mathrm{d}\!\left(\frac{m_s}{\varPhi_m}\right).\tag{b}$$

The boundary conditions for $m_s = 0$ are:

$$\xi_A \equiv 0 \quad \text{and} \quad T = T_0 = 450 \,°\text{C}.$$

Because of the assumed constancy of molar specific heat we may write for c_p:

$$c_p = C_p(1 + \xi_A)/M_A = 2.40(1 + \xi_A) \, 10^3 \, \text{J/kg} \,°\text{C}.$$

If the porosity of the catalytic bed, ε, is assumed to be 0.4, we find that the quantity $U/\varrho_s(1 - \varepsilon)R_h = 1.58$ W/kg °C.

A step-by-step method should again be followed for the simultaneous solution of (a) and (b):
– Consider a "slice" Δm_s at the feed point.
– Find $|r_s|_A$ from Fig. IV-4 at $\xi_A = 0$ and $T = T_0$.
– Calculate $\Delta\xi_A$ from (a) and ΔT from (b).
– Calculate the average values of ξ_A and T over the interval Δm_s, and with these recalculate $\Delta\xi_A$ and ΔT.

– Repeat this until (a) and (b) have been consistently solved, and then proceed to the next interval.

The results of these calculations are shown in Fig. IV-5 where ξ_A and T have been plotted against m_s/Φ_m. In this case of an endothermic reaction, the reaction temperature T decreases rapidly at first and then passes through a minimum. In Fig. IV-4 the path of $|r_s|_A$ has been indicated as a dotted line.

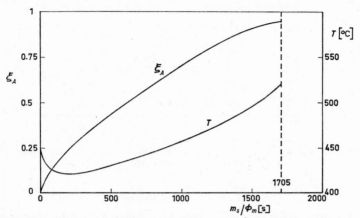

FIG. IV-5. Degree of conversion and temperature as a function of the amount of catalyst in a tubular reactor with an endothermic reaction; Illustration IV.4a.

From Fig. IV-5 it appears that for $\xi_{AL} = 0.95$ the value of m_{sL}/Φ_m must be 1705 kg cat. per kg/s of feed. Since the mass flow Φ_m per tube is:

$$\Phi_m = \frac{100,000}{25 \times 24 \times 3600} = 46.3 \times 10^{-3} \text{ kg/s} ,$$

the amount of catalyst required per tube is:

$$m_{sL} = 1705 \times 46.3 \times 10^{-3} = 79 \text{ kg} .$$

A tube length of 2.0 m is needed to accommodate this amount of catalyst. The pressure drop over this tube can be calculated to be approximately 9×10^4 N/m^2 $\approx$ 0.9 atm.

The outlet temperature of the reaction mixture is about 520°C. This may well be too high a value in view of thermal decomposition of the organic material involved. This can be avoided by lowering the temperature T_h of the heating medium and/or by diminishing the heat consumption per unit volume (e.g., by diluting the feed or the catalyst). These changes would result in a considerable increase in reaction volume and pressure drop.

Maximum temperature with exothermic reactions

In the previous example of an endothermic reaction it was seen that the reaction temperature passes through a minimum. Similarly, the temperature in a cooled tubular reactor may pass through a maximum value in the case of exothermic reactions. This is qualitatively shown in Fig. IV-6, which demonstrates that, depending on the heat effect and the possibilities for heat exchange, the value of this maximum temperature $T_{\max}$ may lie between T_0 and $T_0 + \Delta T_{ad}$. The adiabatic temperature rise ΔT_{ad} of the reaction mixture on complete conversion is defined, from Eq. IV-16, as:

111

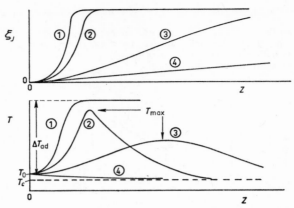

FIG. IV-6. Qualitative conversion and temperature profiles for an exothermic reaction in a cooled tubular reactor; 1 — adiabatic operation; 2,3 and 4 — low, rather high and extremely high capacity for heat removal, respectively.

$$\Delta T_{ad} = -w_{J0}(\Delta h_r)_J/c_p . \qquad \text{IV-17}$$

Now, in many cases it is required that T_{max} (often called the "hot spot temperature") does not exceed a prescribed value, because undesired side reactions might otherwise occur, such as thermal decomposition of the product. Since this highest permissible temperature is often much lower than the temperature obtainable under adiabatic conditions, it is of great importance to know the influence on the value of T_{max} of the properties of the reaction mixture, of the operating variables and of the capacity for heat exchange.

Not only dT/dz will be zero at the "hot spot", but $dT/d\xi_J$ as well. Therefore, after eliminating the variable z from Eqs. IV-16 and II-9 with the result:

$$0 = c_p dT + (\Delta h_r)_J d\xi_J + \frac{U(T - T_c)}{|r|_J R_h} d\xi_J , \qquad \text{IV-18}$$

we may, if $T = T_{max}$, put $dT = 0$, so that:

$$T_{max} - T_c = -(\Delta h_r)_J |r|_J R_h/U .$$

In this equation, the conversion rate $|r|_J$ must be taken at the temperature and the degree of conversion in the hot spot; since these quantities are determined by the entire history of the reaction mixture between the feed point and the hot spot, the latter equation does not permit direct calculation of T_{max}. It can be seen, however, that, with a large capacity for heat exchange U/R_h and a low coolant temperature T_c, T_{max} may in principle be kept below any desired value. It is not practical to choose too low a value of T_c because this will appreciably reduce the rate of conversion in the final section of the reactor; this would involve a large reactor volume. For this reason, high temperature coolants (e.g., molten salts) are often used for cooling tubular (catalytic) reactors. The most powerful variable at our disposal for

112

keeping the reaction temperature between desired limits is R_h, the ratio of the reactor volume and the heat transfer surface. The smaller its value, i.e. the smaller the tube diameter, the better the reaction temperature can be controlled.

Although no general expression can be given for the quantitative evaluation of T_{max}, it is possible to approach it to some extent by solving IV-18 after the introduction of a few approximations. We shall here follow the procedure developed by BARKELEW [85].

The reaction temperature will be taken with reference to the cooling temperature T_c, which is assumed to be constant. A dimensionless temperature difference $\Delta\vartheta$ is defined as:

$$\Delta\vartheta \equiv \frac{E}{RT_c{}^2} (T - T_c) .$$

The following rate equation will furthermore be used:

$$|r|_A = k\varrho w_{A0} (1 - \zeta_A) g(\zeta_A) .$$

The function $g(\zeta_A)$ serves to introduce deviations from first order kinetics:

$$g(\zeta_A) = \frac{1 + \alpha\zeta_A}{1 + \beta\zeta_A} .$$

When $\alpha = \beta = 0$ the reaction is of the first order; with $\alpha = -1$ and $\beta = 0$ it is of second order in A, and with $\beta > 1$ a product-inhibited reaction can be simulated. For the reaction velocity constant k we write:

$$k = k_\infty \exp(-E/RT) =$$
$$= k_\infty \exp(-E/RT_c) \exp\left[\frac{E}{RTT_c} (T - T_c)\right] \approx$$
$$\approx k_c \exp\left[\frac{E}{RT_c{}^2}(T - T_c)\right] = k_c e^{\Delta\vartheta}.$$

The approximation used here is that the ratio of the absolute temperatures T and T_c has been made equal to unity. By introducing ΔT_{ad} and the above substitutions into Eq. IV-18, we obtain the following result:

$$\frac{d(\Delta\vartheta)}{d\zeta_A} = N_{ad} - N_c \frac{\Delta\vartheta e^{-\Delta\vartheta}}{(1 - \zeta_A) g(\zeta_A)} , \qquad \text{IV-19}$$

where:

$$N_{ad} = \frac{E\Delta T_{ad}}{RT_c{}^2} , \quad \text{and} \quad N_c = \frac{U}{k_c \varrho c_p R_h} .$$

The dimensionless number N_{ad} accounts for the adiabatic temperature rise; N_c is a measure of the cooling capacity by means of which the temperature rise can be reduced. N_c is very sensitive to the coolant temperature (since it contains k_c) whereas N_{ad} is not.

Equation IV-19 can be solved by numerical methods for a given set of

113

values of N_{ad}, N_c, α and β, and for the boundary condition:
$$\Delta\vartheta = \Delta\vartheta_0 \quad \text{for} \quad \zeta_A = 0 .$$
Such solutions are shown in Fig. IV-7 for $\alpha = \beta = 0$ (first order reactions), $\Delta\vartheta_0 = 0$, $N_c/N_{ad} = 2$ and 5, and various values of N_{ad}. This figure also contains the locus of the maxima in the $\Delta\vartheta - \zeta_A$ curves for $N_c/N_{ad} = 2$. This locus can be calculated from Eq. IV-19 with $d(\Delta\vartheta)/d\zeta_A = 0$; on its left $d(\Delta\vartheta)/d\zeta_A$ is positive and on its right $\Delta\vartheta$ decreases with increasing conversion. It is seen from Fig. IV-7 that as N_{ad} increases, $\Delta\vartheta_{max}$ becomes higher. Particularly, above a certain value of N_{ad} (in Fig. IV-7 between 24 and 28) the $\Delta\vartheta - \zeta_A$ curve completely misses the lower part of the locus of $\Delta\vartheta_{max}$ with the result that $\Delta\vartheta_{max}$ will become very high and close to the value for adiabatic operation. We shall return later to this great sensitivity of T_{max} to a variation in parameters.

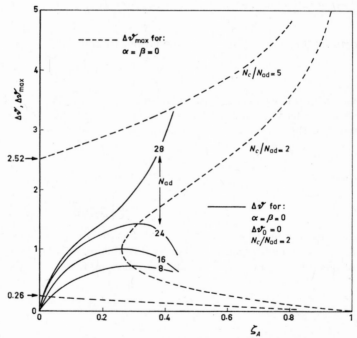

FIG. IV-7. Temperature rise and locus of maximum temperatures for first order exothermic reactions in cooled tubular reactors, Eq. IV-19.

The curves of $\Delta\vartheta_{max}$ as a function of ζ_A as shown in Fig. IV-7 can be very helpful in estimating the requirements for keeping $\Delta\vartheta_{max}$ below a desired value. When the cooling capacity is relatively small (say $N_c/N_{ad} < 2$), the locus lies very much to the right and the chance that, at constant N_{ad}, $\Delta\vartheta_{max}$ will exceed a certain value is increased. On the other hand, if N_c/N_{ad}

114

is large a great region exists where $d(\Delta\vartheta)/d\zeta_A$ must be negative. Thus, for $N_c/N_{ad} = 5$ (see Fig. IV-7) and with a value of $\Delta\vartheta_0$ between 0.26 and 2.52 no maximum in $\Delta\vartheta$ will occur; accordingly, $\Delta\vartheta$ will be consistently lower than $\Delta\vartheta_0$. In case $\Delta\vartheta_0$ lies below 0.26, the reaction temperature will initially rise with increasing conversion but $\Delta\vartheta_{max}$ will remain below the value of 0.26. Finally, if the feed temperature corresponds to $\Delta\vartheta_0 > 2.52$, the reaction temperature will rise to a high value.

Since the locus of $\Delta\vartheta_{max}$ does not intersect the $\zeta_A = 0$ axis for $N_c/N_{ad} < e$ some care must be taken particularly in this range not to let the reaction temperature run away. Starting from Eq. IV-18, BARKELEW [85] had a large number of $\Delta\vartheta - \zeta_A$ curves computed for different values of α, β, N_c/N_{ad}, N_{ad} and $\Delta\vartheta_0$. The results of these calculations were used by him for the derivation of a criterion for the boundary between a region where $\Delta\vartheta_{max}$ remains limited ("stable" region) and a region where $\Delta\vartheta_{max}$ may easily become excessively high ("unstable" region). Fig. IV-8 shows three such boundary lines for a few values of α, β and $\Delta\vartheta_0$; lines for other conditions may be found in BARKELEW's original paper. As to the significance of his criterion, it can be seen from the figure that for the conditions of Fig. IV-7 ($N_c/N_{ad} = 2$) N_{ad} should be smaller than about 20, while the latter figure indicates that $\Delta\vartheta_{max}$ will rapidly increase when $N_{ad} > 24$.

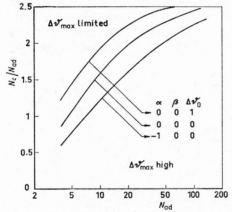

FIG. IV-8. Lines above which $\Delta\vartheta_{max}$ remains small, and below which $\Delta\vartheta_{max}$ may become large; after BARKELEW [85].

The fact that, in a certain range of parameters, the hot spot temperature T_{max} is very sensitive to a change in these parameters ("parametric sensitivity") has also been very clearly demonstrated by BILOUS and AMUNDSON [86]. These authors examined the concentration and temperature profiles for a first order exothermic reaction A → P under various circumstances by means of an analog computer. Some of their results have been collected in Figs. IV-9 and 10. In the first figure it is seen that the very high maximum

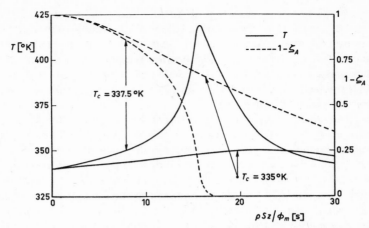

FIG. IV-9. Influence of a twofold change in cooling capacity on the temperature and concentration distribution in a tubular reactor, AMUNDSON [86, 87]; exothermic first order reaction with $k = 3.94 \times 10^{12} \exp(-11400/T)$ s^{-1}, $\Delta T_{ad} = 146°$C, $T_0 = 340°$K, $U/R_h c_p \varrho = 0.20$ s^{-1}.

in T practically disappears when the rate of heat removal at the inlet $[\sim (T_0 - T_c)]$ is doubled; Fig. IV-10 shows that in a certain range a relatively small increase in T_c, ΔT_{ad} and R_h/U may cause T_{max} to change from T_0 to a value near $T_0 + \Delta T_{ad}$. This phenomenon is closely related with the course of the $\Delta \vartheta - \zeta_A$ curve relative to the locus of $\Delta \vartheta_{max}$, as demonstrated in Fig. IV-7.

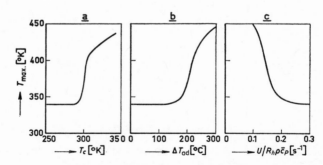

FIG. IV-10. Influence of T_c, ΔT_{ad} and the capacity for heat removal on T_{max} in a tubular reactor [86, 87]; conditions:

	a	b	c	
k	15.9	15.9	7.89	$\times 10^3 \exp(-5700/T)$ s^{-1}
ΔT_{ad}	200	var.	200	°C
T_0	340	340	340	°K
T_c	var.	300	320	°K
$U/R_h c_p \varrho$	0.20	0.20	var.	s^{-1}

116

Because of the analogy between the ideal tubular reactor and the mixed batch reactor, the above considerations apply equally well to the latter reactor type. A practical difference between the two types is that a predetermined temperature and conversion course with time can be enforced in a batch reactor by properly programming the rate of heat supply and/or removal; this was demonstrated in Illustration IV.2a. In a continuously operated tubular reactor similar variable heat exchange requirements can only be realized if the reactor is divided into different sections, or if it is approximated by a cascade of tank reactors operated under different thermal conditions. The choice of the proper temperature sequence in such systems offers great possibilities for obtaining high product yields with complicated reactions. This aspect is connected with reactor optimization and will be discussed in Section VI.3.

ILLUSTRATION IV. 4b. *Maximum reaction temperature*

Find for the reaction system specified in Fig. IV-9:
 i. below which value of T_c no hot spot will occur,
 ii. for what value of T_c the reactor will still have a reasonably low value of T_{max} according to BARKELEW's criterion.

From the data in Fig. IV-9 we have:

$$E/R = 11,400°K, \qquad k_c = 3.94 \times 10^{12} \exp\left(-\frac{11,400}{T_c}\right) s^{-1},$$

$$\Delta\vartheta_0 = \frac{11,400}{T_c^2}(340 - T_c), \qquad N_{ad} = \frac{11,400}{T_c^2} \times 146,$$

$$N_c = 0.20/k_c.$$

With these data the following table can be drawn up:

T_c °K	E/RT_c^2 °K^{-1}	k_c 10^3 s^{-1}	$\Delta\vartheta_0$ —	N_{ad} —	N_c —	N_c/N_{ad} —
345	0.096	19.6	−0.48	13.9	10.2	0.73
340	0.098	12.1	0	14.4	16.5	1.15
338	0.100	9.9	0.20	14.5	20.2	1.39
336	0.101	8.1	0.40	14.7	25	1.68
334	0.102	6.6	0.61	14.9	31	2.0
330	0.104	4.4	1.04	15.2	46	3.0
320	0.111	1.5	2.2	16.2	133	8.2

Since a first order reaction is involved, $\alpha = \beta = 0$, and Figs. IV-7 and IV-8 may be used.
 As to question (*i*), T_c must be so low that $\Delta\vartheta_0$ falls on the locus for $\Delta\vartheta_{max}$, or to its right. By plotting several loci in Fig. IV-7 for N_c/N_{ad} between 2 and 3, and by subsequent interpolation we find that the highest cooling temperature at which no maximum is developed in the temperature profile is $331°K$, corresponding to $\Delta\vartheta_0 = 0.92$.
 Question (*ii*) can be answered by interpolation between the two upper curves of Fig. IV-8, from which it appears that a value of $N_c/N_{ad} = 2.0$ with $T_c = 334°K$ would just be safe according to BARKELEW's criterion. It can be deduced from Fig. IV-9 that T_{max} would then remain somewhat below 350°C.
 Since this hypothetical reaction exhibits a high conversion rate at the inlet, only a change of a few degrees in the cooling temperature profoundly influences the temperature

profile and the average rate of conversion. It can thus be estimated from the k_c values listed in the above table that for $T_c = 331°K$ the reactor would have to be about 3 times longer than with $T_c = 334°K$.

IV.5. Autothermal reactor operation

When an exothermic reaction is carried out, it is generally desirable to employ the liberated heat of reaction somewhere in the plant in a useful manner. The heat of reaction is often used for preheating the feed to the reactor, particularly when the reaction takes place at a high temperature level and the reactants are available at a much lower temperature. A reactor system in which such a feed-back of reaction heat to the incoming reactant stream is applied is said to be operated under autothermal conditions.

The term "autothermal" stems from the fact that such a system is to a great extent self-supporting in its thermal energy requirements, so that it is possible to operate at a high temperature level without preheating the feed by external means. As a consequence of this feed-back, an autothermally working reactor has the property that in many cases the reactor has to be "ignited" in order to attain steady state operation. In this respect, the ordinary flame and, in general, all rapid combustion reactions are autothermal as well, since the reactants are likewise preheated to the reaction temperature by thermal conduction and radiation (see also Section V.5).

The theory of steady state behaviour of reactors under autothermal conditions was first proposed by WAGNER [88] and was later treated extensively by VAN HEERDEN [89, 90]. Of the different possibilities for obtaining the required feed-back, we shall discuss in this section:

i. The tank reactor in which the cold feed is heated by mixing with the reactor contents.

ii. An adiabatic tubular reactor with heat exchange between the outgoing and the incoming stream.

iii. A multitube reactor with internal heat exchange between the incoming stream and the reaction mixture.

The tank reactor

For the purposes of this discussion we shall simplify Eq. IV-14 by assuming that the specific heat of the reaction mixture does not depend on the temperature and the composition and that, consequently, the heat of reaction is independent of temperature. The heat balance can then be written in the form:

$$-\xi_{J1}(\Delta h_r)_J = c_p(T_1 - T_0) + \frac{UA}{\Phi_m}(T_1 - T_c) . \qquad \text{IV-20}$$

Evidently, the reaction temperature T_1 in the steady state must have a value which satisfies this equation.

The left-hand side of Eq. IV-20 represents the heat produced per unit mass of reaction mixture. This specific production of heat is proportional to the

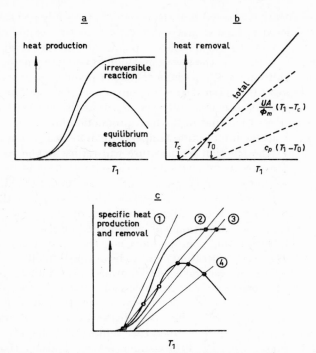

FIG. IV-11. Heat production and heat removal in an autothermally operating tank reactor (*a* and *b*), and different possibilities of steady operation (*c*); ● — stable solutions, ○ — unstable solutions.

heat of reaction and the degree of conversion, which in turn is determined by the residence time $\bar{\tau}$ and the conversion rate (see Eq. II-13). Fig. IV-11a shows how, in principle, the heat production depends on T_1 for an irreversible and an equilibrium reaction.

The two right-hand terms of Eq. IV-20 represent the heat removed per unit mass of the reaction mixture as a result of the heat absorbed by the cold feed and of the heat transferred to the cooling medium, respectively. Both terms are represented schematically in Fig. IV-11b.

The reaction temperature T_1 is obtained, e.g., graphically by combining the two diagrams IV-11a and b, into one graph, as shown in Fig. IV-11c*. At an intersection of a heat production curve and a heat removal line, Eq. IV-20 is obeyed so that steady operation would be possible at the corresponding reaction temperature. It is seen from Fig. IV-11c that several solutions may exist.

If the heat removal is represented by line 1 in Fig. IV-11c, the reaction

---

* The heat production and heat removal functions can be plotted in various ways; each has its own advantages and several methods will be applied in the following.

mixture is so effectively cooled that steady operation is only possible at a low temperature and a very low degree of conversion. If the cooling capacity is reduced, line 2 is obtained which has three points of intersection with the heat production curves; those at the lowest and highest reaction temperature represent stable conditions, and especially the latter point is of practical interest since it represents a high degree of conversion. The stability of these two operating conditions is related to the fact that the slope of the heat removal line is greater than that of the heat production line. Thus, on a positive deviation from the intersection temperature more heat is removed than produced so that the reaction temperature will return to the steady state value; similarly, a negative deviation will cause more heat to be produced than removed so that the temperature will rise. In the intermediate intersection point, on the other hand, the situation is reversed. Since the slope of the heat production curve is here greater than that of the heat removal line, any positive temperature deviation will be amplified until the reactor works in the upper stable operating point and any negative temperature deviation will cause the lower stable operating point to be attained finally; in the latter case we may say that the reaction is "extinguished". The intermediate intersection point is unstable because of this behaviour. If it is desired to operate the reactor at the upper stable point, the lower stable condition has to be by-passed, e.g. by temporarily preheating the feed or by operating under a smaller load; such a procedure is called the "ignition" of the reaction.

If the feed temperature T_0 and the cooling capacity are such that the heat removal line 3 in Fig. IV-11c prevails, only the upper stable working point is a possible solution to Eq. IV-20 and no special measures need be taken to start the reaction. Finally, line 4 shows that a relatively small slope of the heat removal line (which may mean that the cooling capacity is too low) may give rise to high reaction temperatures and, in the case of an equilibrium reaction, to a reduction in the degree of conversion.

It is of interest to study the sensitivity of the autothermal tank reactor to a change in operating variables, such as the feed temperature and concentration, the throughput and the cooling capacity. To this end, we further simplify Eq. IV-20 by assuming constant density of the reaction mixture and by introducing the relative degree of conversion ζ_A of a reactant A and the adiabatic temperature rise ΔT_{ad} defined by Eq. IV-17. With these substitutions IV-20 can be written as:

$$\zeta_{A1} = \frac{T_1 - T_0}{\Delta T_{ad}} + \frac{UA(T_1 - T_c)}{\varrho c_p V_r \Delta T_{ad}} \bar{\tau}. \qquad \text{IV-21a}$$

If a reaction is of the first order in A with a reaction-rate constant k, we have from the material balance (e.g. Eq. II-19):

$$\zeta_{A1} = \frac{k\bar{\tau}}{1 + k\bar{\tau}}, \qquad \text{IV-21b}$$

in which k is still a function of T_1. As an example, Fig. IV-12 shows the

120

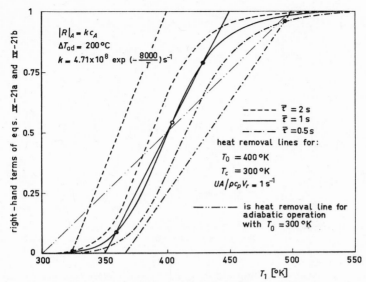

FIG. IV-12. Tank reactor with first order exothermic reaction; influence of the average residence time $\bar{\tau}$ on stable autothermal operation.

functions IV-21a and IV-21b as a function of T_1 for $\bar{\tau} = 0.5$, 1 and 2 seconds under otherwise specified conditions in order to demonstrate the influence of a fourfold variation in reactor load. At $\bar{\tau} = 1$ s the reactor has three possible operating points (of which the intermediate one is unstable). When the reactor throughput is halved ($\bar{\tau} = 2$ s) the reaction is extinguished; when it is doubled ($\bar{\tau} = 0.5$ s), stable operation results with a high degree of conversion. Under the latter conditions the reactor can be started without any special measures.

Fig. IV-12 then shows that — if a throughput corresponding to $\bar{\tau} = 0.5$ s is the normal operating condition — underloading of the reactor results in a *decrease* of conversion because the cooling becomes relatively too effective. This situation could be improved by lowering the feed temperature and at the same time diminishing the rate of heat removal by heat transfer, $UA(T_1 - T_c)$.

If the reactor is operated without heat exchange with a cooling medium (i.e., adiabatically) and if $T_0 = 300°$K, Fig. IV-12 shows that the reaction temperature and the degree of conversion slightly *increase* when the throughput is diminished; in this case, however, the reactor would have to be ignited. In view of the above considerations, a proper combination of inlet temperature and cooling facilities can bring about a situation of minimum sensitivity to load variations.

Another aspect of autothermal operation is the occurrence of hysteresis. If the feed temperature T_0 is increased at a constant feed rate, the reaction will be ignited at a certain feed temperature $(T_0)_{ign}$ and the reactor will work

121

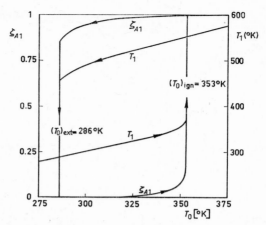

FIG. IV-13. Hysteresis with autothermal operation of a tank reactor; constructed from Fig. IV-12 for adiabatic operation and $\bar{\tau} = 0.5$ s.

at the upper stable operating point. If T_0 is then lowered again, the reactor continues operating at a high conversion level until extinction takes finally place at a feed temperature $(T_0)_{ext}$. Fig. IV-13 shows such a hysteresis diagram for adiabatic operation; it was constructed on the basis of the data of Fig. IV-12. In this particular case the hysteresis interval is $(T_0)_{ign} - (T_0)_{ext}$ = 67°C; consequently, the ignited adiabatic tank reactor is rather insensitive to disturbances in T_0. When additional cooling is applied, the hysteresis interval is generally narrowed, and the sensitivity to feed temperature changes increased, as can be seen from Fig. IV-12.

It is, of course, equally possible to examine the influence of a change in other operating variables such as the feed concentration. This will not be discussed further, but it should be noted that the method of analysis used above is only applicable to changes which are so slow that the corresponding change in reactor operation can be regarded as a succession of pseudo-stationary states (static stability). The dynamic behaviour and stability of an autothermally operating tank reactor under the influence of relatively rapid fluctuations of the various parameters are of great interest, especially for the purpose of automatic control; it will be treated separately in Appendix 2.

ILLUSTRATION IV. 5. *Static stability of tank reactors in a cascade*

It is required to check whether the three tank reactors of Illustration IV.3 will perform under statically stable conditions.

After introducing:

$$\Delta T_{ad} = - \frac{c_{A0} M_A}{\varrho c_p} (\Delta h_r)_A \ (= 39.9°C) \ ,$$

the heat balances become (Eq. IV-20):

122

Reactor 1: $\qquad \zeta_{A1}\Delta T_{ad} = T_1 - T_0 + \dfrac{UA_1}{\Phi_m c_p}(T_1 - T_c)\,.$

Reactor 2: $\qquad (\zeta_{A2} - \zeta_{A1})\Delta T_{ad} = T_2 - T_1 + \dfrac{UA_2}{\Phi_m c_p}(T_2 - T_c)\,.$

Reactor 3: $\qquad (\zeta_{A3} - \zeta_{A2})\Delta T_{ad} = T_3 - T_1 + \dfrac{UA_3}{\Phi_m c_p}(T_3 - T_c)\,.$

The left-hand and the right-hand side of each equation have to be examined as a function of the corresponding reaction temperature (T_1, T_2 and T_3, respectively). It is found from Illustration IV.3 that:

$$\zeta_{A1} = k\bar{\tau}/(1 + k\bar{\tau})\,,$$
$$\zeta_{A2} - \zeta_{A1} = (1 - \zeta_{A1})k\bar{\tau}/(1 + k\bar{\tau})\,,$$
$$\zeta_{A3} - \zeta_{A2} = (1 - \zeta_{A2})k\bar{\tau}/(1 + k\bar{\tau})\,.$$

With these substitutions, the heat balances can be written in the form:

$$\frac{k\bar{\tau}}{1 + k\bar{\tau}} = \frac{1}{\Delta T_{ad}}\left[T_1 - T_0 + \frac{UA_1}{\Phi_m c_p}(T_1 - T_c)\right],$$
$$\frac{k\bar{\tau}}{1 + k\bar{\tau}} = \frac{1}{\Delta T_{ad}(1 - \zeta_{A1})}\left[T_2 - T_1 + \frac{UA_2}{\Phi_m c_p}(T_2 - T_c)\right],$$
$$\frac{k\bar{\tau}}{1 + k\bar{\tau}} = \frac{1}{\Delta T_{ad}(1 - \zeta_{A2})}\left[T_3 - T_2 + \frac{UA_3}{\Phi_m c_p}(T_3 - T_c)\right].$$

These equations can be solved by plotting the left-hand and the right-hand sides as a function of the operating temperatures T_1, T_2 and T_3, respectively. The left-hand terms are equal; they are shown in Fig. IV-14 for $\bar{\tau} = 600$ s and $k = 4 \times 10^6 \exp(-7900/T)$ s^{-1}. With the data of Illustration IV.3, the right-hand terms become, respectively:

Reactor 1: $\qquad \dfrac{1}{39.9}[T_1 - 73.6 + 0]\,.$

Reactor 2: $\qquad \dfrac{1}{18.4}[T_2 - 95 + 0.128\,(T_2 - 20)]\,.$

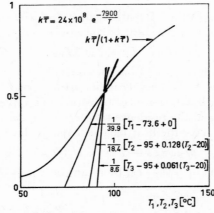

FIG. IV-14. Investigation into the static stability of three tank reactors in cascade; Illustration IV.5.

123

Reactor 3: $\dfrac{1}{8.6}\,[T_3 - 95 + 0.061\,(T_3 - 20)]$.

The three corresponding heat removal lines have been drawn in Fig. IV-14, from which it is seen that all three tank reactors in the cascade show static stability.

An adiabatic tubular reactor with heat exchange between reactants and products

Fig. IV-15 shows a system in which the heat of reaction is used to preheat the feed by countercurrent heat exchange between the feed and product streams. It is seen that the temperature rise in the reactor, $T_L - T_0$, is equal to the temperature difference available for heat transfer. Thus, the feed will not be preheated if no conversion takes place. On the other hand, when the reactor has been ignited a temperature rise $T_L - T_0$ results which makes it possible to preheat the reactor feed to a temperature level which may be sufficiently high to keep the reactor going with a high degree of conversion.

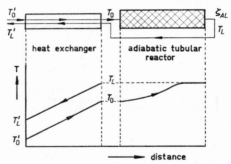

FIG. IV-15. Adiabatic tubular reactor with heat exchange between feed and reaction product.

After introduction of the adiabatic temperature rise of the reaction mixture ΔT_{ad} we obtain from the heat balance over the reactor:

$$T_L - T_0 = \zeta_{AL}\Delta T_{ad}\,. \qquad\qquad \text{IV-22}$$

Here, ζ_{AL} has to be determined from the conversion rate expression and the operating conditions in the manner indicated in Section IV.4 for adiabatic tubular reactors. With a given feed composition and conversion rate formula, ζ_{AL} depends on T_0 and the residence time τ_L in the reactor.

Furthermore, we have the heat balance over the heat exchanger:

$$\Phi_m c_p(T_0 - T'_0) = UA(T_L - T_0)\,,$$

and after elimination of $(T_L - T_0)$ by means of Eq. IV-22 we obtain:

$$T_0 - T'_0 = \zeta_{AL}\Delta T_{ad}\,\frac{UA}{\Phi_m c_p}\,. \qquad\qquad \text{IV-23}$$

It is seen that the temperature rise of the feed stream in the heat exchanger

124

is equal to the temperature rise in the reactor multiplied by the factor $UA/\Phi_m c_p$; in practice, this factor is often greater than 1.

The left-hand term of Eq. IV-23 is proportional to the heat taken up in the heat exchanger per unit mass of feed, and the right-hand term is proportional to the heat production by chemical conversion. Both terms can be plotted separately as a function of the reactor inlet temperature T_0, which in this case is the primary variable. The points of intersection between the two functions represent possible points of operation of the system.

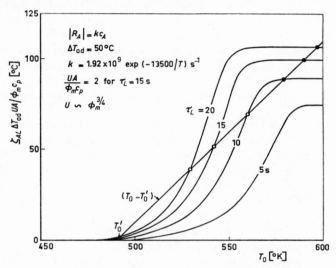

FIG. IV-16. Operating points of system shown in Fig. IV-15 for first order reaction at different residence times in the reactor.

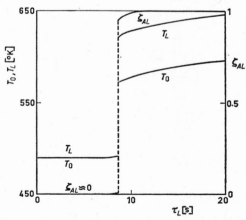

FIG. IV-17. Relative conversion, and inlet and outlet temperatures as a function of residence time; from Fig. IV-16.

This has been done in Fig. IV-16 for a first order reaction of which the relevant parameters have been indicated in the graph. Various values of τ_L were selected in order to demonstrate the influence of the throughput. It was assumed that the volume of the reactor was fixed, so that τ_L is inversely proportional to Φ_m; moreover, the over-all heat transfer coefficient U was assumed to be proportional to $\Phi_m{}^{3/4}$.

It is seen from Fig. IV-16 that stable operation with a high degree of conversion is possible above a certain value of τ_L. In this region, the temperature level of the reactor is rather sensitive to the throughput. When the mass flow through the system is increased, the reaction is extinguished at a certain value of τ_L. This occurs in this example when τ_L is about 8.6 s, as shown in Fig. IV-17. The reaction can be started by temporarily preheating the feed (for example, with an electric heater) at a relatively low value of Φ_m.

A multi-tube reactor with internal heat exchange between the reaction mixture and the feed.

The autothermal behaviour of a catalytic tubular reactor in which the gas feed is taking up heat from the reacting mixture was also discussed by VAN HEERDEN [89]. Fig. IV-18 shows a schematic diagram of such a reactor and its temperature distribution, which is typical of a converter for NH_3 synthesis from H_2 and N_2 at high pressure and temperature. Since this is an exothermic equilibrium reaction, a high capacity and a high degree of conversion necessitate a high reaction temperature when the degree of conversion is still low, as well as a drop in temperature as the conversion proceeds. This is achieved in a reactor of the type shown in Fig. IV-18.

For the calculation of the conversion and the temperature distribution, a

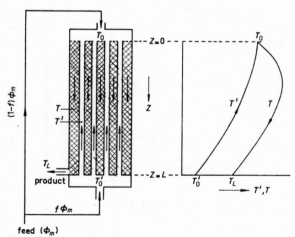

FIG. IV-18. Autothermal multi-tube reactor with internal heat exchange.

126

material balance (e.g., Eq. II-8) has to be combined with differential energy balances, one for the gas which is preheated:

$$0 = f\Phi_m c_p dT' + U(T - T')\frac{A}{L}dz ,$$

IV-24

and one for the reaction mixture:

$$0 = \Phi_m c_p dT + \Phi_m(\Delta h_r)_A d\xi_A + U(T - T')\frac{A}{L}dz .$$

IV-25

In these equations, c_p has been assumed to be constant, and the heat transfer resistance $1/U$ between the two streams has been supposed to be localized at the dividing wall; A is the total heat exchange area, f is the fraction of feed flowing through the heat exchanger, and the fraction $(1 - f)$ is injected directly at the feed end of the catalyst bed. The boundary conditions are:

$$T' = T'_L \quad \text{for} \quad z = L,$$

$$T = T_0 = (1 - f)T'_L + fT'_0 \quad \text{for} \quad z = 0 ,$$

and

$$\xi_A \equiv 0 \quad \text{for} \quad z = 0 .$$

With a known rate expression, the above system of equations can be solved with a computer, e.g. for various values of the main parameters ΔT_{ad}, $UA/c_p\Phi_m$ and f [91].

For a qualitative discussion of the autothermal character of this reactor type, the problem is simplified by taking $f = 1$ (no cold feed injection at the entrance of the catalyst bed) and then combining Eqs. IV-24 and IV-25 to yield:

$$\Phi_m c_p d(T - T') = -\Phi_m(\Delta h_r)_A d\xi_A = -\Phi_m(\Delta h_r)_A w_{A0} d\zeta_A .$$

In view of the last two boundary conditions and of $f = 1$, we find:

$$T - T' = -\frac{(\Delta h_r)_A w_{A0}}{c_p}\zeta_A = \Delta T_{ad}\zeta_A .$$

By substitution of $(T - T')$ into Eq. IV-24 we obtain:

$$\frac{c_p\Phi_m}{UA}dT' = -\frac{\Delta T_{ad}}{L}\zeta_A dz ,$$

and after integration between $z = 0$ and $z = L$:

$$\frac{(T_0 - T'_L)}{UA/c_p\Phi_m} = \frac{\Delta T_{ad}}{L}\int_0^L \zeta_A dz = \Delta T_{ad}\langle\zeta_A\rangle ,$$

IV-26

where $\langle\zeta_A\rangle$ is the degree of conversion averaged over the reactor length, and $\Delta T_{ad}\langle\zeta_A\rangle$ the average driving force for the heat exchange (compare Eq. IV-23 where the temperature difference between both streams in the heat exchanger was constant and equal to $\Delta T_{ad}\zeta_A$). For a given system $\langle\zeta_A\rangle$ will depend on T_0 and on $UA/c_p\Phi_m$, and for an equilibrium reaction it will pass through a maximum as a function of T_0.

127

In a similar manner as in Eq. IV-23, the first term in Eq. IV-26 is proportional to the heat taken up by the feed before it enters into the catalyst bed $[c_p\Phi_m(T_0 - T'_L)]$; the total temperature increase of the feed is equal to the average driving force $\Delta T_{ad}\langle\zeta_A\rangle$, multiplied by a factor $UA/c_p\Phi_m$. Both terms of Eq. IV-26 have been plotted in Fig. IV-19 as a function of the inlet temperature of the catalyst bed T_0 for several values of $UA/c_p\Phi_m$ (after VAN HEERDEN [89]). It is seen that not only the heat removal lines but also the heat production curves depend on the value of $UA/c_p\Phi_m$. With too small a heat exchange capacity, the bed entry temperature will become too low and no conversion will result. In the situation 1 in Fig. IV-19, the reactor is on the verge of stable operation. If too much heat exchange capacity has been built in (e.g., situation 3 in Fig. IV-19), the reaction temperature is too high and the equilibrium is adversely affected. Accordingly, it is desirable not to make the heat exchange capacity much greater than necessary, as e.g. in situation 2 in Fig. IV-19.

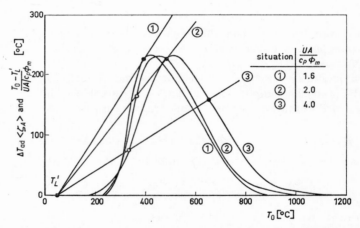

FIG. IV-19. Possible operating points of the reactor of Fig. IV-18 for an equilibrium reaction with $f = 1$; NH_3 converter, according to VAN HEERDEN [89].

In actual practice, once the reactor has been designed, the parameter $UA/c_p\Phi_m$ is rather insensitive to load variations since the over-all heat transfer coefficient U is approximately proportional to $\Phi_m^{3/4}$. A reactor will, therefore, be designed with too large a heat exchange area A, and part of the cold feed will be by-passed ($f < 1$) and injected directly at the entrance of the catalyst bed. As the heat exchange area becomes fouled or the catalyst becomes less active during operation, f is steadily increased in order to maintain high conversion levels. The simplified qualitative discussion for $f = 1$ is no longer valid under such circumstances.

IV.6. Maximum permissible reaction temperatures

Although high reaction temperatures may have the advantage of producing high rates of conversion, there may be several reasons for keeping the reaction temperature below, and sometimes above, a certain value. Once temperature limits have been set, it is possible to predict the measures to be taken in order to comply with these requirements; the methods outlined in the preceding sections can be used for this purpose, provided enough information is available on the reaction and on the reactor to be used.

A very important argument for keeping the reaction temperature within a limited region originates from the possible occurrence of undesired side reactions. If, for example, the selectivity of the desired reaction in a complex reaction decreases with increasing temperature, an upper temperature limit must be adhered to if both the yield and the capacity of the installation are to have acceptable values. In most cases, however, a statement that the reaction temperature in a given system should not exceed a certain fixed value would be entirely inadequate.

The yield of a desired product in complex reactions is determined not only by the temperature (range) at or in which the reaction is carried out, but also by other variables, such as the reaction or residence time and the reactor type used. Especially if the side reactions are accompanied by important heat effects, the manner of heat supply or removal may likewise have a great effect on the result of the reaction. Since the above circumstances will generally be entirely different in laboratory experiments and under actual plant conditions, temperature specifications derived from laboratory data may not be valid for practical use. A knowledge of the reaction scheme and of the rate expressions for the reactions involved as a function of temperature is a much more dependable basis for finding the appropriate reaction conditions. It is realized that such information is hard to obtain in many practical cases; a few indications of a more or less qualitative nature may nevertheless be helpful in this respect.

We shall demonstrate the points raised above by considering a set of parallel reactions and a set of consecutive reactions with heat effects carried out in a continuous *tank reactor*. These examples were treated in a paper by WESTERTERP [92], to which the reader is referred for more details.

Suppose that a key reactant A can be converted to a desired product P and an undesired product X. Molar concentrations will be used and it will be assumed that ϱ and c_p remain constant, that the feed contains neither P nor X ($c_{P0} = c_{X0} = 0$) and that the sum of the concentrations of A, P and X is constant ($c_{A0} = c_A + c_P + c_X$). The material balances for the species P and X become for steady state operation in a tank reactor:

$$0 = -c_{P1} + R_P \bar{\tau} ,$$
$$0 = -c_{X1} + R_X \bar{\tau} ,$$

in which R_P and R_X have to be taken at the reaction conditions. Assuming first order kinetics, we have:

$$\left.\begin{array}{l} R_P = k_1 c_A \\ R_X = k_2 c_A \end{array}\right\} \text{ for parallel reactions },$$

and:

$$\left.\begin{array}{l} R_P = k_1 c_A - k_2 c_P \\ R_X = k_2 c_P \end{array}\right\} \text{ for consecutive reactions .}$$

In examining the influence of temperature it is convenient to introduce the reference temperature T_R at which k_1 and k_2 are equal and have the value k_R. T_R and k_R follow from:

$$k_R \equiv k_1|_{T_R} = k_{1\infty} e^{-E_1/RT_R} = k_2|_{T_R} = k_{2\infty} e^{-E_2/RT_R} .$$

The composition of the reaction mixture can now be calculated as a function of the dimensionless absolute reactor temperature T_1/T_R and the dimension-

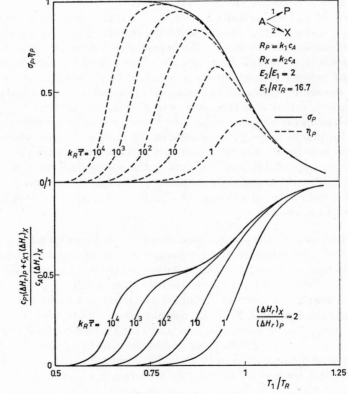

FIG. IV-20. Selectivity, yield and relative heat production for exothermic parallel reactions in a tank reactor.

less average time of residence $k_R \bar{\tau}$, while the reaction system is characterized by k_R, T_R and the ratio of the activation energies E_2/E_1 which influences the selectivity. As a result of such calculations the upper parts of Figs. IV-20 and IV-21 show, for a parallel and a consecutive reaction system respectively, the selectivity:

$$\sigma_P = c_{P1}/(c_{A0} - c_A) ,$$

and the yield:

$$\eta_P = c_{P1}/c_{A0} ,$$

as a function of the dimensionless temperature T_1/T_R and for $E_2/E_1 = 2$. The relative degree of conversion of A, ζ_A, equals the ratio of σ_P and η_P; the reactant A is completely converted, therefore, if the latter two magnitudes coincide.

It is seen that for both reaction systems the yields have a maximum value which is higher as the reaction temperature is farther removed from

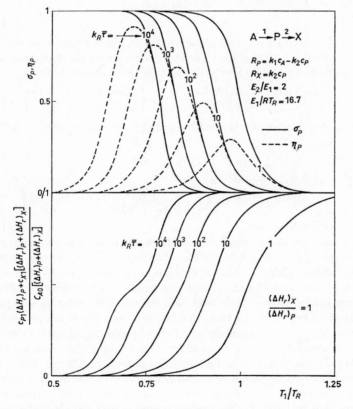

FIG. IV-21. Selectivity, yield and relative heat production for exothermic consecutive reactions in a tank reactor.

131

T_R. An increase in maximum yield can, in this case, only be obtained at the expense of a great increase in residence time and a corresponding reduction in reactor capacity. It is also observed from these figures that the same value of η_P can be obtained in a whole range of operating temperatures. Thus, an a priori specification of a maximum temperature at which a side reaction would be sufficiently suppressed has no significance.

Another point is that, if both the main reaction and the side reaction have a heat effect, these effects have to be taken into account, so that the reactor may be operated in a proper (i.e., stable) manner. In writing the heat balance over a tank reactor in a form similar to Eq. IV-20 the heat production of all reactions has to be considered. We thus obtain for the above parallel reactions:

$$- c_{P1}(\Delta H_r)_P - c_{X1}(\Delta H_r)_X = \varrho c_p(T_1 - T_0) + \frac{\varrho U A}{\varPhi_m}(T_1 - T_c) , \quad \text{IV-27a}$$

and for the consecutive reactions:

$$- c_{P1}(\Delta H_r)_P - c_{X1}[(\Delta H_r)_P + (\Delta H_r)_X] = \varrho c_p(T_1 - T_0) + \frac{\varrho U A}{\varPhi_m}(T_1 - T_c).$$

$$\text{IV-27b}$$

$(\Delta H_r)_X$ is the heat of reaction associated with the formation of one molar unit of X. Division of the heat production terms on the left-hand side of these equations by the highest possible heat production yields:

$$\frac{- c_{P1}(\Delta H_r)_P - c_{X1}(\Delta H_r)_X}{- c_{A0}(\Delta H_r)_X} = \eta_P \left[\frac{(\Delta H_r)_P}{(\Delta H_r)_X} + \frac{1 - \sigma_P}{\sigma_P} \right] \quad \text{IV-28a}$$

for the relative heat production with parallel reactions [assuming $(\Delta H_r)_X > (\Delta H_r)_P$], and:

$$\frac{- c_{P1}(\Delta H_r)_P - c_{X1}[(\Delta H_r)_P + (\Delta H_r)_X]}{- c_{A0}[(\Delta H_r)_P + (\Delta H_r)_X]} =$$

$$= \eta_P \left[\frac{(\Delta H_r)_P}{(\Delta H_r)_P + (\Delta H_r)_X} + \frac{1 - \sigma_P}{\sigma_P} \right] \quad \text{IV-28b}$$

with consecutive reactions.

If η_P and σ_P are known as a function of $k_R\bar\tau$ and of the dimensionless reaction temperature T_1/T_R, these relative heat production functions can be plotted for fixed values of $(\Delta H_r)_X/(\Delta H_r)_P$. This has been done in Figs. IV-20 and IV-21 for the reactions considered, on the assumption that they are exothermic. Under conditions where a high yield η_P is obtained, the relative heat production curves show a tendency to form a plateau. As a consequence, 5 solutions of the heat balance can in principle be found by comparing such a curve with the heat removal line when the autothermal behaviour of the reactor is studied (compare Section IV.5). Two solutions are unstable; of the 3 stable ones, the lowest corresponds to practically no conversion and the highest to an almost complete conversion of reactant to the product involving the highest heat of reaction. If this product is not wanted, the reactor must work at the intermediate stable operating point. It will be clear that, especially with reactions producing large heat effects, a proper combination of feed concentration and temperature, heat transfer area and cooling temperature have to be chosen to keep the reactor operating under the desired conditions. An example will be given in the illustration at the end of this section.

It should be noted that this section deals with very simple kinds of complex reactions carried out in a continuous tank reactor. Much more complicated reactions may occur in practice (such as shown by HOFTIJZER and ZWIETE-RING [93]), and a similar treatment for, e.g., tubular reactors with heat exchange will also become extremely involved. However, a qualitative analysis of the influence of side reactions with a heat effect on the autothermal behaviour of tank reactors and on the parametric sensitivity of tubular reactors can lead to valuable results, even if simplified rate equations are introduced in order to make the problem more tractable (VAN HEERDEN [90]).

ILLUSTRATION IV. 6. *The oxidation of naphthalene in a fluidized bed.*

This example serves to illustrate how the operating temperature and the corresponding cooling requirements can be found for a highly exothermic reaction followed by additional exothermic reactions.

The catalyzed gas-phase reaction between naphthalene and oxygen occurs along the following scheme:

$$
\text{naphthalene} \begin{cases} \overset{3}{\nearrow} \text{naphthoquinone} \\[4pt] \underset{4}{\searrow} \text{phthalic anhydride} \end{cases} \quad \begin{matrix} \downarrow 5 \\[4pt] \overset{6}{\rightarrow} \text{maleic anhydride,} \end{matrix}
$$
$$
CO_2, \; H_2O.
$$

DEMARIA, LONGFIELD and BUTLER [94] studied the kinetics of these reactions in a fluidized bed with two different catalysts, "A" and "B". On deriving the reaction-velocity constants k_3 to k_6 they considered all reactions to be homogeneous and of the first order with respect to the concentrations of the species converted; the concentration of oxygen in the reaction mixture, which was in great excess, was taken as constant. They furthermore assumed the reaction mixture to have a uniform composition in the fluidized bed so that it was considered to behave like a tank reactor. They showed that k_5 was several times greater than k_3, and that k_3 was equal to k_4. Hence we shall further simplify the above reaction scheme to:

$$
\underset{(A)}{\text{naphthalene}} \overset{1}{\rightarrow} \underset{(P)}{\text{phthalic anhydride}} \overset{2}{\rightarrow} \underset{(X)}{\text{combustion products,}}
$$

where P is the desired product.

For the first-order reaction-velocity constants we take:

$$
k_1 = k_3 + k_4, \quad \text{and} \quad k_2 = k_6.
$$

The values of k_1 and k_2 as derived from the measurements by DEMARIA, LONGFIELD and BUTLER have been plotted in Fig. IV-22 against $1/T$. On extrapolating the lines beyond the range of the experiments we find the values of T_R and k_R for both catalysts (see the table below); the values of E_2/E_1 are found from the ratio of the slopes of k_2 and k_1.

In order to obtain a high yield, η_P, k_1 should be one or two orders of magnitude greater than k_2; this means that the reaction temperature should be well above T_R (224°C) for catalyst "A", and for catalyst "B" well below its corresponding T_R value (497°C). It is seen from Fig. IV-22 that a reaction temperature in the vicinity of 350°C will be desirable for both catalysts.

133

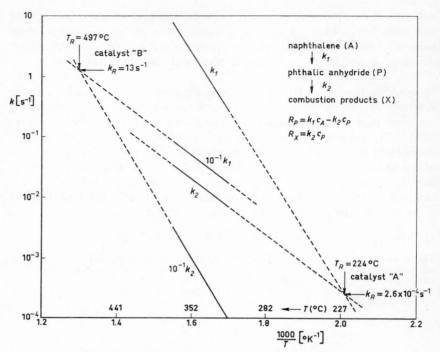

FIG. IV-22. Reaction velocity constants for the oxidation of naphthalene with two different catalysts [92]; Illustration IV.6.

It is now assumed that the residence time distribution in an industrial fluidized bed reactor is very similar to that of the ideal tank reactor★. On this assumption, η_P curves can be calculated as a function of T_1/T_R for various values of the dimensionless residence time $k_R \bar{t}$ in the manner indicated earlier in this section and with a result very similar to the top graph of Fig. IV-21. For each value of $k_R \bar{t}$ a maximum in η_P occurs at a certain value of T_1/T_R; the corresponding reaction temperature T_1 will be called the optimum temperature $(T_1)_{\text{opt}}$ at a given residence time $\bar{t}$. For further calculations, we adopt two residence times (0.4 and 20 s) for catalyst "A", with corresponding reaction temperatures $(T_1)_{\text{opt}}$ of 423 and 331°C, respectively; a residence time of 5 s is selected for catalyst "B" with $(T_1)_{\text{opt}} = 365°C$. These figures are shown in the table below, together with the product distribution obtained. It is seen that with catalyst "A" the yield of phthalic anhydride increases with increasing reaction temperature, provided the contact time is reduced in order to keep to the maximum within the yield curve. A comparison between catalysts "A" and "B" at the longer residence times shows that a higher yield is obtained with "A", but that "B" gives a better selectivity under the conditions indicated.

For investigating the requirements of heat removal, the relative heat production curves (compare Fig. IV-21, bottom graph) are constructed for the three cases mentioned above. These are shown in Fig. IV-23, where the operating points have been indicated by S_{A1}, S_{A2} and S_B. The data used for the calculation of the curves have been collected in the accompanying table.

The heat removal lines which must pass through the operating points have the formula (see Eqs. IV-27b and 28b):

★ It should be noted that this is not necessarily true; see Section III.9.

$$\frac{\varrho c_p (T_1 - T_0) + \varrho UA(T_1 - T_c)/\Phi_m}{-c_{A0}[(\Delta H_r)_P + (\Delta H_r)_x]} = f(T_1) \ .$$

If it is desired to run the reactor adiabatically with a given feed temperature T_0 (say, 150°C), the indicated points of operation could only be realized by proper adjustment of the naphthalene feed concentration c_{A0}. However, stable operation might result only in the case of catalyst "A" with $\bar{\tau} = 0.4$ s (line a in Fig. IV-23). The feed mole fraction c_{A0}/c would then have to be 0.00438, but if it became higher than 0.00456 (line b) a nearly complete combustion of the desired product would result at $T_1/T_R = 2.36$, or $T_1 = 900$°C. Below a mole fraction of 0.00423 (line c), on the other hand, the reaction is extinguished. It will be clear that this range of feed concentrations is too narrow for safe operation; moreover, these concentrations are rather low. It is necessary, therefore, to work with much steeper heat removal lines, which means that the reactor has to be cooled with a medium having a relatively high cooling temperature T_c.

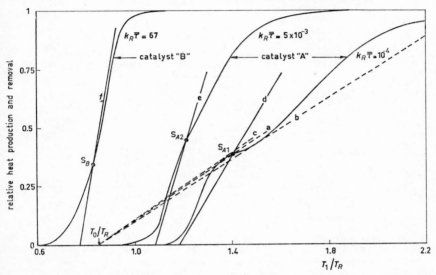

FIG. IV-23. Heat production and heat removal lines for the oxidation of naphthalene; Illustration IV.6.

Fig. IV-23 contains the heat removal lines d, e and f for the three different cases treated here and for $c_{A0}/c = 0.010$. Only one stable operating condition is possible with these lines, so that the possibility of excessive combustion of the phthalic anhydride is excluded. The lines have the character of a compromise: when the slope of the lines through the operating points is diminished, the flexibility of the reactor is greatly reduced; an increase of the slope means that more heat transfer area has to be built in and that a higher coolant temperature has to be used. The values of UA/Φ_m and T_c associated with the heat removal lines d, e and f — as indicated in the table on the next page — must therefore be regarded as minimum values.

It is seen from the tabulated results that a high yield of phthalic anhydride would be obtained with catalyst "A" at $\bar{\tau} = 0.4$ s, but that an extremely high heat exchange area per unit reactor volume would be required. This can only be achieved by rapid circulation of catalyst through an external heat exchanger [95]*. A reasonably small heat

---

* For calculating such a system, the last term in Eq. IV-27 should be replaced by $\Phi_s c_{ps}(T_1 - T'_0)/\Phi_m$, where Φ_s is the mass flow, c_{ps} the specific heat and T'_0 the entrance temperature of the circulating catalyst. The design of the catalyst heat exchanger then becomes a separate problem.

135

exchange area is required with $\bar{t} = 20$ s, and a once-through yield of about 77% is obtainable. The same yield but a better selectivity results with catalyst "B" and $\bar{t} = 5$ s; the cooling area is rather large and the temperature of the coolant must be high.

This illustration should be regarded merely as a rough approximation on the basis of rather crude simplifications and extrapolations. It shows, however, in a semi-quantitative manner that the maximum permissible reaction temperature is an elastic concept and that very special cooling conditions are required.

TABLE

Data for Illustration IV.6

Oxidation of naphthalene with air at atmospheric pressure;
kinetic data: see Fig. IV-22

$(\Delta H_r)_P = -1880 \times 10^6$ J/kmol
$(\Delta H_r)_X = -3280 \times 10^6$ J/kmol
$c_p \quad = 1040$ J/kg°C
$U \quad = 350$ W/m² °C
$c_{A0}/c = 0.010$
$T_0 \quad = 150$°C

	Catalyst "A"		Catalyst "B"
T_R(°K)	497		770
k_R(s^{-1})	2.6×10^{-4}		13
E_2/E_1	0.47		2.19
$k_R\bar{t}$	10^{-4}	5×10^{-3}	67
$\bar{t}$(s)	0.4	20	5
$(T_1)_{opt}/T_R$	1.41	1.22	0.83
$(T_1)_{opt}$(°C)	423	331	365
$\zeta_A = 1 - c_A/c_{A0}$	0.977	0.941	0.787
$\sigma_P = c_P/(c_{A0} - c_A)$	0.957	0.814	0.955
$\eta_P = c_P/c_{A0}$	0.934	0.768	0.752
heat removal line in Fig. IV-23	d	e	f
A/V_r(m²/m³)	32.8	1.4	7.4
T_c(°C)	348	275	334

CHAPTER V

CHEMICAL REACTIONS
IN HETEROGENEOUS SYSTEMS

V.1. The role of mass transfer

In the preceding chapters the conversion rate was used as a quantity to be employed for purposes of calculation. It expressed the number of mass or molar units of a certain component converted per unit time and per unit volume (or per unit mass of catalyst), and it was supposed to be a known function of the temperature, the pressure and the composition of the reaction mixture. No attention was paid to the question whether the reaction was proceeding uniformly or whether the conversion rate would turn out to vary locally when inspected on a smaller scale. In fact, the material balances were applied on a scale which was generally small with respect to the reactor dimensions, but still large with respect to the scale of possible local variations.

Such local variations in the nature and composition of the reaction mixture will occur even in systems consisting of one phase only, if mixing on a molecular scale is not complete. Above all, however, marked variations will be encountered in systems made up of more than one phase; these will be called heterogeneous systems.

Contrary to reactions in a single phase mixed on a molecular scale, not all reactants present in heterogeneous systems may be available for chemical reaction. Thus, to give an example, a *homogeneous reaction* between two reactants A and B may have to be carried out in one phase, although A is originally present in a different phase. Apparently, conversion can only take place when A is transferred to the phase in which the reaction can occur. The rate of this mass transfer may therefore influence the conversion rate, especially if the rate of the chemical reaction proper is high with respect to the rate at which A can be supplied. Another example is a *heterogeneous reaction* at the interface between two phases (e.g., at a catalyst surface). Here the reactants have to be transported by a diffusional process to the interface where the reaction takes place; in this case mass transfer to the reaction surface may considerably influence the over-all conversion rate. Hence, chemical reactions in heterogeneous systems are, in principle, combinations of chemical reaction and mass transfer phenomena.

The design of a reactor for a heterogeneous system is in full agreement with

the general theory developed in the preceding chapters, as long as an over-all
(or macroscopic) conversion rate is used. The difference between the conversion rate expressions for a homogeneous well-mixed system and a heterogeneous system lies in the mathematical formulation. In the latter case it has to
account for the interaction between chemical reaction and mass transfer.
The main purpose of this chapter is to analyse this interaction and to develop
expressions for the over-all conversion rate from this analysis.

In view of the great diversity of problems arising in this area, we shall
limit the discussion to a few types of applications commonly encountered in
practice. They have been indicated in Table V-1, where a classification has
been made according to the location of the reaction (homogeneous or heterogeneous reaction) and to the distribution of the reactants. In the cases to be
treated in Sections V.2, 3, 4 and 5, all the principal "tools" for handling
such problems will be dealt with.

TABLE V-I

Different cases of reactions in heterogeneous systems

	Reactant(s) present in one of the phases only	*Reactants distributed over more than one phase*
Homogeneous reaction in one or more phases	Homogeneous reaction with the possibility of removal of product (e.g., by liquid-liquid extraction, V.2)	Mass transfer with chemical reaction (e.g., chemical gas absorption, V.3)
Heterogeneous reaction at the interface between two phases	Surface-catalysed reactions (e.g., solid catalyst, V.4 and 5)	Fluid-solid reactions (e.g., combustion of solids, V.4 and 5)

Since mass transfer plays an important part in most of the examples to be
treated, the definition of the mass transfer coefficient β may be recalled.
It is formally defined as the ratio of the material flux to or from the boundary
and the concentration difference between the interface and the bulk of the
phase under consideration. We thus have for the material flux of a species J
in molar units:

$$J_J \equiv \beta(c_{Ji} - \langle c_J \rangle) \quad [\text{kmol/m}^2\text{s}] , \qquad \text{V-1a}$$

or in mass units:

$$j_J \equiv \beta\varrho(w_{Ji} - \langle w_J \rangle) \quad [\text{kg/m}^2\text{s}] . \qquad \text{V-1b}$$

The mass transfer coefficient β, which has the dimension of a velocity, is determined by the geometry of the system and by the flow conditions and the
physical properties of the phase considered; it may be slightly different for

different components, but in the following it will not be given an index for reference to the component under consideration.

When we have mass transfer from a phase f to a phase g, both mass transfer coefficients β_f and β_g have to be taken into account as well as the equilibrium relation between the two phases. Because of the conditions of continuity we have (e.g., in molar units):

$$J_{Jf} = \beta_f(\langle c_J \rangle - c_{Ji})_f =$$
$$J_{Jg} = \beta_g(c_{Ji} - \langle c_J \rangle)_g \,. \qquad \text{V-2}$$

It can be assumed for nearly all practical cases that equilibrium exists between the two phases at the interface. Therefore, c_{Jf} and c_{Jg} at the interface are connected by an equilibrium relation:

$$(c_{Jf} = K_J c_{Jg})_i \,, \qquad \text{V-3}$$

in which the dimensionless distribution coefficient K_J for species J generally depends on the composition of the two phases and on the temperature and the pressure. If K_J is independent of the concentration of J under otherwise constant conditions, Eq. V-3 indicates a proportionality similar to Henry's law for liquid-gas equilibrium and to Nernst's law for liquid-liquid equilibrium.

At a constant value of K_J, the concentrations at the interface can be easily eliminated from Eq. V-2, giving for the molar flux:

$$J_J = \left(\frac{1}{\beta_f} + \frac{K_J}{\beta_g}\right)^{-1} (\langle c_J \rangle_f - K_J \langle c_J \rangle_g) =$$
$$= \left(\frac{1}{K_J \beta_f} + \frac{1}{\beta_g}\right)^{-1} \left(\frac{\langle c_J \rangle_f}{K_J} - \langle c_J \rangle_g\right) \,. \qquad \text{V-4}$$

A similar expression can be developed for the mass flux j_J in terms of mass fractions w_J.

During the past decades a considerable amount of data has been accumulated on physical mass transfer in dispersed systems. The theoretical and experimental results can most conveniently be expressed in terms of the dimensionless Sherwood number for physical mass transfer:

$$Sh \equiv \beta d/D \,, \qquad \text{V-5}$$

where d is a characteristic dimension of the dispersion (e.g. bubble size, drop size, liquid film thickness, particle size) and D is the coefficient of molecular diffusion of the species considered. A few orders of magnitude of Sh are given below.

For mass transfer between the interior of a small bubble or drop and its surface we have roughly:

$$10 < Sh < 25 \;;$$

the lower figure applies approximately when the inside fluid is stagnant and the higher figure can be used in case of free internal circulation [96, 97, 98]. For liquid films flowing by gravity over a packing, the Sh number, based on film thickness, lies in the same range.

Mass transfer between the surface of a single bubble, drop or particle and a surrounding fluid moving with a relative velocity v_r is in general described by:

$$Sh = C Re^m Sc^n ,$$

where $Re = v_r d/v$. When the interface is stagnant, $C \approx 0.6$, $m \approx \frac{1}{2}$ and $n = \frac{1}{3}$; for a freely moving interface we have approximately $C = 1.1$, $m = \frac{1}{2}$ and $n = \frac{1}{2}$ [99,100, 101]. At very low Reynolds numbers, Sh approaches the value 2. For swarms of bubbles and for particles dispersed in liquids, the continuous-phase mass-transfer properties were recently summarized by CALDERBANK and MOO-YOUNG [102].

The total transport across a phase boundary for a given system is equal to the product of the mass or molar flux and the interfacial area A. This quantity per unit reactor volume, the specific surface area A_v, is an extremely important variable in heterogeneous reaction systems and its value is closely related to the degree of dispersion.

If one of the phases is a solid (such as in a fixed bed, a fluidized bed or a slurry), the value of A_v can be easily calculated from geometric considerations, since a particle-size analysis is not difficult to obtain. The problem of estimating A_v becomes somewhat more complicated if, for example, its value is required for a gas-liquid interface, where the liquid flows over a packing of known geometry (e.g., in packed distillation and absorption columns and in "trickle" reactors). In the industrial applications where one fluid is dispersed in another (gas in liquid, liquid in gas, liquid in liquid), a dependable prediction of the specific surface area may be very difficult. In general, one must then rely on published data for similar systems, or on special experiments (for agitated gas-liquid contactors, see, e.g., a study by WESTERTERP, VAN DIERENDONCK and DE KRAA [103]).

There is a relation between the interfacial area A in a system consisting of two phases with a total volume V_r, their volume fractions and the fineness of dispersion. Suppose we have two phases f and g with volumes V_f and V_g. The porosity ε is generally defined as the fraction of the total volume which is taken up by the *continuous* phase; therefore, if g is dispersed in f, the porosity of the system is:

$$\varepsilon = V_f/(V_f + V_g) = V_f/V_r . \qquad \text{V-6}$$

If the total volume V_r contains N_g particles of the dispersed phase, and if we assume these particles to be spherical and to have different diameters d, the total interfacial area A will be:

$$A = N_g \pi \langle d^2 \rangle .$$

Since we can also write for the volume of the dispersed phase, V_g:

$$V_g = N_g \frac{\pi}{6} \langle d^3 \rangle ,$$

the last three equations give for the total interfacial area in the volume V_r:

$$A = 6 V_g \langle d^2 \rangle / \langle d^3 \rangle \equiv 6 V_g / d_{av},$$

and for the specific surface area per unit volume, A_v:

$$A_v = \frac{A}{V_r} = \frac{6(1 - \varepsilon)}{d_{av}}. \qquad \text{V-7}$$

This shows that A and A_v are inversely proportional to the average size of the dispersed particles. If these are bubbles or drops, their size does not only depend on the fluid properties of both phases but also to a large extent on the interplay between the mechanisms responsible for their breaking up and mutual coalescence.

For each species participating in a reaction in a heterogeneous system, a formal *material balance* can be written down for each phase separately. The general expression I-1 will, of course, still be valid. However, in specifying the term $-\Delta \Phi_{mJ}$ (which denotes the net supply of J) a distinction must be made between a convective part, $-\Delta(\Phi_m w_J)$, and a part representing the mass flow of J from the interface to the bulk of the phase considered, $j_J A$. Such balances become for a total volume V_r (large with respect to the scale of dispersion, but so small as to be governed by uniform conditions) containing two phases f and g with a reaction going on in phase f only:

$$\frac{dm_{Jf}}{dt} = -\Delta(\Phi_{mf} w_{Jf}) + j_{Jf} A_v V_r + \langle \overset{*}{r_J} \rangle_f V_f, \qquad \text{V-8a}$$

and:

$$\frac{dm_{Jg}}{dt} = -\Delta(\Phi_{mg} w_{Jg}) + j_{Jg} A_v V_r. \qquad \text{V-8b}$$

The last term of Eq. V-8a is the production rate by homogeneous chemical reaction in the phase f. Since, due to mass transfer the composition may vary on a much smaller scale than the volume V_r considered, an average space value has to be used. The over-all production rate r_J on the basis of the total volume V_r is defined by means of a balance over both phases together:

$$\frac{dm_J}{dt} = -\Delta(\Phi_{mf} w_{Jf} + \Phi_{mg} w_{Jg}) + r_J V_r. \qquad \text{V-8c}$$

A comparison between Eq. V-8c and the sum of Eqs. V-8a and V-8b, yields for the over-all conversion rate r_J:

$$r_J = \langle \overset{*}{r_J} \rangle_f \frac{V_f}{V_r} + (j_{Jf} + j_{Jg}) A_v. \qquad \text{V-8d}$$

With *homogeneous reactions*, no reaction takes place at the interface, and hence:

$$j_{Jf} = -j_{Jg},$$

from which:

$$r_J = \langle \overset{*}{r_J} \rangle_f \frac{V_f}{V_r}. \qquad \text{V-8e}$$

141

If the reaction is very slow with respect to the highest possible mass transfer rate of J, the composition in phase f is uniform and in equilibrium with the other phase. For a system with known chemical kinetics, r_J is then easily evaluated (see, e.g., Section V.2). If the reaction is relatively fast, the concentration distribution is greatly influenced by the interaction of mass transfer and homogeneous chemical reaction; $\langle r_J{}^* \rangle_f$ can be found only after an examination of these phenomena on the scale of the dispersion (see Section V.3).

With purely *heterogeneous reactions*, a homogeneous reaction does not occur; hence, in Eq. V-8d:

$$\langle r_J^* \rangle_f = 0 \,.$$

On the other hand, since there is a net production or consumption at the interface:

$$j_{Jf} + j_{Jg} \neq 0 \,,$$

and accordingly the over-all production rate becomes:

$$r_J = (j_{Jf} + j_{Jg})A_v \,.$$

Mostly, one of the phases, e.g., phase g, is a material reacting with (or catalysing the reaction of) components in a fluid f, in which case $j_{Jg} = 0$. The above equation then states that the rate of production of J is equal to the mass flow of J from the interface into the fluid f; it is positive for a product and negative for a reactant. The value of this mass flow can only be found by considering the combination of mass transfer and chemical reaction at the interface on a smaller scale (see Sections V.4 and 5).

A section (V.6) at the end of this chapter will be devoted to mixing phenomena in fixed and fluidized bed reactors.

V.2. Reaction in a liquid-liquid system with simultaneous extraction

Of the many possible examples in the field of liquid-liquid systems we select a set of consecutive first order reactions:

$$A \overset{1}{\to} P \overset{2}{\to} X \,,$$

which occur homogeneously in the phase f of an emulsion. The other liquid phase, g, is used to extract the desired product P from the reaction phase in order to improve the reaction yield. It is assumed that the reaction is carried out in one stirred continuous tank reactor in the steady state and at constant temperature, and furthermore that:

– A and X are insoluble in phase g.
– The distribution coefficient $K_P = c_{Pg}/c_{Pf}$ is constant.
– The composition in phase f is uniform.
– The conversion rate is small with respect to the highest possible mass

142

transfer of product P, so that the two phases are in equilibrium with respect to this component.
– The densities of the two feed streams are equal to the corresponding densities at the outlet.
Reference is made to Fig. V-1 for the symbols used.

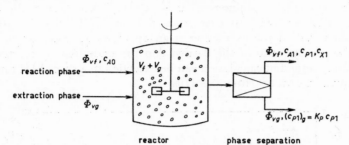

reactor   phase separation

FIG. V-1. Consecutive reactions in liquid system with simultaneous extraction of the intermediate product P by phase g.

In view of the above assumptions, the material balance for species A (which occurs only in the phase f) is according to Eq. V-8a:

$$0 = \Phi_{vf}(c_{A0} - c_{A1}) - k_1 c_{A1} V_f . \qquad \text{V-9}$$

Since for P equilibrium is assumed between both phases, the following material balance can be drawn up for the entire reactor contents (Eqs. V-8a + V-8b):

$$0 = -\Phi_{vf} c_{P1} - \Phi_{vg} K_P c_{P1} + k_1 c_{A1} V_f - k_2 c_{P1} V_f . \qquad \text{V-10}$$

c_{A1} and c_{P1}, upon introduction of the average residence time of the reaction phase $\bar{\tau}_f = V_f/\Phi_{vf}$ and the extraction factor $E_P = K_P \Phi_{vg}/\Phi_{vf}$, are found to be:

$$\frac{c_{A1}}{c_{A0}} = \frac{1}{1 + k_1 \bar{\tau}_f} ,$$

and:

$$\frac{c_{P1}}{c_{A0}} = \frac{k_1 \bar{\tau}_f}{(1 + k_1 \bar{\tau}_f)(1 + E_P + k_2 \bar{\tau}_f)} .$$

The yield η_P is the ratio of the moles of P produced per mole of A fed:

$$\eta_P = \frac{\Phi_{vf} c_{P1}(1 + E_P)}{\Phi_{vf} c_{A0}} = (1 + E_P) \frac{c_{P1}}{c_{A0}} . \qquad \text{V-11}$$

It is seen that the yield has a maximum as a function of $\bar{\tau}_f$ when k_1, k_2 and E_P remain constant. From the condition:

$$\frac{\partial \eta_P}{\partial \bar{\tau}_f} = 0 ,$$

we find that this maximum occurs at:

$$k_1 \bar{\tau}_f = \sqrt{(1 + E_P) k_1/k_2} ,$$

at which:

$$\eta_P = \frac{(1 + E_P)k_1/k_2}{\left[1 + \sqrt{(1 + E_P)k_1/k_2}\right]^2}.$$ V-12

Apparently, $k_1\bar{\tau}_f$ and η_P depend on a single parameter $(1 + E_P)k_1/k_2$ for a maximum yield. These functions are shown in Fig. V-2. Since the value of E_P would be zero without extraction of P, it can be reasoned that the optimum result of the extraction is an apparent increase, by the factor $(1 + E_P)$, of the ratio of the desired and the undesired conversion rates. The above method of calculation can be extended to a cascade of tank reactors, as was shown by HOFMANN [104].

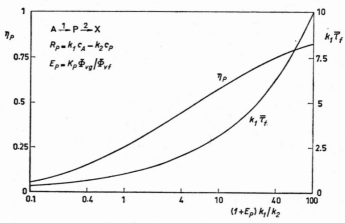

FIG. v-2. Maximum yield of P and corresponding dimensionless residence time (Eq. V-12) for consecutive reactions in a tank reactor with simultaneous extraction.

The improvement in yield by extraction of P entails the need for a greater reaction volume. It is seen from Eq. V-12 that with respect to the case $E_P = 0$ the average residence time of the reaction phase must be increased by the factor $\sqrt{(1 + E_P)}$. Furthermore, the extraction liquid g has to be accommodated, which implies that a further factor of $(V_f + V_g)/V_f = V_r/V_f$ must be applied for obtaining the total reaction volume.

As to the volume ratio V_g/V_f, its value is determined mainly by the requirements of obtaining a sufficiently large mass transfer surface per unit volume, and to a lesser extent by the value of E_P to be applied. It was shown, e.g. by TRAMBOUZE [105], that by taking special measures at the outlet of an agitated emulsion reactor the value of V_g/V_f can be made different from the ratio of the volumetric flow rates Φ_{vg}/Φ_{vf}.

The theory of this section was successfully applied by SCHOENEMANN and HOFMANN [106, 107, 108, 109] to the preparation of furfural from xylose in water containing hydrochloric acid. They found that the reaction was relatively slow and proceeded according to the scheme:

xylose (A)

$\downarrow$

intermediate product $\left.\begin{array}{l} \\ \downarrow \\ \\ \end{array}\right\} \rightarrow$ condensation product (Y)

furfural (P)

$\downarrow$

resin (X)

The production rate of furfural could be satisfactorily described by:

$$R_P = k_1 c_A - k_2 c_A c_P - k_3 c_P ,$$

in which the rate constants depend on the temperature and the HCl concentration. It is seen that it is desirable to keep the value of c_P in the reaction phase low so as to suppress the side reactions leading to the products X and Y. This can be achieved by extracting the furfural from the reaction mixture. This problem was extensively studied by SCHOENEMANN and HOFMANN, who calculated — on the basis of the experimental rate data and distribution ratios K_P — the furfural yield for various reactor types and process variables (xylose concentration in the feed, HCl concentration and reaction temperature). They verified experimentally that a yield η_P of 0.63 could be obtained in a cascade of three identical tank reactors with tetraline as solvent phase g and with a value of $\Phi_{vg}/\Phi_{vf} = 10$. In a batch process carried out under the same conditions, but without extraction, the maximum yield would have been only 0.10.

V.3. Mass transfer with homogeneous reaction

In this section a homogeneous reaction between the species A and B will be considered in one phase (the reaction phase), while A is supplied by mass transfer from another, adjoining phase. Analysis of the interaction between mass transfer and chemical reaction will ultimately lead to expressions for the flux of reactant A across the interface and for the over-all conversion rates of A and B to be used in material balances of the type of V-8c, by means of which a reactor calculation can be carried out in the manner indicated in Chapter II.

The reaction phase is supposed to be a flowing medium and the other phase can be either a nonmiscible fluid or a solid. In the present analysis, it will be rather arbitrarily assumed that the reaction phase is a liquid and that the phase providing the reactant A is a gas. In the following, therefore, we consider the absorption of a gas A by a liquid in which A reacts; however, the results will be equally applicable to other operations which are entirely similar: liquid-liquid extraction with chemical reaction, dissolution of a reacting solid, etc.

Now, with regard to gas absorption, we shall consider a heterogeneous

145

system with a gas-liquid interfacial area per total two-phase volume of $A_v(\text{m}^2/\text{m}^3)$ and with a fractional volume ε of the (liquid) reaction phase. We shall further assume that the bulk concentration of B in the liquid, $\langle c_B \rangle$, is known and also that the concentration of A in the liquid at the interface, c_{Ai}, is given. The latter value can be found by conventional methods from the gas composition, the mass transfer coefficient for A between the gas and the interface, the flux of A and its physical solubility in the absorption liquid. We shall, therefore, be concerned only with the proceedings in the liquid phase so that no special index, indicating the phase, will be attached to the concentrations and the various physical properties of this phase.

Concentration distribution in the reaction phase

A qualitative picture of the various possible concentration distributions of A and B in the boundary region of the liquid is shown in Fig. V-3. The curves 1 refer to a case where the reaction between A and B is relatively slow. Most of the conversion takes place in the bulk of the liquid, and the drop in concentration of A over the boundary region is mainly due to diffusional resistance. Should the ratio of bulk volume and interfacial area be increased, this concentration drop would become greater since more A would then have to be supplied per unit area for reaction in the main body of the reaction phase.

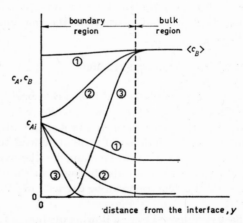

FIG. V-3. Possible concentration profiles in the boundary region for a homogeneous reaction between a component A transferred through the interface $y = 0$ and a component B present in the bulk.

The curves 2 give qualitative concentration distributions for a moderately high chemical reaction velocity. Here, a relatively great deal of A coming from the interface is already converted within the boundary region; this can be seen from, e.g., the concentration distribution of B which has to be supplied by diffusion from the bulk region. In comparison with the pre-

146

ceding case, the *surface area* of the interface has become more important for the total conversion rate relative to the *volume* of the reaction phase.

Finally, distributions of type 3 will be found when the reaction is so fast that it occurs entirely within the boundary region in a rather narrow reaction zone towards which A and B have to be transported by diffusion. No reaction takes place in the bulk region, and the total conversion rate is proportional to the interfacial area. The position of this reaction zone greatly depends on the ratio $\langle c_B \rangle / c_{Ai}$.

The above qualitative discussion makes it clear that at least 3 important parameters play a part in a mass transfer process with a reaction between A and B. They are:
– the surface-volume ratio of the reaction phase,
– the ratio of chemical reaction velocity and maximum mass transfer rate, and
– the ratio $\langle c_B \rangle / c_{Ai}$.

A more quantitative study of the influence of these parameters would require a detailed knowledge of the mechanism of mass transfer without chemical reaction. Fluid flow along solid boundaries in a dispersed system mainly involves steady state diffusion through a developing boundary layer. A nonsteady diffusion model – more appropriate in the case of flow along mobile surfaces – has become known under the name "penetration theory". In confined stagnant volumes, too, mass transfer occurs by nonsteady diffusion. The resulting mass transfer coefficients β can be expressed in terms of the dimensionless Sherwood number, Sh, and its order of magnitude has been indicated in Section V.1 for several cases.

The mass transfer rate increases due to the chemical reaction; in Fig. V-3, for example, the concentration gradient of A at the interface increases in the order 1-2-3, as the chemical reaction accelerates. Now many studies in this field indicate that in a given reaction system the ratio of mass transfer rate with chemical reaction and physical mass transfer rate is rather independent of the mass transfer mechanism itself. This makes possible an almost quantitative discussion of the influence of chemical reaction on mass transfer based on the simplest but otherwise unrealistic model: steady state diffusion through a laminar film. According to this "film theory" (LEWIS and WHITMAN [110]), the mass transfer coefficient for a component A, β_A, is formally ascribed to steady diffusion through a film of thickness δ, so that:

$$\beta_A = D_A / \delta .$$

Complications due to a first order reaction of a diffusing species were first formulated by HATTA [111], and the influence of a second order reaction between a reactant A transferred from the interface and a component B dissolved in the reaction phase was treated by VAN KREVELEN and HOFT-IJZER [112] for the film model.

We shall now follow these theories for the reaction:

147

$$\nu_A A + \nu_B B \rightarrow \text{products},$$

with a homogeneous chemical production rate given by:

$$R_A^* = -kc_A c_B.$$

Steady state diffusion in the boundary film with a thickness δ will be considered, and it will be assumed that the bulk of the reaction phase is well mixed and that its properties do not change with time.[*]

The concentration distributions in the film follow from the material balances for A and B:

$$0 = D_A \frac{d^2 c_A}{dy^2} - kc_A c_B, \qquad\qquad \text{V-13}$$

$$0 = D_B \frac{d^2 c_B}{dy^2} - kc_A c_B \nu_A/\nu_B, \qquad\qquad \text{V-14}$$

along with the boundary conditions for A:

$$
\left.
\begin{aligned}
y = 0 \quad & c_A = c_{Ai}; \\
y = \delta \quad & -A_v D_A \frac{dc_A}{dy} = kc_A \langle c_B \rangle (\varepsilon - A_v \delta),
\end{aligned}
\right\}
$$

· and those for B:

$$
\left.
\begin{aligned}
y = 0 \quad & \frac{dc_B}{dy} = 0 ; \quad y = \delta \quad c_B = \langle c_B \rangle .
\end{aligned}
\right\}
\qquad \text{V-15}
$$

The second condition for A states that the flux of A through the plane $y = \delta$ is used for reaction in the well-mixed bulk of the reaction phase. The first condition for B implies that there is no transport of B to the gas phase.

Solution for (pseudo) first order reactions

A general solution of Eqs. V-13, 14 and 15 is very complicated. The problem is simplified when the concentration of B is practically constant over the film and equal to $\langle c_B \rangle$. In that case, the chemical reaction rate is only of the first order in A and the concentration distribution of A is found from Eq. V-13 with its boundary conditions.

The solution contains a very important parameter, φ, which is defined by:

$$\varphi \equiv \delta \sqrt{\frac{k \langle c_B \rangle}{D_A}} = \frac{\sqrt{k \langle c_B \rangle D_A}}{\beta_A}. \qquad\qquad \text{V-16}$$

φ^2 is equal to the ratio of the maximum conversion rate of A in the film $(= kc_{Ai} \langle c_B \rangle \delta)$ and the maximum diffusional transport through the film $(= c_{Ai} D_A/\delta)$. When $\varphi \ll 1$, hardly any reaction takes place in the film, and when $\varphi \gg 1$ the reactant A coming from the interface is converted entirely within the film.

---

[*] A few more simplifications are introduced: the density, the diffusivities and the temperature do not change over the film, and a possible systematic velocity perpendicular to the interface due to the diffusion itself is disregarded.

148

Integration of Eq. V-13 yields for the concentration distribution of A in the film $(0 < y < \delta)$:

$$\frac{c_A}{c_{Ai}} = \cosh\frac{y}{\delta}\,\varphi - \frac{\left(\dfrac{\varepsilon}{A_v\delta} - 1\right)\varphi + \tanh\varphi}{\left(\dfrac{\varepsilon}{A_v\delta} - 1\right)\varphi\tanh\varphi + 1}\ \sinh\frac{y}{\delta}\,\varphi\,. \qquad \text{V-17}$$

For $y > \delta$, c_A is given by the above equation with $y = \delta$. It is seen that Eq. V-17 contains a second dimensionless parameter, $\varepsilon/A_v\delta$, which is the ratio of the total volume of the reaction phase and the volume of the mass transfer film of this phase; in view of the definition of δ it can be written in various forms:

$$\frac{\varepsilon}{A_v\delta} = \frac{\varepsilon\beta_A}{A_vD_A} = \frac{\varepsilon}{A_vd}\times\frac{\beta_A d}{D_A} = \frac{\varepsilon}{A_vd}Sh\,, \qquad \text{V-18}$$

where d is a characteristic length of the dispersion (compare Eq. V-5).

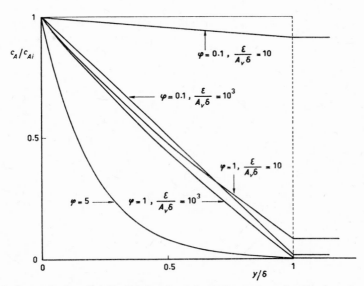

FIG. V-4. Concentration distribution in a hypothetical mass transfer film for a first order reaction in A, Eq. V-17.

To illustrate the influence of φ and $\varepsilon/A_v\delta$, a few concentration distributions of A are shown in Fig. V-4. With $\varphi = 0.1$, hardly any reaction occurs in the film, which appears from the practically linear concentration profiles; the concentration drop over the film increases as the volume-surface ratio (or $\varepsilon/A_v\delta$) becomes greater. For $\varphi = 1$, part of the reaction already occurs in the film; this is seen from the fact that the concentration gradients at $y/\delta = 1$ are smaller than at $y/\delta = 0$. With $\varphi = 5$, the reactant A is entirely converted within the film; the concentration distribution is no longer dependent on $\varepsilon/A_v\delta$. This also follows from Eq. V-17 since with $\tanh \varphi \approx 1$ for $\varphi \gg 1$ this equation gives:

$$\frac{c_A}{c_{Ai}} = \mathrm{e}^{-y\varphi/\delta} \, . \qquad\qquad \text{V-17a}$$

The molar flux of A into the reaction phase can be found from the concentration distribution V-17:

$$J_A = -D_A \frac{\mathrm{d}c_A}{\mathrm{d}y}\bigg|_{y=0} = c_{Ai}\sqrt{k\langle c_B\rangle D_A}\; \frac{\left(\dfrac{\varepsilon}{A_v\delta}-1\right)\varphi + \tanh \varphi}{\left(\dfrac{\varepsilon}{A_v\delta}-1\right)\varphi\,\tanh \varphi + 1} \, . \qquad \text{V-19}$$

When A is supplied to the reaction phase by mass transfer only, the product $J_A A_v$ is equal to the over-all conversion rate of A. It is of interest to compare this quantity with the greatest possible conversion rate which would occur if the entire reaction phase were in equilibrium with the interface ($= kc_{Ai}\langle c_B\rangle\varepsilon$). The ratio of these two conversion rates, which might be called the degree of utilization of the reaction phase, results from Eq. V-19:

$$\frac{J_A A_v}{kc_{Ai}\langle c_B\rangle\varepsilon} = \frac{A_v\delta}{\varphi\varepsilon}\; \frac{\left(\dfrac{\varepsilon}{A_v\delta}-1\right)\varphi + \tanh \varphi}{\left(\dfrac{\varepsilon}{A_v\delta}-1\right)\varphi\,\tanh \varphi + 1} \, . \qquad \text{V-20}$$

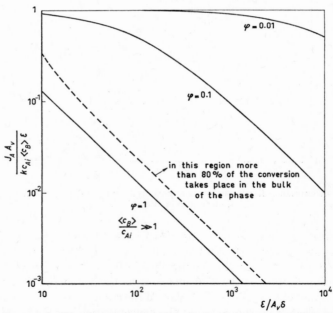

FIG. V-5. Degree of utilization of reaction phase volume for mass transfer of A with reaction between A and B, when $c_B = \langle c_B\rangle$.

Since tanh $\varphi \approx \varphi$ for $\varphi < 0.2$, the right-hand side of Eq. V-20 becomes approximately equal to $[1 + \varphi^2(\varepsilon/A_v\delta - 1)]^{-1}$ in this region. Hence it follows that the degree of utilization approaches unity for relatively small values of φ and $\varepsilon/A_v\delta$ (see Fig. V-5). For a good utilization of the reaction phase, $\varepsilon/A_v\delta$ has to be decreased as φ becomes greater; in other words, a large interfacial area has to be utilized with fast reactions.

As long as the greatest part of the conversion takes place in the bulk of the liquid, the degree of utilization is independent of the ratio $\langle c_B \rangle / c_{Ai}$. Fig. V-5 indicates in which region this would apply if we take as a criterion that 80% or more of the reaction takes place in the bulk.

A similar theory can be set up for a reaction rate which is first order in c_B and independent of c_A. This was recently shown by VAN DE VUSSE [113], who pointed out that many oxidation processes of hydrocarbons belong to this class.

Solution for rapid second order reactions

It has been shown that in the case of relatively rapid reactions most of the conversion of A takes place in the film. Consequently, the reactant B must be transported from the bulk and its concentration in the film may be appreciably lower than $\langle c_B \rangle$ (see Fig. V-3). We shall limit our further analysis to situations where A is entirely converted within the film; evidently, the second boundary condition for A in Eq. V-15 can then be simplified to:

$$y = \delta \qquad c_A = 0. \qquad\qquad \text{V-15a}$$

The solution of Eqs. V-13 and V-14 with the modified boundary conditions was discussed by VAN KREVELEN and HOFTIJZER [112].

Simple analytical solutions to this problem only exist for two extreme cases, i.e. for a pseudo first order reaction in $A(\langle c_B \rangle / c_{Ai} \gg 1)$, and for an "infinitely" fast reaction between A and B.

For the former case, the concentration distribution was already given by Eq. V-17a, from which the molar flux of A through the plane $y = 0$ is calculated as (cf. Eq. V-19 with tanh $\varphi \approx 1$):

$$J_A = c_{Ai}\sqrt{k\langle c_B \rangle D_A}. \qquad\qquad \text{V-21}$$

This equation is valid for practical purposes when $\varphi > 2$ and $\nu_A \langle c_B \rangle / \nu_B c_{Ai} > 10\varphi$.

In the extreme case of an infinitely fast reaction between A and B, this reaction takes place in a plane parallel to the surface; the curves 3 in Fig. V-3 represent a situation where this case is approached. The reaction plane is situated at a distance $y = y_r$ from the interface; its value follows from the condition that A and B have to be supplied in their stoichiometric ratio by steady diffusion from the interface and from the inner boundary of the film, respectively. This condition reads:

$$\frac{c_{Ai}D_A}{\nu_A y_r} = \frac{\langle c_B\rangle D_B}{\nu_B(\delta - y_r)},$$

from which results:

$$J_A = \frac{c_{Ai}D_A}{y_r} = c_{Ai}\beta_A\left(1 + \frac{\nu_A\langle c_B\rangle D_B}{\nu_B c_{Ai}D_A}\right). \qquad \text{V-22}$$

This equation can be used when $\varphi > 10\ \nu_A\langle c_B\rangle D_B/\nu_B c_{Ai}D_A$. The J_A values which are intermediate between Eqs. V-21 and V-22 can only be obtained by numerical computation.

For a general presentation of the mass transfer rate of A with a homogeneous second order reaction in the film, it is convenient to use the factor by which the maximum physical mass transfer rate is increased as a result of chemical reaction. This "chemical acceleration factor" F_A is accordingly defined as:

$$F_A \equiv \frac{J_A}{c_{Ai}D_A/\delta} = \frac{J_A}{c_{Ai}\beta_A},$$

and we find, using Eqs. V-21 and V-22, respectively:

$$F_A = \frac{\sqrt{k\langle c_B\rangle D_A}}{\beta_A} = \varphi \qquad \left(\varphi > 2\ ,\quad \frac{\nu_A\langle c_B\rangle}{\nu_B c_{Ai}} > 10\ \varphi\right), \qquad \text{V-23}$$

FIG. v-6. The chemical acceleration factor F_A for mass transfer of A with a second order homogeneous reaction; film model, after VAN KREVELEN and HOFTIJZER [112].

and: $$F_A = 1 + \frac{\nu_A \langle c_B \rangle D_B}{\nu_B c_{Ai} D_A} \qquad (\varphi > 10\, \nu_A \langle c_B \rangle / \nu_B c_{Ai}) . \qquad \text{V-24}$$

F_A has been plotted in Fig. V-6 as a function of φ with $\nu_A \langle c_B \rangle D_B / \nu_B c_{Ai} D_A$ as a parameter. The data for the curves between Eqs. V-23 and V-24 were provided by VAN KREVELEN and HOFTIJZER [112].

When a more realistic picture of the mass transfer phenomenon is used as a starting point for the above calculations, only relatively small deviations from the curves for F_A given in Fig. IV-6 are found. This can be verified by studying the literature on the same problem in conjunction with the boundary layer theory [114, 115, 116, 117] and with the penetration theory [118, 119, 120].

The over-all conversion rate

The derivation of the various expressions for J_A was based on the assumption of a steady state and a supply of A to the reaction phase by mass transfer only. Under these conditions the material balance V-8a for the reaction phase gives:

$$\langle R_A^* \rangle \varepsilon = -J_A A_v .$$

Combining this with Eq. V-8e, we find for the over-all production rate of A (R_A in kmol/s m³ total reactor volume):

$$R_A = -J_A A_v . \qquad \text{V-25}$$

For a high reactor capacity, this quantity should be sufficiently great. Whether this is obtained with a large value of ε (the volume fraction of the reaction phase), or with a large value of A_v (the interfacial area per unit volume), depends primarily on φ. In this respect we can roughly distinguish 3 regions:

i. $\varphi < 0.02$; here $J_A A_v \approx k c_{Ai} \langle c_B \rangle \varepsilon$ so that ε should be near unity for a high capacity; a fairly large value of $\varepsilon / A_v \delta$ is still permissible (Fig. V-5).

ii. $0.02 < \varphi < 2$; as φ is increased the degree of utilization of the reaction phase is reduced; this can be partially compensated by making $\varepsilon / A_v \delta$ smaller, i.e. by increasing the specific surface area.

iii. $\varphi > 2$; the reaction occurs only in the boundary layer and $J_A A_v = \beta_A c_{Ai} F_A A_v$; hence the main requirement for a large reactor capacity is a high value of A_v.

To illustrate this, Table V-2 gives some representative figures for A_v, ε and $\varepsilon / A_v \delta$ for a few current types of equipment used for gas absorption with chemical reaction in the liquid phase. It is seen that bubble contactors are particularly suitable for slow reactions and that high capacities will be obtainable in an agitated gas-liquid contactor also with moderately fast reactions. The several types of absorption columns are to be preferred for very fast reactions, particularly when fairly big gas streams have to be handled. An increase of the absorption rate by chemical reaction may cause the mass transfer resistance on the gas side to become relatively more important; this effect must be taken into account by applying Eq. V-2.

153

TABLE V-2

Characteristic data of equipment for gas absorption with chemical reaction in aqueous systems

type of gas-liquid contactor	specific surface, A_v (m^{-1})	volume fraction liquid phase, ε	$Sh =$ $\beta_A d/D_A$	$\varepsilon/A_v\delta =$ $(\varepsilon/A_v d)Sh$
spray column	60	0.05	10–25	2–10
plate column	150	0.15	200–600	40–100
packed column	100	0.08	10–100	10–100
wetted-wall column	50	0.05	10–50	10–50
bubble contactor	20	0.98	400–1000	$4000–10^4$
agitated bubble contactor	200	0.90	100–500	150–800

The calculation of an absorption column with chemical reaction is very similar to the calculation of a physical absorption process [121]. VAN KRE-VELEN and HOFTIJZER [122] developed a graphic method for this purpose. Cocurrent or countercurrent flow of gas and liquid can be selected. When the reactant A is to be removed almost completely from the gas stream, the latter type of operation is to be preferred because the lean gas is then contacted with liquid having the highest concentration of reactant B.

Heat effects will occur in consequence of dissolution of A in the reaction phase as well as of the reaction itself. They can be taken into account by means of heat balances over the various phases as long as the heat absorption or liberation proceeds rather uniformly over the reaction phase ($\varphi \ll 1$). With rapid reactions ($\varphi > 1$), the heat production is concentrated near the interface from which appreciable local temperature differences may result. The reader is referred to the paper by DANCKWERTS [123] for a further orientation in this field.

ILLUSTRATION V. 3. *Chemical absorption of CO_2 from air in a packed column*

CO_2 is scrubbed from air at 15 atm. pressure by a 1N NaOH solution flowing in countercurrent through a packed column. It is required to calculate the height L of the column, when the following data are given:

Mean temperature:	20°C
Air flow rate, 50,000 m³/day (NTP), Φ_{vg}:	0.0414 m³/s
Liquid flow rate, 2.5 m³/h, Φ_{vf}:	0.694×10^{-3} m³/s
CO_2 content in air feed, p_{A0}/p:	1 vol %
CO_2 content at outlet, p_{AL}/p:	5×10^{-3} vol %
Column diameter:	0.52 m
Cross-sectional area of column, S:	0.212 m²
Diameter of Raschig ring packing material:	0.025 m
Specific surface of Raschig rings:	220 m²/m³
Effective specific surface for mass transfer, A_v, estimated at 50%:	110 m²/m³

The gas is assumed to behave ideally. The CO_2 (component A) is dissolved by the caustic solution, diffuses inwards and at the same time reacts with the OH^- ions (species B) according to a second order reaction $R_A^* = -kc_Ac_B$. The relevant properties of this system can be found in the literature (see, e.g., [124, 125, 126]), which also contains sufficient information on the influence of the ionic strength of the solution:

Distribution coefficient, $K_A = \dfrac{c_{Ai}}{p_{Ai}/RT}$: 0.535

Diffusivity of A in the liquid, D_A: 1.77×10^{-9} m²/s

Reaction rate constant at 20°C, k: 5700 m³/s kmol

The mass transfer coefficients for component A are:

Gas-side mass transfer coefficient, β_g: 15.7×10^{-3} m/s

Liquid-side mass transfer coefficient, β_f: 0.37×10^{-3} m/s

It appears that under the conditions given above the reaction occurs entirely in the boundary region next to the liquid-gas interface. Hence, the bulk concentration of A in the liquid is zero. Taking into account the gas-side mass transfer coefficient and the liquid-side mass transfer coefficient multiplied by the chemical acceleration factor F_A, we obtain, according to Eq. V-4, for the molar flux J_A:

$$J_A = \frac{p_A}{RT} \frac{K_A F_A \beta_f}{1 + K_A F_A \beta_f / \beta_g} . \tag{a}$$

The change in CO_2 content of the gas at the height z above the inlet is given by the material balance for A over the gas phase:

$$0 = -\Phi_{vg} d\left(\frac{p_A}{RT}\right) - J_A A_v S dz ; \tag{b}$$

it has here been assumed that longitudinal dispersion in the gas flow can be neglected. The required length L of the column can be found by integrating (b) after (a) has been substituted:

$$\frac{SL}{\Phi_{vg}} = -\int_{p_{A0}}^{p_{AL}} \frac{1 + K_A F_A \beta_f / \beta_g}{K_A F_A \beta_f} \frac{dp_A}{A_v p_A} . \tag{c}$$

On integration, the values of K_A, β_f, β_g and A_v may be assumed to be constant. The chemical acceleration factor F_A, however, depends on the values of $\varphi = \sqrt{k\langle c_B \rangle D_A}/\beta_f$ and $\langle c_B \rangle / c_{Ai}$, both of which change along the column height. The value of c_{Ai} follows from p_{Ai}, which is found from:

$$J_A = \beta_g \frac{p_A - p_{Ai}}{RT} , \tag{d}$$

and $\langle c_B \rangle$ is calculated from the stoichiometric condition that for the conversion of each mole of CO_2 two moles of OH^- are needed:

$$\Phi_{vg} d\left(\frac{p_A}{RT}\right) = \tfrac{1}{2}\Phi_{vf} d\langle c_B \rangle , \tag{e}$$

with the boundary condition that at the top of the column $\langle c_B \rangle = 1$ kmol/m³ and $p_{AL}/p = 5 \times 10^{-5}$. In Eq. (e), longitudinal dispersion in the liquid phase has been neglected.

F_A can now be found for various values of p_A by the simultaneous solution of (a), (d) and (e) and by using the theory of the preceding section. The results are shown in the table, given on the next page.

It is seen from this column that only 5 to 10% of the mass transfer resistance lie on the gas side. Moreover, the values of $\langle c_B \rangle / c_{Ai}$ are so high that the theory for first order reaction in A can be applied and that $F_A = \varphi$. The values in the last column can be plotted against p_A, and graphic integration according to Eq. (c) yields:

p_A N/m^2	$\langle c_B\rangle$ $kmol/m^3$	p_{Ai} N/m^2	$\dfrac{\sqrt{k\langle c_B\rangle D_A}}{\beta_f} = \varphi$	$\langle c_B\rangle/c_{Ai}$ —	$F_A = \varphi$ (eq. V-23)	$\dfrac{1 + K_A F_A \beta_f/\beta_g}{K_A F_A \beta_f A_v p_A}$ $10^3\ m^2\ s/N$
15000	0.25	14200	4.3	80	4.3	0.75
10000	0.50	9300	6.1	245	6.1	0.81
5000	0.75	4600	7.4	740	7.4	1.36
2000	0.90	1800	8.1	2280	8.1	3.13
1000	0.95	900	8.4	4800	8.4	6.05
500	0.975	450	8.4	9900	8.4	12.1
200	0.99	180	8.5	25000	8.5	29.9
100	0.995	90	8.5	51000	8.5	59.8
75	1.00	68	8.5	67000	8.5	79.7

$$\frac{SL}{\varPhi_{vg}} = 34.4\ s, \quad \text{or} \quad L = \frac{34.4 \times 0.0414}{0.212} = 6.75\ m.$$

It still has to be ascertained whether the assumptions of isothermal operation and of the absence of longitudinal dispersion in both phases are correct. The heat liberated by the reaction is approximately 90×10^6 J/kmol of CO_2 converted. This heat is mainly taken up by the liquid stream, and it can be calculated that its temperature increase would be about 8°C. This would result in only a slight increase in absorption rate; although k rapidly rises with increasing temperature, this effect is offset partly by a decrease of the solubility of CO_2.

With regard to longitudinal dispersion, STEMERDING [81] mentions a value of $D_l \approx 15 \times 10^{-4}$ m²/s for the flow of liquid over 0.013 m Raschig rings. For the liquid, therefore, the value of $N' = \langle v\rangle L/D_l$ will be of the order of 15. Longitudinal dispersion will also occur to some extent in the gas stream. No data are as yet available on the magnitude of the latter effect. It will be safe to compensate for longitudinal dispersion in both phases by making the column about 20% longer than calculated; compare, e.g., Fig. III-8.

V.4. The influence of mass transfer on heterogeneous reactions

As discussed in V.1, a heterogeneous reaction takes place at the interface between two adjacent phases. In the case of heterogeneous catalysis, this interface is the surface of a phase of catalyst, and the reactants are present in the fluid phase surrounding the catalyst. With a non-catalysed heterogeneous reaction, the interface is the surface of a more or less pure material which itself reacts with components of the surrounding fluid phase. In both cases the chemical conversion at the surface (which can be expressed as a chemical conversion rate per unit surface) is, in principle, influenced by the fact that the reactants have to be transferred to the interface, and the products away from it*. Accordingly, it is of interest to investigate the interplay between the true *chemical* reaction rate and the physical transport phenomena in order to arrive at an expression for the *over-all* conversion rate (per unit

---

* In fluid-solid reactions it may occur that the reaction product forms a new solid phase, e.g. in the thermal decomposition of calcium carbonate [127] and in the oxidation of zinc sulphide in an air stream [128].

reactor volume or per unit mass of catalyst). The latter expression can then be used for reactor calculations in the manner indicated in Chapters II and IV.

To this end, let us consider the general case of a reaction at the surface of a particle of porous catalyst along which flows a fluid containing the reactant(s)*. It is generally recognized that the following steps occur successively in such a system:

i. Mass transfer of reactant(s) from the main flow to the external surface of the particle;

ii. Transport of reactant(s) by a diffusional process through the pores into the particle;

iii. Adsorption of reactant(s) on internal catalyst surface;

iv. Chemical conversion in the adsorbed state;

v. Desorption of product(s);

vi. Transport of product(s) by a diffusional process through the pores out of the particle;

vii. Mass transfer of product(s) from the external surface into the main flow.

The steps *i*, *ii*, *vi* and *vii* are entirely of a physical nature. If the particle is nonporous, the steps *ii* and *vi* do not occur.

The maximum use is made of a porous catalyst when the entire internal surface is readily accessible to the reactants; this will be the case when the chemical conversion rate is slow with respect to the greatest possible rates of transport according to the mechanisms *i* and *ii*, and *vi* and *vii*. Such a situation may also be realized for moderately fast reactions provided the external mass transfer is made sufficiently high (by a high fluid velocity along the particle) and if the diffusional resistance inside the particle is made sufficiently small (by a high internal porosity and a small particle diameter). If the chemical reaction is very fast with respect to the greatest possible physical transport, it will occur in the outer part of the particle. In the extreme case, only the external particle surface will be of use to the reaction; the internal surface then plays no part and may equally well be absent.

A quantitative treatment of the conversion rate along the lines given above for a given reaction system is very difficult to undertake. No sufficient general data are available for an a priori evaluation of steps *ii* to *vi*. The internal diffusion greatly depends on the pore texture of the particle of catalyst (pore size distribution and the connection between the pores) and on the fact whether the transport is brought about by normal molecular diffusion, Knudsen diffusion (with gases, when the mean free path of the molecules exceeds the average pore size) or migration in the adsorbed state.

---

* The treatment of a heterogeneous reaction between a fluid and a solid is entirely similar but for the fact that the solid is consumed whereas in general a solid catalyst retains its geometry.

In the first case the coefficient of internal diffusion D_i may be 10 to 100 times smaller than the molecular diffusivity in the free fluid. For these matters, the reader is referred to the more general papers by THIELE [129], ZELDO-WITCH [130], WAGNER [131], WICKE [132] and VAN KREVELEN [133].

A vast amount of work has been done on the kinetics of the heterogeneous reaction itself, particularly on the basis of kinetic measurements where the interference by physical transport resistances was eliminated as much as possible. In general, the expression for the kinetics of the surface conversion rate contains all three effects *iii*, *iv* and *v* since it is almost impossible to study these separately. This is reflected by the complexity of many experimental rate expressions for heterogeneous catalytic reactions; see, e.g., HOUGEN and WATSON [12].

A number of quantitative studies has been made of the external mass transfer between a fluid flow and aggregates of particles. The experimental results obtained by THOENES and KRAMERS [134] for a packed bed of spherical particles may be summarized within $\pm$ 10% by the formula:

$$\frac{\beta d_p}{D} = 1.9 \left(\frac{v d_p}{\nu}\right)^{0.5} \left(\frac{\nu}{D}\right)^{0.33}. \qquad \text{V-26}$$

It is to be noted that β is here an average value over the outer particle surface area and that large deviations from this average value occur locally. For mass transfer between a fluid and particles in a fluidized bed, the experimental results of RICHARDSON and SZEKELY [135] may be used as a guide to the value of β:

$$\left.\begin{aligned}
\frac{\beta d_p}{D} &= 0.37 \left(\frac{v d_p}{\nu}\right)^{1.18}, & 0.1 < Re_p < 15 \\
\frac{\beta d_p}{D} &= 2.0 \left(\frac{v d_p}{\nu}\right)^{0.5}, & 15 < Re_p < 250
\end{aligned}\right\} Sc \approx 1. \qquad \text{V-27}$$

In the following we shall illustrate the combined effect of the abovementioned phenomena on the conversion rate and the selectivity. The treatment is rather similar to that first given by THIELE [129] and ZELDOWITCH [130], to which WHEELER, among others, made important contributions [136].

Conversion rate

An equilibrium reaction A $\rightarrow$ P is carried out with a porous catalyst in the form of spherical particles with radius R. The following assumptions will be made:

– The chemical rate of the forward reaction is given by $k'_1 c_A$, and that of the reversed reaction by $k'_2 c_P$ (both in kmol/m²s); the ratio k'_1/k'_2 is equal to the chemical equilibrium constant K.

– The temperature in the particle is uniform.

– The specific internal surface area A_i(m²/m³) is distributed uniformly over the particle.

– The effective internal coefficient of diffusion, D_i, and the external mass transfer coefficient β are constants and have the same value for A and for P.
– The composition of the fluid outside the particle is given by $\langle c_A \rangle$ and $\langle c_P \rangle$.

The material balance for species A in the catalyst particle gives the differential equation for spherical symmetry and in the steady state:

$$0 = \frac{\mathrm{d}}{\mathrm{d}r}\left[r^2 D_i \frac{\mathrm{d}c_A}{\mathrm{d}r}\right] - r^2 A_i (k'_1 c_A - k'_2 c_P), \qquad \text{V-28}$$

where c_A and c_P are the concentrations of A and P in the pores and functions of the distance r from the centre of the particles (see Fig. V-7). The boundary conditions are:

$$r = 0 \qquad \frac{\mathrm{d}c_A}{\mathrm{d}r} = 0,$$

$$\text{V-29}$$

$$r = R \qquad D_i \frac{\mathrm{d}c_A}{\mathrm{d}r} = \beta(\langle c_A \rangle - c_A) - k'_1 c_A + k'_2 c_P.$$

In the latter condition it is taken into account that A and P may react at the external surface of the particle which is assumed to be equal to its geometric surface.

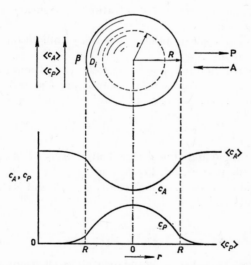

FIG. v-7. Heterogeneous equilibrium reaction in a spherical porous particle; concentration distributions calculated from Eq. V-30 with $K = 5$, $\varphi' = 2$, $D_i/\beta R = 0.1$ and $A_i R = 10^5$.

If we write the corresponding equations for component P, it is found that:

$$c_A + c_P = \langle c_A \rangle + \langle c_P \rangle,$$

so that c_P can be expressed in terms of c_A and Eqs. V-28 and V-29 can be solved. The concentration distribution in the particle is found to be:

$$c_A = \langle c_A \rangle - \frac{K \langle c_A \rangle - \langle c_P \rangle}{K + 1} \times$$

$$\times \left[1 - \frac{\dfrac{R}{r} \sinh \dfrac{r}{R}\, \varphi'}{\dfrac{D_i}{\beta R}\, \varphi' \cosh \varphi' + \left[1 + \dfrac{D_i}{\beta R} \left(\dfrac{\varphi'^2}{A_i R} - 1 \right) \right] \sinh \varphi'} \right], \quad \text{V-30}$$

where:

$$\varphi' = R \sqrt{\frac{k'_1 A_i (K + 1)}{D_i K}}.$$

It is seen that the following quantities appear as parameters in this complicated expression:

$K =$ the equilibrium constant.

$D_i/\beta R =$ a measure of the ratio of external mass transfer resistance and internal diffusional resistance.

$\varphi' =$ a measure of the ratio of internal diffusional resistance and "chemical reaction resistance".

$A_i R =$ a measure of the ratio of internal and external surface area.

Fig. V-7 gives an example of a concentration distribution according to Eq.
V-30.

Eq. V-30 can be greatly simplified for a few combinations of extreme values of these parameters, e.g.:

– for a very slow reaction in a porous particle, $\varphi' \ll 1$ and $c_A \approx \langle c_A \rangle$;

– for a rapid irreversible reaction in a porous particle with a negligible external mass transfer resistance, $\varphi' \gg 1$, $K = \infty$ and $D_i/\beta R \ll 1$:

$$c_A \approx \langle c_A \rangle \frac{R}{r}\, e^{-\varphi'(1 - r/R)},$$

which indicates a rapid and almost exponential decrease of c_A just below the
outer surface of the particle (cf. Eq. V-17a);

– when no internal surface area is present, $\varphi' = 0$ and $A_i R = 0$ (also see,
e.g., FRANK-KAMENETSKI [5]):

$$c_A \big|_{r=R} = \frac{\beta K \langle c_A \rangle + k'_1 (\langle c_A \rangle + \langle c_P \rangle)}{\beta K + k'_1 (1 + K)}.$$

We can now obtain from Eq. V-30 the over-all production rate to be used in
reactor calculations. If the production rate of A is expressed in molar units
per unit time and per unit mass of solid, it is equal to the molar flow of A
from the particle divided by its mass:

$$R_{sA} = -\beta \left(\langle c_A \rangle - c_A \big|_{r=R} \right) 4\pi R^2 \Big/ \frac{4}{3} \pi R^3 \varrho_s$$

and with Eq. V-30:

160

$$R_{sA} = -\frac{3\beta}{R\varrho_s} \left[\frac{\varphi' + \left(\frac{\varphi'^2}{A_i R} - 1\right) \tanh \varphi'}{\varphi' + \left(\frac{\beta R}{D_i} + \frac{\varphi'^2}{A_i R} - 1\right) \tanh \varphi'} \right] \times \frac{K\langle c_A\rangle - \langle c_P\rangle}{K + 1}. \quad \text{V-31}$$

Table V-3 shows a few special forms of this equation. When $\varphi' \ll 1$, the concentration in the particle is uniform at a level determined by the relative importance of the mass transfer coefficient β. If β is sufficiently large, neither external mass transfer nor internal diffusion limits the rate of conversion, and the surface area is utilized to the greatest possible extent [form (b)].

The reaction occurs almost entirely near the periphery of the particle if $\varphi' > 3$. With a sufficiently high mass transfer coefficient, the conversion rate is proportional to $\sqrt{k'_1 D_i A_i}$ [form (e)]; this result is analogous to the expression describing the mass flux for dissolution combined with a fast reaction, see Eq. V-21.

With nonporous particles, two extreme cases may occur where either the chemical reaction rate or the mass transfer rate is entirely in control [forms (h) and (j), respectively]. The expression (j) is identical with (c) and (f) since in all three cases it was assumed that the external mass transfer would be the main limiting factor in the conversion rate. In practice, however, the conditions to which (c) and (f) apply are rarely encountered.

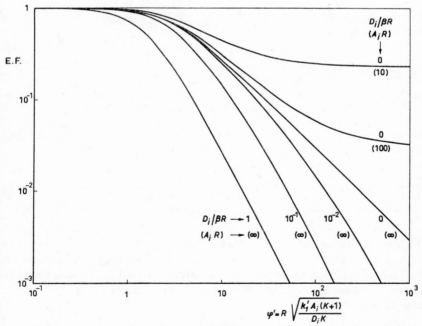

FIG. V-8. The effectiveness factor $E.F.$ of a porous catalyst for a first order equilibrium reaction.

TABLE V-3

Special forms of Eq. V-31

Slow reaction in a porous particle

$\varphi' \ll 1$:

$\left(\tanh \varphi' \approx \varphi' - \dfrac{\varphi'^3}{3}\right)$

$$R_{sA} \approx - \frac{\beta k'_1 (K+1)(A_i R + 3)}{R \varrho_s [\beta K + k'_1(K+1)(1 + A_i R/3)]} \times$$
$$\times \frac{K\langle c_A \rangle - \langle c_P \rangle}{K+1}, \quad (a)$$

special cases:

$K\beta/k'_1(K+1) \gg 1$

$$R_{sA} \approx - \frac{k'_1(K+1)(A_i R + 3)}{R \varrho_s K} \times$$
$$\times \frac{K\langle c_A \rangle - \langle c_P \rangle}{K+1} \quad (b)$$

(greatest possible conversion rate),

$K\beta/k'_1(K+1) \ll 1$

$$R_{sA} \approx - \frac{3\beta}{R \varrho_s} \times \frac{K\langle c_A \rangle - \langle c_P \rangle}{K+1}. \quad (c)$$

Fast reaction in a porous particle

$\varphi' > 3$ and $A_i R \gg \varphi'$:

(tanh $\varphi' \approx 1$)

$$R_{sA} \approx - \frac{3\beta(\varphi' - 1)}{R \varrho_s(\varphi' - 1 + \beta R/D_i)} \times$$
$$\times \frac{K\langle c_A \rangle - \langle c_P \rangle}{K+1}, \quad (d)$$

special cases:

$\left.\begin{array}{r} \beta R/D_i \gg \varphi' \\ \varphi' \gg 1 \end{array}\right\}$

$$R_{sA} \approx - \frac{3}{R \varrho_s} \sqrt{\frac{k'_1 D_i A_i (K+1)}{K}} \times$$
$$\times \frac{K\langle c_A \rangle - \langle c_P \rangle}{K+1}, \quad (e)$$

$\beta R/D_i \ll \varphi'$

$$R_{sA} \approx - \frac{3\beta}{R \varrho_s} \times \frac{K\langle c_A \rangle - \langle c_P \rangle}{K+1}. \quad (f)$$

With porous catalysts, the term "effectiveness factor" (*E.F.*) is frequently used to indicate the fraction of surface area utilized for chemical reaction. This magnitude can be defined as the ratio of actual conversion rate and greatest possible conversion rate. If the temperature of the particle is uniform, we have:

$$E.F. = \frac{R_{sA}(\text{Eq. V-31})}{R_{sA}(\text{Eq.(b) in Table V-3})}.$$

TABLE V-3

(continued)

Reaction at the outer surface of a nonporous particle

$A_i = 0$:

$$R_{sA} \approx - \frac{3\beta k'_1(K+1)}{R\varrho_s[K + k'_1(K+1)]} \times$$
$$\times \frac{K\langle c_A \rangle - \langle c_P \rangle}{K+1}, \quad \text{(g)}$$

special cases:

$K\beta/k'_1(K+1) \gg 1$ $\qquad R_{sA} \approx - \frac{3k'_1(K+1)}{R\varrho_s K} \times \frac{K\langle c_A \rangle - \langle c_P \rangle}{K+1}$ (h)

(greatest possible conversion rate),

$K\beta/k'_1(K+1) \ll 1$ $\qquad R_{sA} \approx - \frac{3\beta}{R\varrho_s} \times \frac{K\langle c_A \rangle - \langle c_P \rangle}{K+1}.$ (j)

Fig. V-8 shows a few curves of *E.F.* as a function of the parameter φ' for a porous catalyst of which $A_i R \gg 1$. The curves show that the degree of utilization of the internal catalyst surface decreases as the chemical reaction rate and the physical resistance to the transport of reactant become greater. It is seen that, with a given combination of reaction system and catalyst, the variables available for improving the effectiveness factor are the particle size and, to a lesser extent, the mass transfer coefficient β [which is roughly proportional to $(v/R)^{\frac{1}{2}}$]. Inversely, a variation of these two parameters in conversion experiments makes it possible to ascertain to what extent physical transport influences the over-all conversion rate. Thus, if it is found that the conversion rate is not influenced by the fluid velocity, it may be concluded that the effect of external mass transfer is negligible; internal diffusion may, however, still be the controlling factor. Whether this is true can be decided by investigating the influence of the particle diameter.

The effect of temperature on the conversion rate greatly depends on the relative importance of the physical transport phenomena, which are much less temperature-dependent than the chemical reaction velocity itself. This is qualitatively shown in Fig. V-9, where the logarithm of $|R_s|_A$ has been plotted as a function of $1/T$ for various cases; the slope of a curve in this diagram is a measure of the "activation energy" of the over-all conversion rate. The slope will indicate the activation energy of the chemical reaction only at such a low temperature that Eq. (b) in Table V-3 applies. On increasing the temperature, the external mass transfer may directly become rate-determining (Curve 1, for a relatively small value of $\beta R/D_i$), or eventually, after a temperature region has been passed where Eq. (e) of Table V-3 applies

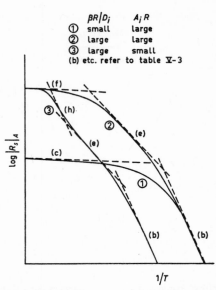

FIG. V-9. Schematic representation of the effect of temperature on the conversion rate with a porous catalyst.

approximately (Curve 2). In this particular region, the apparent activation energy of the over-all conversion rate is approximately one half of the chemical activation energy. With catalyst particles having a relatively small internal surface area, it is possible that a second intermediate region occurs with the chemical activation energy [Curve 3, section (h)]. In this situation, the internal surface is no longer active but the chemical reaction at the external surface still determines the conversion rate. It may be concluded that experimentally determined activation energies of heterogeneous reactions (catalysed or not) may often not be equal to the activation energy of the reaction proper, and that extrapolation of experimental results of this nature to other temperatures may be hazardous. This will also be true for extrapolation to other particle sizes.

A curve analogous to Curve 2 of Fig. V-9 is found for the reaction between oxygen and coal (WICKE [137, 138]. Fig. V-10 shows as an example the over-all conversion rate of oxygen (A) in a bed of porous coke particles as determined by HEDDEN [139].

In the above analysis, three effects which may modify the results given above have been neglected. Firstly, in the case of catalysed gas reactions the actual chemical kinetics in combination with the adsorption equilibria on the catalyst surface were disregarded. It appears from a paper by CHIEH CHU and HOUGEN [140] that these microkinetic phenomena should be taken into account for proper interpretation of catalytic effectiveness.

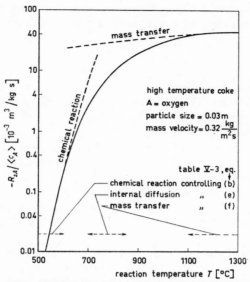

FIG. V-10. Over-all conversion rate for first order reaction between air oxygen (A) and porous coke; HEDDEN [139].

Secondly, in gas reactions it may occur that the number of moles changes upon conversion. In such a case, a net molar flow in radial direction is established; this flow sensibly affects the diffusive transport of reactants into and of products out of the catalyst particle if this transport is brought about by free molecular diffusion in the pores. If, on the other hand, the mean free path of the gas molecules is much longer than the diameter of the pores, Knudsen diffusion prevails and the various species migrate independently of each other; this effect needs not be considered in this case.

The third effect not taken into account relates to the possibility that the temperature in a porous particle is not uniform. This may occur in relatively large and poorly conducting particles of catalyst in which a reaction with a high heat effect takes place. This phenomenon has only recently drawn general attention. A paper by CARBERRY [141] indicates that the factor of catalytic effectiveness is significantly affected when:

$$\left| \frac{E}{R\langle T \rangle} \times \frac{\langle c_A \rangle (\Delta H_r)_A D_i}{\lambda_s} \right| > 1 \, .$$

SCHILSON and AMUNDSON [142] developed an elegant method for calculating the factor of catalytic effectiveness for exothermic and endothermic reactions with Knudsen diffusion in the pores.

Selectivity

It can now be qualitatively understood that the selectivity of a heterogeneous reaction system will be reduced when the conversion rate is influenced by external or internal physical transport. For example, with a reaction:

$$A \overset{k'_1}{\to} P \overset{k'_2}{\to} X$$

the desired product formed at the interface must be transported back to the main stream. Due to the presence of diffusional resistance the concentration of P at the interface will be higher than in the main stream. As a result, the undesired reaction will be favoured with respect to a case in which the entire active surface is easily accessible.

This can be shown quantitatively when the above consecutive reactions are of the first order with chemical surface rate constants k'_1 and k'_2. The isothermal production rates of A and P can then be calculated along the same lines as was done earlier in this section. A few special results are shown in Table V-4; in calculating these it was assumed that the mass transfer coefficients β and the internal diffusivities D_i have the same value for both components A and P.

At the bottom of Table V-4 a formal representation is given of the production rates in which k_1 and k_2 are pseudo-homogeneous conversion rate constants. We shall use it for calculating the maximum yield, $(\eta_P)_{max}$ (i.e. the maximum value of $\langle c_P \rangle / c_{A0}$), in a tubular reactor for the purpose of demonstrating the influence of the various physical resistances on $(\eta_P)_{max}$. For the isothermal tubular reactor, we then have the material balances (compare, e.g., Eq. II-11):

$$0 = \Phi_v d \langle c_A \rangle + \frac{k_1}{\varrho_s} \langle c_A \rangle \, dm_s \, ,$$

and:

$$0 = \Phi_v d \langle c_P \rangle - \frac{k_1}{\varrho_s} \Big[\psi \langle c_A \rangle - \frac{k_2}{k_1} \langle c_P \rangle \Big] dm_s \, .$$

After substituting $\tau_s = m_s / \varrho_s \Phi_v$, which is proportional to the residence time of the fluid, and with the boundary conditions:

$$\tau_s = 0 \, , \quad \langle c_A \rangle = c_{A0} \quad \text{and} \quad \langle c_P \rangle = 0 \, ,$$

the following solutions are obtained:

$$\langle c_A \rangle = c_{A0} e^{-k_1 \tau_s} \, ,$$

$$\langle c_P \rangle = c_{A0} \frac{\psi k_1}{k_1 - k_2} \Big(e^{-k_2 \tau_s} - e^{-k_1 \tau_s} \Big) \, .$$

The latter expression passes through a maximum as a function of τ_s. This maximum occurs at:

$$k_1 \tau_s = \frac{k_1}{k_1 - k_2} \ln \frac{k_1}{k_2} \, , \qquad\qquad\qquad \text{V-32}$$

and the corresponding value of the maximum yield is:

$$(\eta_P)_{max} = \psi \Big(\frac{k_1}{k_2} \Big)^{-k_2/(k_1 - k_2)} \, . \qquad\qquad \text{V-33}$$

166

TABLE V-4

Over-all production rates for the heterogeneous reaction $A \rightarrow P \rightarrow X$ *in a porous catalyst of uniform temperature; a few special cases.*

Case 1

Slow reactions, no diffusional and mass transfer resistance:

$$R_{sA} = -\frac{A_i R + 3}{R \varrho_s} k'_1 \times \langle c_A \rangle \,, \qquad (b)\star$$

$$R_{sP} = \frac{A_i R + 3}{R \varrho_s} k'_1 \times \left[\langle c_A \rangle - \frac{k'_2}{k'_1} \langle c_P \rangle \right] .$$

Case 2

Fast reactions, no external mass transfer resistance:

$$R_{sA} \approx -\frac{3}{R \varrho_s} \times \sqrt{k'_1 D_i A_i} \times \langle c_A \rangle \,, \qquad (e)\star$$

$$R_{sP} \approx \frac{3}{R \varrho_s} \times \sqrt{k'_1 D_i A_i} \times$$

$$\times \left[\frac{\langle c_A \rangle}{1 + \sqrt{k'_2/k'_1}} - \langle c_P \rangle \sqrt{k'_2/k'_1} \right] .$$

Case 3

Reactions at the surface of a nonporous particle, $A_i = 0$:

$$R_{sA} = -\frac{3}{R \varrho_s} \times \frac{k'_1}{1 + k'_1/\beta} \times \langle c_A \rangle \,, \qquad (g)\star$$

$$R_{sP} = \frac{3}{R \varrho_s} \times \frac{k'_1}{1 + k'_1/\beta} \times$$

$$\times \left[\frac{\langle c_A \rangle}{1 + k'_2/\beta} - \frac{k'_2(1 + k'_1/\beta)}{k'_1(1 + k'_2/\beta)} \langle c_P \rangle \right] .$$

Formal representation:

$$R_{sA} = -\frac{1}{\varrho_s} k_1 \langle c_A \rangle \,,$$

$$R_{sP} = \frac{1}{\varrho_s} k_1 \left[\psi \langle c_A \rangle - \frac{k_2}{k_1} \langle c_P \rangle \right] .$$

⋆ Compare the corresponding equations in Table V-3.

For the various cases treated in Table V-4 we have

Case 1: $\dfrac{k_1}{k_2} = \dfrac{k'_1}{k'_2}$, $\qquad\qquad \psi = 1$.

Case 2: $\dfrac{k_1}{k_2} = \sqrt{\dfrac{k'_1}{k'_2}}$, $\qquad\qquad \psi = [1 + \sqrt{k'_2/k'_1}]^{-1}$.

Case 3: $\dfrac{k_1}{k_2} = \dfrac{k'_1(1 + k'_2/\beta)}{k'_2(1 + k'_1/\beta)}$, $\qquad \psi = [1 + k'_2/\beta]^{-1}$.

It is seen that the selectivity parameter k_1/k_2 comes nearer to unity as the influence of physical transport makes itself more felt.* Fig. V-11 shows $(\eta_P)_{max}$ as a function of k'_1/k'_2 for the various cases treated. It is evident that if a catalyst is chosen for the purpose of obtaining a high selectivity, it should be used under circumstances where its effectiveness factor is high. It can be deduced from Eq. V-32 that a reduction of the selectivity parameter always entails an increase in the residence time required for obtaining the maximum yield, i.e. a decrease in the reactor capacity. Finally, it is to be noted that if a reactor shows a considerable spread in the residence time distribution (such as a continuous tank reactor), the value of $(\eta_P)_{max}$ and the capacity are still further reduced; cf. Illustration II.7.

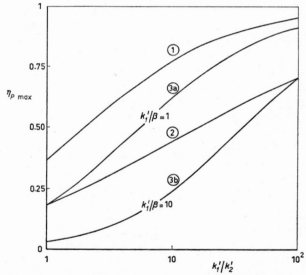

FIG. V-11. Influence of physical transport resistance on the maximum yield for heterogeneous consecutive reactions of the first order; 1 — slow reactions, no physical limitation (Table V-4, Case 1); 2 — fast reactions with internal diffusion controlling (Table V-4, Case 2); 3 — reactions at external surface of nonporous particle (Table V-4, Case 3).

---

* Similarly, a non uniform particle temperature will entail a diminishing of the selectivity of a complex reaction (CARBERRY [143]).

V.5. Autothermal behaviour of exothermic gas-solid reactions

In Section IV.5 we discussed the autothermal operation of an entire reactor system in which an exothermic reaction was carried out. It was shown that this phenomenon is brought about by the feed-back of liberated heat of reaction to the cold feed. A similar situation may occur on a much smaller scale with rapid heterogeneous exothermic reactions. It is encountered in the catalytic combustion of NH_3 with air on a surface of platinum catalyst (see Illustration V.5) as well as in certain gas-solid reactions, such as the combustion of carbon. The latter process will be used for the following discussion.

Let us consider a particle of lean coal or coke in a fixed bed through which air is flowing. When the coal is burning, the over-all reaction between oxygen and carbon may be represented by:

$$O_2 + C \rightarrow CO_2 .$$

Actually, the reaction mechanism has not been entirely elucidated; CO is probably produced at the coal surface, either by oxidation of carbon or by reduction of CO_2, while CO is oxidized to CO_2 very near the surface (VAN LOON [144], VAN DER HELD [145]). However, for the present analysis it may be assumed that the reaction takes place at the coal surface, and accordingly that the net heat of reaction is released at this surface.

Since a burning piece of coal is consumed very slowly, a pseudo-steady state may be assumed to exist in the coal bed, and the temperature of a coal particle may be thought to be constant. In such case, all of the heat produced by the reaction must be transported from the coal surface to the surroundings. Since, at least in the middle of the burning coal bed, radiation equilibrium will approximately exist, the reaction heat will be transferred by convection to the gas stream. In this way the feed-back of heat is established from the reaction site to the gaseous reactant.

Under the above conditions the molar flux J_A of oxygen (which we call the reactant A) to the surface of the particle, multiplied by the heat liberated per molar unit of A converted, $-(\Delta H_r)_A$, must be equal to the heat flux q coming from the surface:

$$-J_A(\Delta H_r)_A = q . \qquad \text{V-34}$$

The value of J_A depends on the texture of the particle and on the chemical and physical rate parameters as indicated in the preceding section. At a low value of T_s (the temperature of the solid), J_A is mainly determined by the rate of the chemical surface reaction; as T_s increases, a situation is reached where the oxygen is converted at the external particle surface at such a high rate that its concentration at the surface is zero and J_A is entirely determined by mass transfer:

$$J_A = \beta_A \langle c_A \rangle \, \star . \qquad \text{V-35}$$

$\star$ Also see Eqs. (f) and (j) in Table V-3.

With a constant gas velocity, the mass transfer coefficient β_A does not greatly depend on temperature so that J_A will be practically constant for a certain value of $\langle c_A \rangle$ and at high temperatures. Accordingly, the left-hand term of Eq. V-34, i.e. the chemical heat production rate per unit external area, will depend on T_s in the manner indicated in Fig. V-12, Curves 1a and 1b.

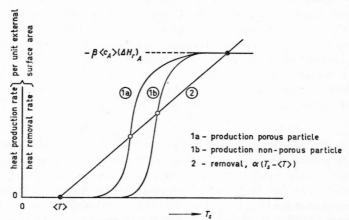

FIG. V-12. Heterogeneous exothermic reaction; possible solutions to Eq. V-34: ● stable, ○ unstable.

The rate of heat transfer to the gas flow (q in Eq. V-34) can be described by means of a heat transfer coefficient α:

$$q = \alpha(T_s - \langle T \rangle) , \qquad \text{V-36}$$

where $\langle T \rangle$ is the average gas temperature. Since it was assumed that α does not contain a contribution due to thermal radiation, it is rather independent of temperature. Hence, at a constant gas load and for a given value of $\langle T \rangle$, q is practically a linear function of T_s, as shown in Fig. V-12, line 2.

The intersections of a curve 1 and a line 2 in a diagram like Fig. V-12 represent solutions to Eq. V-34. When there are three solutions, the middle one is unstable for the same reasons as discussed with reference to Fig. IV-11c. The right-hand intersection corresponds with a high conversion rate which can only be obtained after ignition. The corresponding surface temperature lies between 1500 and 2000°C for the burning of coal in atmospheric air [144]. Its value is rather insensitive to variations in gas velocity and the degree of oxygen conversion in a fixed bed; this will be shown below.

In the range where the combustion rate is entirely controlled by mass transfer, we find from Eqs. V-34, 35 and 36 for the difference between the solid's surface temperature and the average temperature of the gas stream $\langle T \rangle$:

$$T_s - \langle T \rangle = -\frac{\beta_A}{\alpha} \langle c_A \rangle (\Delta H_r)_A ;$$

this equality prevails only in the *upper* stable operating point (Fig. V-12). As a consequence of the analogy between heat and mass transfer in convective flow (known as either the Nusselt or the Chilton-Colburn analogy), we have:

$$\frac{\beta_A}{\alpha} = \frac{1}{\varrho c_p} Le^{-2/3} ;$$

the dimensionless Lewis number of the gas mixture ($= \lambda/c_p\varrho D_A$) is practically constant at the temperatures and pressure considered. With the latter substitution we obtain:

$$T_s - \langle T \rangle = - \frac{\langle c_A \rangle}{\varrho c_p} (\Delta H_r)_A Le^{-2/3}, \qquad \text{V-37}$$

the value of which does not depend on the gas flow rate for constant $\langle T \rangle$ and $\langle c_A \rangle$.

For finding the reaction temperature T_s as a function of the degree of conversion, we consider the coal bed a tubular reactor with a negligible longitudinal dispersion of matter and heat. At the entrance of the combustion zone ($z = 0$), the oxygen concentration and the gas temperature are $\langle c_{A0} \rangle$ and $\langle T_0 \rangle$, respectively. With adiabatic steady operation, the combined heat and material balances give for a differential length dz of the reactor (see, e.g., Eqs. IV-16 and II-9):

$$0 = d(\Phi_m c_p \langle T \rangle) - (\Delta H_r)_A d(\Phi_m \langle c_A \rangle / \varrho) .$$

When the increase of the mass flow Φ_m (due to the fact that the product CO_2 is heavier than the reactant O_2) is neglected, and after putting $c_A = p_A/RT$ and $\varrho T = \varrho_0 T_0$, we obtain on integration:

$$\langle T \rangle - \langle T_0 \rangle = - (\Delta H_r)_A \frac{\langle c_{A0} \rangle}{c_p \varrho_0} \left(1 - \frac{\langle c_A \rangle \varrho_0}{\langle c_{A0} \rangle \varrho} \right) = \Delta T_{ad}(1 - p_A/p_{A0}) . \qquad \text{V-38}$$

The following expression for T_s results from Eqs. V-38 and V-37:

$$T_s - \langle T_0 \rangle = \Delta T_{ad} \left[1 - \frac{p_A}{p_{A0}} (1 - Le^{-2/3}) \right] . \qquad \text{V-39}$$

Since the Lewis number for gases is of the order of unity, Eq. V-39 shows that $(T_s - \langle T_0 \rangle)$ will always remain of the order of ΔT_{ad}, irrespective of the degree of conversion (of which $1 - p_A/p_{A0}$ is a measure). If $Le > 1$, $(T_s - \langle T_0 \rangle)$ will rise to the final value ΔT_{ad} when the reaction is completed. If $Le < 1$, it will drop to this final value; therefore, in the latter case in the reaction zone, $(T_s - \langle T_0 \rangle)$ will be higher than ΔT_{ad}. The value of Le for an O_2–N_2 mixture is about 1.15.

An elegant demonstration of the influence of Le was given by WICKE [146]. When p_A/p_{A0} is eliminated from Eqs. V-38 and V-39, the following equation for the upper stable operating temperature T_s as a function of $\langle T_0 \rangle$, ΔT_{ad} and $\langle T \rangle$ is obtained:

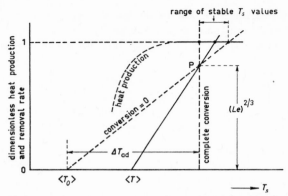

FIG. V-13. Dimensionless representation of Fig. V-12 showing the influence of Le on the course of the solids temperature (●) with the conversion.

$$\frac{T_s - \langle T \rangle}{\langle T_0 \rangle + \Delta T_{ad} - \langle T \rangle}\, Le^{2/3} = 1\,. \qquad\qquad \text{V-40}$$

This equation, as shown in Fig. V-13, can be solved graphically by finding the intersection between a horizontal line at a height 1 and an inclined straight line through the point P ($\langle T_0 \rangle + \Delta T_{ad}$, $Le^{2/3}$). Actually, such a line represents the heat removal rate as a function of T_s in dimensionless form; as the degree of conversion increases, the point of intersection $\langle T \rangle$ of this line with the abscissa moves from $\langle T_0 \rangle$ to $\langle T_0 \rangle + \Delta T_{ad}$, and the line pivots around the point P. With $Le < 1$, the value of T_s giving a solution to Eq. V-40 moves to the left; with $Le > 1$ it would move to the right with increasing conversion.

Finally, the degree of conversion can be calculated as a function of the active bed length z from the material balance:

$$0 = \mathrm{d}(\Phi_m \langle c_A \rangle /\varrho) + \beta_A \langle c_A \rangle\, A_v S\,\mathrm{d}z\,,$$

in which A_v is the external surface area of the particles per unit volume. Simple integration is not possible since not only $\langle c_A \rangle$, but also Φ_m, ϱ and β_A depend on z. An approximation of the partial pressure distribution is obtained when Φ_m and $\beta_A \varrho$ are assumed to be constant. The solution then becomes:

$$\frac{\langle c_A \rangle \varrho_0}{\langle c_{A0} \rangle \varrho} = \frac{p_A}{p_{A0}} = \exp\left(-\frac{\beta_A \varrho A_v S}{\Phi_m}\, z\right) \equiv \mathrm{e}^{-z/z_e}\,, \qquad \text{V-41}$$

where a characteristic length z_e has been introduced; it is the distance along the packed bed over which p_A has decreased by a factor of e (relaxation or decay length, or "Abklinglänge", WICKE [147]). If we use Eq. V-26 for the mass transfer coefficient β_A, we obtain:

$$z_e = \frac{\Phi_m}{S\varrho} \times \frac{1}{A_v} \times \frac{1}{\beta_A} \approx v \times \frac{d_p}{6(1-\varepsilon)} \times \frac{d_p}{1.9\, D_A} \left(\frac{v d_p}{\nu}\right)^{-1/2} \left(\frac{\nu}{D_A}\right)^{-1/3}.$$

172

With the usual value of $\varepsilon \approx 0.4$ for fixed beds, z_e becomes:

$$z_e \approx 0.15 \, d_p \left(\frac{v d_p}{\nu}\right)^{1/2} \left(\frac{\nu}{D_A}\right)^{2/3} = 0.15 \, d_p \, Re_p^{1/2} Sc^{2/3} \ .$$

Re_p lies between 10 and 1000 for most practical applications, while Sc is of the order of 1 for gases. Accordingly, z_e will vary between 1 and 6 particle diameters for rapid gas-solid reactions of which the conversion rate is entirely determined by mass transfer [147]. Actually, z_e may be somewhat increased by longitudinal dispersion and/or a nonuniform velocity distribution. As a result, it may be concluded that, with such a reaction as the combustion of coal with atmospheric air, 90% of the oxygen conversion take place within a bed length equal to about 3 to 15 particle diameters, as the value of Re_p goes from 10 to 1000. Consequently, the oxygen in the air passing through a burning coal bed of the height indicated is almost completely converted, particularly if no heat is lost at the end of the reaction zone by radiation to cold surfaces. Because of the consumption of solid fuel, the burning zone moves slowly in the direction of the gas flow, leaving the ashes behind.

In the above we have given only the essential outlines of the theory of rapid heterogeneous exothermic reactions between a gas and a solid. The theory is treated more extensively in a recent book by VULIS [148]; practical applications to the combustion and gasification of coal were discussed by VAN LOON [144] and by HEDDEN [139, 149]. The same principles can be applied to other rapid heterogeneous reactions such as the catalytic recombination of H_2 and O_2 and the catalytic combustion of NH_3 with air. The latter process will be discussed more quantitatively in the next illustration.

ILLUSTRATION V. 5. *Catalytic combustion of NH_3 with atmospheric air*

Some of the data published by OELE [150] will be used to analyse the conversion of NH_3 and the temperature distribution in a catalytic burner in which the gas mixture passes at atmospheric pressure through three flat platinum gauzes in succession. Under operating conditions (platinum temperature between 800 and 900°C), the chemical reaction velocity at the platinum surface is so high that the rate of conversion is determined entirely by the rate of mass transfer of the reactant which is not in excess. For several reasons this reactant is ammonia (reactant B). At a lower temperature, the rate of the chemical reaction would become the limiting factor. As a consequence, the system will show autothermal behaviour with a cold feed gas, so that the reaction has to be ignited by preheating temporarily either the gas or the gauze.

The following values of the operating variables are selected for calculating the stable reaction conditions:

Pressure, p	1 atm.
Feed temperature, $\langle T_0 \rangle$	60°C
NH_3 in feed, p_{B0}/p	0.11
Number of gauzes	3
Gauze wire diameter, d	60×10^{-6} m
Platinum surface/m² gauze, $A_v \Delta z$	1.2 m²/m²
Mass velocity of gas, ϱv	0.4 kg/m²s

OELE's paper supplies the values of the heat of reaction $[(\Delta H_r)_B = -226 \times 10^3 \text{ kJ/kmol at } 800°C]$ and of the specific molar heat of the feed gas ($C_p = 31.8$ kJ/kmol°C between 60 and 800°C) with which the adiabatic temperature rise for complete conversion is calculated:

$$\Delta T_{ad} = \frac{-(\Delta H_r)_B p_{B0}}{C_p p} = 782°C .$$

The partial pressures p_{B1}, p_{B2} and p_{B3} after the first, second and third gauze, respectively, have to be calculated for arriving at the gas and solids temperature. Eq. V-41 will be used in the form:

$$\frac{p_{B1}}{p_{B0}} = \exp\left[-\frac{\beta \varrho A_v \Delta z}{\varrho v}\right], \tag{a}$$

and similar expressions for p_{B2}/p_{B1} and p_{B3}/p_{B2}.

The value of the mass transfer coefficient β is calculated by analogy from an empirical heat transfer correlation for gas flow across thin wires [151]:

$$\frac{\beta d}{D} = 0.42 \left(\frac{v}{D}\right)^{0.2} + 0.57 \left(\frac{\varrho v d}{\mu}\right)^{0.5} \left(\frac{v}{D}\right)^{0.33} .$$

For average film temperatures of about 400°C (first gauze) and 800°C (third gauze), this produces with the physical properties indicated:

	400°C	800°C	
μ	31	42	10^{-6} kg/m s
ϱ	0.49	0.31	kg/m³
$Sc = v/D$	0.63	0.63	—
$Re = \varrho v d/\mu$	0.775	0.570	—
$Sh = \beta d/D$	0.82	0.75	—
β	1.37	2.7	m/s
$\beta \varrho$	0.67	0.83	kg/m²s
$\beta \varrho A_v \Delta z/\varrho v$	2.0	2.5	—

Accordingly we find with Eqs. (a) and V-38:

$$\frac{p_{B1}}{p_{B0}} \approx e^{-2.0} = 0.13 , \qquad\qquad \langle T_1 \rangle = 740°C ,$$

$$\frac{p_{B2}}{p_{B1}} \approx e^{-2.3} = 0.10 , \quad \frac{p_{B2}}{p_{B0}} = 0.013 , \qquad \langle T_2 \rangle = 832°C ,$$

$$\frac{p_{B3}}{p_{B2}} \approx e^{-2.5} = 0.08 , \quad \frac{p_{B3}}{p_{B0}} = 0.001 , \qquad \langle T_3 \rangle = 841°C .$$

With $v/D = 0.63$ and $\mu c_p/\lambda = Pr = 0.75$, we have $Le = Sc/Pr = 0.84$. This value is used in Eq. V-40 for calculating the gauze temperature. Because of the large gas temperature difference, particularly over the first gauze, an average temperature of the gas passing through the gauze should be taken for $\langle T \rangle$, such as the arithmetic average of the temperatures of the incoming and of the outgoing gas. The results are:

Gauze no.	1	2	3	
$\langle T \rangle$	400	786	837	°C
$T_s - \langle T \rangle$	495	63	6	°C
T_s	895	849	843	°C

It is seen that, since $Le < 1$, the catalyst temperature is higher than corresponds with the adiabatic temperature rise. It decreases towards this value as the reaction is completed.

This example furthermore shows that, with 3 gauzes at atmospheric pressure and with $\varrho v = 0.4$ kg/m²s, the final conversion is nearly complete. Since the value of $\beta \varrho$ is rather insensitive to pressure changes, it appears from Eq. (a) that the conversion will be reduced when ϱv is increased by increasing either the velocity or the pressure. A larger number of gauzes must be used for obtaining a complete conversion under these circumstances; burners containing up to 20 gauzes exist [150].

V.6. Mixing phenomena in fixed and fluidized bed reactors

This section stands somewhat apart from the previous ones in which the nonuniform conditions were examined at the scale of dispersion. The scale of scrutiny will now be enlarged, but it will still remain rather small with respect to the smallest reactor dimension. The purpose is to discuss some effects of insufficient internal exchange of heat and matter which, particularly in solid catalysed gas reactions, may give rise to undesirable variations in temperature and concentration. The effects to be discussed for fixed and fluidized bed reactors are essentially different.

The *catalytic tubular reactor* (in general a pipe or a number of pipes in parallel, filled with solid pellets of catalyst) was already mentioned in Section II.2 with respect to isothermal operation. The theory was developed further in Section IV.4, consideration being given to the heat effect of the reaction and to the external heat exchange. In that treatment, both the temperature and the composition of the reaction mixture were assumed to be uniform over the cross section of the reaction tube. This, however, depends very much on the possibilities of the transport of heat and matter perpendicular to the direction of the main flow. If these possibilities are limited, in the case of, for instance, an exothermic reaction in a cooled tubular reactor containing particles of catalyst, the temperature at the axis of the tube may become considerably higher than near the wall; consequently, the degree of conversion may be higher near the axis than near the wall. The greater part of this section will be devoted to the transverse mixing effects associated with a gas flow through packed beds and to their implications with respect to the design and operation of such reactors.

The internal exchange of heat presents no problem in the *fluidized bed reactor*. The mixing of solids generally is so good that no undesired "hot spots" develop. A less satisfactory feature of this type of dispersion lies in the fact that, in most applications, part of the gas feed rises through the bed in the form of large bubbles or gas pockets, the contents of which may be insufficiently exchanged with the gas between the particles (also see Section III.9). The resulting by-passing of reactant feed may severely limit the final conversion of the reaction. This will be discussed briefly at the end of this section.

Transverse mixing with flow through packed beds

As a fluid is passing through a bed of particles, its repeated lateral displacement combined with the mixing of volume elements belonging to different streamlines gives rise to a certain degree of mixing perpendicular to the main flow. The degree of mixing can be characterized by means of an apparent transverse dispersion coefficient D_t. As shown in Section III.9 (Fig. III-17) for a bed of spherical particles, $Pé_t$ approaches a value of 12, which is reached when $\langle v \rangle d_p/v > 100$. Accordingly:

$$D_t = \frac{\langle v \rangle d_p}{12} = \frac{v d_p}{12\varepsilon} \approx 0.2\, v d_p, \qquad \text{V-42}$$

where v is the fluid velocity based on the empty cross section of the bed (i.e. the approach velocity). It can be easily ascertained from Eq. V-42 that, for liquids, D_t will in all practical cases greatly exceed the molecular diffusivity D; with gases this will be so only when Re_p is sufficiently large.

Heat can be transported perpendicularly to the main flow by the same mechanism if a transverse temperature gradient exists. For $Re_p = v d_p/v > 20$, the corresponding transverse thermal conductivity for a packed bed of spherical particles or cylindrical pellets appears to be:

$$\lambda'_t = (0.10 \pm 0.02)\, \varrho c_p v d_p; \qquad \text{V-43}$$

the numerical coefficient was taken from the paper by YAGI and KUNII [152] in which all previously published measurements were assembled.

Apart from this transverse mixing effect, heat can be transported fairly well in a packed bed by conduction through the fluid from particle to particle, and, with gases, by thermal radiation between the particles. If, therefore, there is no flow, an apparent (isotropic) thermal conductivity of the bed, λ_0, already exists. Several methods have been published for estimating λ_0 from the separate thermal conductivities of the particles and the fluid; see, e.g., WILHELM, JOHNSON, WIJNKOOP and COLLIER [153] and the more recent work by YAGI and KUNII [152] in which the effect of thermal radiation is also accounted for.

It is now assumed that λ_0 and λ'_t act rather independently. Accordingly, the total apparent transverse conductivity, λ_t, for a bed of spheroidal particles is given by:

$$\lambda_t = \lambda_0 + \lambda'_t,$$

or:

$$\frac{\lambda_t}{\lambda} = \frac{\lambda_0}{\lambda} + 0.1\, Re_p Pr, \qquad \text{V-44}$$

where λ is the thermal conductivity of the fluid and $Re_p = v d_p/v$. A few experimental results for λ_t are given in Fig. V-14; at higher values of Re_p it appears that transverse mixing is the main mechanism by which heat can be transported perpendicularly to the main direction of flow.

In principle, an additional heat transfer resistance should be taken into account for the transport of heat between the fluid stream and the wall containing the bed. Although the point velocity in the bed can be greater near the wall than its value averaged over the whole cross section (see, e.g.,

176

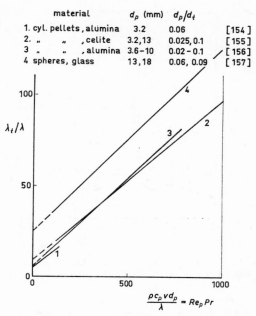

material	d_p (mm)	d_p/d_t	
1. cyl. pellets, alumina	3.2	0.06	[154]
2. „ „ , celite	3.2, 13	0.025, 0.1	[155]
3 „ „ , alumina	3.6–10	0.02 – 0.1	[156]
4 spheres, glass	13, 18	0.06, 0.09	[157]

FIG. V-14. A few experimental results for λ_t in packed beds with air flow.

SCHWARZ and SMITH [158]), the intensity of transverse mixing decreases as the wall is approached. A boundary layer exists at the wall itself; it has an average thickness determined by the velocity of flow and by the eddies produced by the particles adjacent to the wall. These effects can be conveniently combined into a wall heat transfer coefficient α_w. For packed beds containing more than 10 particles on the tube diameter $(d_p/d_t < 0.1)$, YAGI and WAKAO [159] recommend the following correlation, to be used in conjunction with Eq. V-44:

$$Nu_w = \frac{\alpha_w d_p}{\lambda} = 0.20\ Re_p{}^{0.80} Pr^{1/3}, \qquad \text{V-45}$$

established for $20 < Re_p < 2000$, which is in agreement with earlier measurements by PLAUTZ and JOHNSTONE [157].

An estimate of the relative importance of the transverse conductivity and the wall heat transfer coefficient can be obtained by calculating the radial temperature distribution in a packed cylindrical tube under the assumption that the heat generated in it is distributed uniformly over the cross section. A parabolic temperature distribution results (as shown in Fig. V-15, top left). The ratio of $(T_m - \langle T \rangle)$ (temperature in the centre minus average temperature) and $(\langle T \rangle - T_w)$ (average temperature minus wall temperature) is characteristic of the nonuniformity of the temperature distribution. With a uniform heat production it is found that:

177

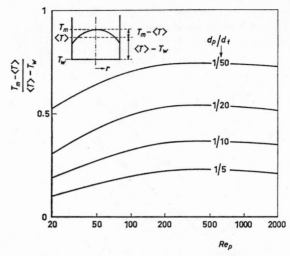

FIG. V-15. Degree of nonuniformity of the radial temperature distribution with uniform heat production, from Eqs. V-44, 45 and 46 with $Pr = 1$ and $\lambda_0/\lambda = 10$.

$$\frac{T_m - \langle T \rangle}{\langle T \rangle - T_w} = \left(1 + 8\,\frac{\lambda_t}{\alpha_w d_t}\right)^{-1}. \qquad \text{V-46}$$

This expression is equal to 1 when thermal conduction is entirely controlling $(\lambda_t/\alpha_w d_t \ll 1)$, and it is equal to 0 when the wall heat transfer is the limiting mechanism $(\lambda_t/\alpha_w d_t \gg 1$, uniform temperature over the cross section). Fig. V-15 shows that the nonuniformity of the temperature depends mainly on d_p/d_t and to a lesser extent on Re_p. It may be concluded that for $d_p/d_t > 0.2$ the temperature is nearly uniform over the cross section and that only α_w needs to be taken into account. Since Eq. V-45 is no longer valid in this region, α_w has to be derived from experimental results obtained under these conditions (see, e.g., KLING [160] and LEVA [161]). The value of α_w can now be combined with the heat transfer coefficient between the wall and the cooling or heating medium to give the over-all heat transfer coefficient U. The calculation of a tubular reactor then proceeds along the lines given in Section IV.4. If the influence of λ_t, and consequently that of D_t, cannot be neglected, a more detailed analysis of the temperature and concentration distribution will be necessary.

Temperature and concentration distribution in a catalytic tubular reactor

Calculation of the axial and radial temperature and concentration distributions requires a material balance and a heat balance to be written down for a small volume element in the reactor. The following reasonable assumptions may be made:

i. There is cylindrical symmetry.

ii. The velocity profile is flat.

iii. D_t and λ_t are independent of the distance r from the axis, of the distance z from the inlet, and of the temperature.

iv. The axial transport of matter and heat by longitudinal diffusion and conduction, respectively, is negligible as compared to convective transport.

The second assumption is justified for values of d_p/d_t below 0.05 [158]. With regard to *iii*, λ_t may well depend on temperature, particularly because of the contribution of the thermal radiation to λ_0. The conditions for *iv* to apply may be derived from the theory in Section III.6 and from the data for packed beds given in Section III.9.

With the above assumptions, the steady state balance for a species A becomes:

$$0 = D_t\left(\frac{\partial^2 c_A}{\partial r^2} + \frac{1}{r}\frac{\partial c_A}{\partial r}\right) - v\frac{\partial c_A}{\partial z} + R_{sA}\varrho_s(1 - \varepsilon) ; \qquad \text{V-47}$$

R_{sA} is the molar production rate of A per unit mass of catalyst; with $\varrho_s =$ density of the catalytic material and $\varepsilon =$ porosity of the catalyst bed, the last term in this equation represents the molar production rate of A per unit reactor volume. R_{sA} in principle contains all effects discussed in Section V.4; for further calculation, it should be known as a function of composition and of temperature for a given catalytic material and particle size. The boundary conditions for Eq. V-47 are:

$$z = 0, \quad 0 < r < R, \quad c_A = c_{A0}$$
$$z \geqslant 0, \quad\quad r = 0, \quad \partial c_A/\partial r = 0 \qquad \text{V-48}$$
$$z \geqslant 0, \quad\quad r = R, \quad \partial c_A/\partial r = 0 .$$

The heat balance becomes:

$$0 = \lambda_t\left(\frac{\partial^2 T}{\partial r^2} + \frac{1}{r}\frac{\partial T}{\partial r}\right) - \varrho c_p v\frac{\partial T}{\partial z} + (\Delta H_r)_A R_{sA}\varrho_s(1 - \varepsilon) , \qquad \text{V-49}$$

with the boundary conditions:

$$z = 0, \quad 0 < r < R, \quad T = T_0$$
$$z \geqslant 0, \quad\quad r = 0, \quad \partial T/\partial r = 0 \qquad\qquad \text{V-50}$$
$$z \geqslant 0, \quad\quad r = R, \quad -\lambda_t\frac{\partial T}{\partial r} = \alpha_w(T - T_w) = U(T - T_c) ;$$

T_c is the temperature of the cooling or heating medium.

An analytical solution of this system of equations is not feasible; even if R_{sA} is assumed to be simply proportional to c_A, its nonlinear dependence on the temperature would pose serious mathematical difficulties. A solution of a given problem can always be obtained by numerical computation; to this end, the differential equations are changed into difference equations by means of which the solution can be built up stepwise. In this case, each step involves a complicated trial-and-error solution because of the coupling between Eqs. V-47 and V-49 through R_{sA}.

179

BARON [162] showed that an elegant graphic step-by-step method can be used (similar to the Schmidt-Binder method for non-steady heat conduction), provided $D_t = \lambda_t/\varrho c_p$. It can be inferred from Eqs. V-42 and V-44 that for gases there will always be a Re_p range where this will approximately apply.

During the last thirty years several solutions to simplified versions of the above problem were published [4, 163, 164, 165, 166] which have been useful for specific cases. A book by KJAER [167] contains a valuable survey of methods hitherto used, while BEEK [168] recently published a monograph on the design of packed catalytic reactors. LÜCK [169] calculated temperature distributions for geometries differing from the circular tube, based on the assumption of uniform heat production; among other things, his work specifies results for a catalytic bed containing cooling tubes.

It should be borne in mind that the assumption of constant D_t and λ_t over the cross section of the bed and a local heat transfer coefficient α_w at the wall are simplifying approximations. These give rise to the still rather simple system of Eqs. V-47 to V-50, the solution of which, however, is involved. Moreover, the solution is very sensitive to the values of λ_t and α_w selected (compare the "parametric sensitivity" discussed in Section IV.4) so that a prediction of the temperature and concentration distribution in a tubular reactor will not be very reliable, especially for reactions with a great heat effect.

ILLUSTRATION V. 6. *Temperature and concentration distribution in an experimental catalytic reactor*★.

It has been decided to build an experimental tubular reactor (diameter: 32 mm; length: 0.4 m) for the catalytic chlorination with HCl of benzene in the vapour phase (component A). The conversion rate is known as a function of temperature and of the degree of conversion of HCl (ζ_A) from measurements carried out in a fluidized bed with small particles of the catalyst to be used (see Fig. V-16). The tubular reactor is to be filled with 2.5 mm particles of catalyst and it has been verified that under the reaction conditions mass transfer and diffusion inside these catalyst pellets do not significantly slow down the chemical conversion rate. The reactor will be cooled with paraffin oil of $T_c = 245°C$ at a rather low flow rate. It is required to calculate the temperature and conversion distribution for the following operating conditions: feed composition as given in Fig. V-16, a mass velocity of 0.314 kg/m²s and an inlet temperature $T_0 = 245°C$.

The solution of this problem depends on a number of parameters which can be obtained by making the differential equations for the concentration and the temperature distribution dimensionless. When these are written down on a mass basis, and when the following new variables are introduced:

$$\zeta_A = 1 - w_A/w_{A0}, \quad \Delta T = T - T_c$$
$$r' = r/R, \quad z' = z/L,$$

Eq. V-47 can be written as:

$$0 = \frac{D_t L}{vR^2}\left(\frac{\partial^2 \zeta_A}{\partial r'^2} + \frac{1}{r'}\frac{\partial \zeta_A}{\partial r'}\right) - \frac{\partial \zeta_A}{\partial z'} - \frac{\varrho_s(1-\varepsilon)L}{\varrho v w_{A0}} r_{sA},$$

★ This illustration was taken from a design problem worked out at the Institute of Chemical Technology, Technische Hochschule, Darmstadt, Germany. The results were kindly made available to us by Dr. H. Hofmann.

180

and Eq. V-49:

$$0 = \frac{\lambda_t L}{\varrho c_p v R^2} \left(\frac{\partial \Delta T}{\partial r'^2} + \frac{1}{r'} \frac{\partial \Delta T}{\partial r'} \right) - \frac{\partial \Delta T}{\partial z'} + \frac{(\Delta h_r)_A w_{A0}}{c_p} \times \frac{\varrho_s (1 - \varepsilon) L}{\varrho v w_{A0}} r_{sA} .$$

The boundary conditions V-48 and V-50 can be easily transformed into the new variables, and the last condition of Eq. V-50 becomes:

$$\frac{\partial \Delta T}{\partial r'} = - \frac{UR}{\lambda_t} \Delta T .$$

The following values of the parameters are obtained by calculation:

$$\frac{D_t L}{v R^2} = 0.53 , \qquad \frac{\lambda_t L}{\varrho c_p v R^2} = 1.83 ,$$

$$\frac{\varrho_s (1 - \varepsilon) L}{\varrho v w_{A0}} = 3400 \text{ s} \left(= \frac{\text{kg of catalyst}}{\text{kg/s of HCl fed}} \right) ,$$

$$\frac{-(\Delta h_r)_A w_{A0}}{c_p} \equiv \Delta T_{ad} \approx 122°C \text{ (increases somewhat with T)} ,$$

$\dfrac{UR}{\lambda_t} = 0.46$ (in which the heat resistance gas-wall, α_w^{-1}, is 14% of the over-all heat resistance, U^{-1}).

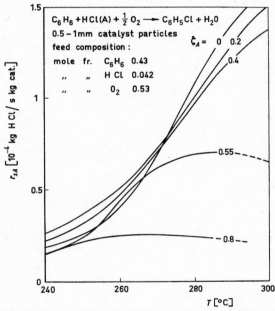

FIG. V-16. Empirical data for the conversion rate of HCl (A) in the gas phase chlorination of benzene, obtained with small catalyst particles in a fluidized bed; Illustration V.6.

With these values of the parameters and with r_{sA} given by Fig. V-16, the differential equations can be numerically solved; the steps taken in the z-direction are 1/40 of the tube length L, and in the r-direction 1/4 of the tube radius R. The resulting temperature distribution is shown in Fig. V-17. Both the temperature at the axis and that near the

181

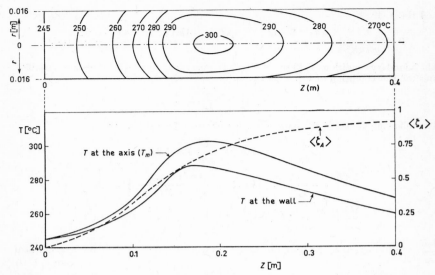

FIG. V-17. Temperature and conversion distribution in an experimental catalytic tubular reactor for the reaction indicated in Fig. V-16; Illustration V.6.

wall show an appreciable increase (30 to 40% of ΔT_{ad}), but the nonuniformity of the temperature over the cross section appears to be relatively small. This is due to the relatively low value of U which is determined mainly by the rather poor heat transfer coefficient between the cooling liquid and the outer surface of the tube.

The degree of conversion averaged over the cross section, $\langle \zeta_A \rangle$, as a function of z is also shown in Fig. V-17. The radial variation of ζ_A is very small in this case. This is caused by the relatively small radial temperature variations and by the fact that, in the lower temperature range and below 50% conversion, the conversion rate is rather independent of ζ_A.

It may be concluded from these calculations that the reactor would not operate under sufficiently isothermal conditions if it were used for kinetic studies. A considerable improvement would be obtained if the outside heat transfer coefficient were greatly increased.

The fluidized bed reactor

The gas fluidized bed has received wide attention during the past 20 years, with regard to its applicability as a chemical reactor as well as for other purposes. A huge amount of information has been assembled on the physical behaviour of fluidized beds, such as fluidization characteristics, heat transfer and mixing of gas and solids. Reference may be made to the books of RIBAUD [170], LEVA [171] and ZENZ and OTHMER [172] and to the proceedings of two symposia on this subject [173].

The main advantage of the fluidized bed as a reactor is its temperature homogeneity. Moreover, the possibility of transporting the solid material (either a catalyst or a reactant) may be an attractive feature, such as for the continuous treatment of solids (reaction) and for recirculation for the purpose of regeneration (of a catalyst) or of heat transfer in an external heat exchanger.

When the conversion of components in the *gas phase* is considered (the solids acting as a catalyst), problems may be encountered in connection with the nonhomogeneous composition of the bed. At fluidizing velocities not more than a few times the velocity for incipient fluidization, only some of the gas seeps through the aggregate of particles (dense phase), while the rest ascends through the bed in the form of bubbles or gas pockets (dilute phase). These bubbles stimulate efficient mixing of the particles and the equalization of temperature differences; on the other hand, the average residence time of the gas in the bubbles is much shorter than its average residence time in the dense phase. Particularly with rather slow reactions and with a low rate of exchange of gas between the dilute and the dense phase, this short-circuiting flow of bubbles will reduce the degree of conversion obtainable in the reactor as a whole.

This effect is evident from several studies published on catalytic gas reactions in a fluidized bed, such as those by LEWIS, GILLILAND and GLASS [174] and MATHIS and WATSON [175]. The former authors compared the catalytic hydrogenation of ethylene in a fixed and in a fluidized bed using the same particles of catalyst. Some typical results are shown in Fig. V-18. It appears that, particularly at high fluidizing velocities, the conversion in the fluidized bed is appreciably reduced; it may even become lower than the conversion in a reactor where the gas is completely mixed (tank reactor model).

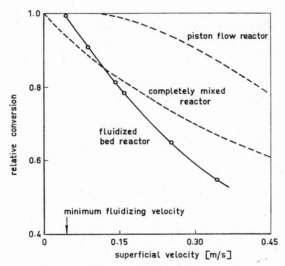

FIG. V-18. Measured conversion in a fluidized bed reactor, compared with calculated conversion for a tubular and a tank reactor model under the same conditions and containing the same amount of catalyst; LEWIS, GILLILAND and GLASS [174].

Several models have been proposed to account for the effect mentioned above, e.g. by MAY [176] and by VAN DEEMTER [78]. The latter takes into account the rate of mass transfer between the dilute and the dense phase (in the form of the height of a transfer unit) and the degree of longitudinal mixing of the gas in the dense phase (assumed to be equal to the degree of mixing of the particles, and expressed as a mixing length) ; he provides graphs from which the degree of conversion can be derived from these two parameters in conjunction with the conversion rate. As yet, no reliable tests of the various proposed models have been published. The main difficulty is that the rate of formation and the ultimate size of the gas pockets (and hence also the degree of mixing of the solids) greatly depends on the density and the size distribution of the particles. In general it can be said that light particles having a large spread in sizes, in the range from 20 to 200 μ, will give the least short-circuiting.

With respect to the conversion of *solids* which are continuously processed in a fluidized bed, the reactor can often be regarded as a tank reactor with segregated flow (compare Section III.8). Hence, an almost complete conversion will require either a high retention time or a cascade of several reactors. The possibility that fine particles resulting from the reaction or from attrition will be carried away by the gas stream must also be taken into account. A theoretical and experimental study on these subjects was recently published by YAGI and KUNII [177].

CHAPTER VI

THE OPTIMIZATION OF CHEMICAL REACTORS

VI.1. The object and means of optimization

Optimization is the activity by which it is endeavoured to have a process advance under such conditions that an extreme value of a specified quantity is attained. It is meaningless to discuss optimization unless the quantity of which the extreme is sought is properly specified. Since the production of chemicals is to be considered an economic activity, the quantity to be optimized is closely related to the economy of the plant; it will ultimately be its financial profit which should be maximized. This means, among other things, that the plant unit should be so designed as to allow the desired amount of product to be obtained at the lowest possible manufacturing costs. Although the chemical reactor proper frequently is only a small part of the total equipment of a manufacturing unit, the reactor may considerably affect the over-all economy of the plant. This will be illustrated below by means of the idealized economic diagrams introduced in Section II.8.

Let us assume that a material A is converted in an existing plant to a desired product P and to by-products X and Y, and that the production rate of P is Φ_P at a plant yield $\bar{\eta}_P$. The plant yield is equal to the reactor yield η_{PL} if no recirculation of the raw material is applied; it is equal to the selectivity σ_{PL} of the reactor section if unconverted A is completely separated from the product stream and recycled to the reactor feed (see Fig. VI-1).

If the by-products have a negligible sales value, the gross profit I of the

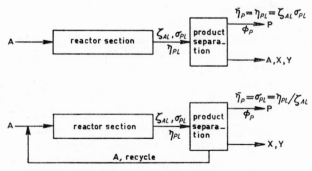

FIG. VI-1. Plant yield $\bar{\eta}_P$ and reactor yield η_{PL}.

plant may be schematically represented by:

$$I = C_P \Phi_P - \left[\frac{C_A \Phi_P}{\bar{\eta}_P} + C_{\text{var}} \Phi_P + C_{\text{fix}} \right] ; \qquad \text{VI-1}$$

C_A and C_P represent the total costs or net sales value of a unit amount of A and P, respectively; C_{var} are the variable costs per unit production rate of P, and C_{fix} the fixed costs of the installation per unit time. The break-even point at which $I = 0$ is obtained at a production rate $(\Phi_P)_{\text{nil}}$; the economic flexibility of the plant and the possibilities for making profit are improved as the ratio of the actual production rate and $(\Phi_P)_{\text{nil}}$ is increased.

Let the existing economic situation according to Eq. VI-1 be represented by Fig. VI-2°. This situation can, in principle, be improved by changes in the reactor section in a number of different ways:

(a) Yield increase by improved process conditions; the raw material costs diminish, and as a consequence the economic flexibility and the profit at the same production rate increase (Fig. VI-2a).

(b) Capacity increase by improved process conditions; in this case the diagram (Fig. VI-2b) is the same as VI-2°; the increased capacity results in greater flexibility and higher profit only if the increased production can be sold.

(c) As (a) after capital investment; it depends on the investment required for yield increase whether the profit is influenced favourably $(\mathrm{d}C_{\text{fix}}/\,\mathrm{d}\bar{\eta}_P < C_A \Phi_P/\bar{\eta}_P{}^2)$, or not (Fig. VI-2c).

(d) As (b) after capital investment; it is seen from Fig. VI-2d that the gross profit and the economic flexibility increase only if the production rate and sales volume rise considerably.

(e) Reduction of the variable costs; this has the same effect as (a).

It appears that the *plant capacity* and the *plant yield* influence the plant economy rather independently, and also that the variable costs, in particular *heat economy* and *energy consumption*, can play an important part. Now, apart from the reactor section, the manufacturing unit will generally contain sections for feed preparation, product separation and product treatment and delivery. Consequently, the extent to which the reactor itself influences the economy of the plant strongly depends on the costs connected with the reactor section in relation to the total costs.

For a few extreme cases it is clear in which direction measures should be taken for improving the plant profitability:

i. If the variable and fixed costs greatly exceed the raw material costs (e.g., $C_{\text{var}} \Phi_P + C_{\text{fix}} \gg C_A \Phi_P/\bar{\eta}_P$) the former costs should be minimized and the reactor capacity made as high as possible, provided the reactor depreciation contributes considerably to the total fixed costs of the plant.

ii. In case the raw material costs are much higher than the other costs (e.g., $C_A \Phi_P/\bar{\eta}_P \gg C_{\text{var}} \Phi_P + C_{\text{fix}}$) it should be attempted to maximize the plant yield for which the reactor is mainly responsible.

186

A relationship between the *technical* properties of the reaction section (such as capacity, yield, heat requirements) and the *economy* of the entire plant will, in general, be very difficult to formulate quantitatively. If, for example, a certain temperature level of the reactor section is surpassed, this may involve the need for an entirely different heating system or the use of different constructional materials; this will result in a discontinuity in the relationship

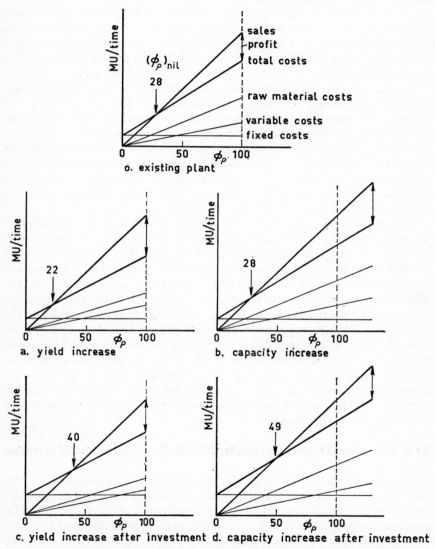

FIG. VI-2. Several ways of improving the economy of a plant.

187

between total costs and operating temperature. Such considerations make the design of a plant which can operate near its economic optimum largely a matter of experience and sound judgment. At the same time, however, it is a wise policy to try to optimize parts of the installation, such as the reactor section, with reference to a more restricted criterion for optimization. In this way, the economic features of the entire plant can be studied for a number of combinations of plant sections which in themselves have been suitably optimized. In view of this procedure it is worthwhile to consider optimization of chemical reactors in a more restricted sense. Accordingly, the rest of this chapter will be devoted to optimization with respect to capacity and/or yield of the reactor section, bearing in mind that its performance should be judged ultimately by standards of economy for the total plant.

Many basic data required for industrial optimization of a reactor are supplied by the chemical laboratory. Information should be available as to the cheapest raw materials, the preferred sequence of reaction steps in a complicated synthesis, the most suitable catalyst, the possible uses for by-products, etc. In evaluating the results of experiments related to these questions, the chemist is mainly guided by the obtainable yield of desired product. When a decision has been made on the particular reaction system to be used, more laboratory data are needed regarding the influence of the operating variables on the conversion rates of all reactions involved.

The principal variables by means of which a reactor can be optimized in the industrial sense on the basis of the above information are: the reaction temperature, the mode of operation and the reactor type, the reaction or residence time and, for a cascade, the number of tank reactors. The reactant concentration is an equally important variable, as discussed in Section II.9. With respect to this quantity it may be said, in general, that the conversion rates, and consequently the capacity, of the reactor will be greater to the extent that the reactant concentrations are higher. At the same time, however, the local heat fluxes will increase for reactions with a great heat effect; this involves greater expenditures for heat transfer purposes in order to maintain optimum conditions. In the next sections we shall no longer discuss the influence of concentration, but restrict the discussions to optimization by the proper choice of reactor type and feed distribution, and of temperature and temperature distribution.

VI.2. The choice of reactor type and feed distribution with isothermal operation

The problem of batch *vs.* continuous operation and, for the latter case, the merits of the tubular reactor and the tank reactor have already been discussed in Section II.8, mainly with respect to the possibility of obtaining *maximum capacity*. It will be recalled that the capacity of a single tank reactor is always lower than that of a tubular reactor under the same reaction conditions. For the intermediate system consisting of a cascade of tank reactors, capacity optimization problems may arise particularly with regard to the distribution of the various tank volumes with which a desired degree of conversion can be obtained with the minimum total volume. Such problems, however, appear to be rather unimportant in most cases. The reduction in total reaction volume obtainable in comparison with a cascade of equal-volume tank reactors may not at all outweigh the increased investment and maintenance costs of a set of different reactors (see, e.g., Illustration VI.4b).

On the other hand, since more than one reaction occurs in most practical cases, it is often of economic interest to consider which reactor system is capable of giving the *highest yield* of desired product. This is especially true if one or more of the reactants are expensive. If, moreover, such reactants cannot easily be recovered from the product, a high final conversion is required as well.

With equilibrium reactions, the final degree of conversion can be increased in various ways, all of which consist essentially of the shifting of the equilibrium composition. Examples of product withdrawal during the reaction have already been given in Illustration II.5b and in Section V.2. The strategies with respect to reaction temperature will be discussed in Section VI.3.

Yield in tubular reactors and tank reactors

With the occurrence of wasteful side reactions or consecutive reactions, the solution to a yield optimization problem greatly depends on the relative rates of the desired and undesired reactions. In this respect we shall consider a complex reaction system with a principal reaction according to:

$$\nu_A A + \nu_B B \to \nu_P P \;,$$

but in which undesired species X, Y etc. may be produced as well. Apparently, the value of:

$$\nu_A |R|_P / \nu_P |R|_A \equiv \psi_P \qquad\qquad \text{VI-2}$$

determines at any place in a reactor to what extent A is being converted to P. According to the definition II-23, ψ_P may be called the *differential selectivity* of the reaction; it has been defined in such a way that $\psi_P = 1$ when no by-products are formed. This concept was introduced by DENBIGH[178] (who used the term "instantaneous yield" for ψ_P) in order to illustrate yield optimization problems along the following lines.

Since the value of ψ_P depends on the composition of the reaction mixture, analysis of this dependence will generally indicate the circumstances under which a high yield may be expected. In particular, when the composition is entirely characterized by the degree of conversion of one of the reactants, ψ_P can be plotted as a function of, say, ζ_A for a given feed composition and temperature. A relation of this kind can be obtained either from the known kinetics of the system or from experiments performed in a continuous tank reactor. Such a graph is shown in Fig. VI-3a for a reaction system in which the differential selectivity decreases with increasing conversion. The yield

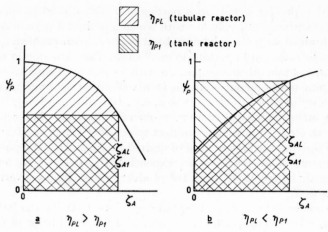

FIG. VI-3. The course of the differential selectivity ψ_P with ζ_A determines what type of continuous reactor gives the highest yield.

obtainable with this system in a tubular reactor and in a tank reactor can be easily derived from the graph, as shown below.

For a tubular reactor, we have the material balances (with constant density):

$$\Phi_v dc_A = - |R|_A S dz ,$$

and

$$\Phi_v dc_P = |R|_P S dz .$$

By taking the ratio of these equations, and with the definitions of the relative degree of conversion ζ_A and of ψ_P, we find:

$$\frac{\nu_A dc_P}{\nu_P c_{A0}} = - \psi_P \frac{dc_A}{c_{A0}} = \psi_P d\zeta_A ,$$

and hence for the yield obtained with the tubular reactor:

$$\eta_{PL} = \frac{\nu_A c_P}{\nu_P c_{A0}} = \int_0^{\zeta_{AL}} \psi_P d\zeta_A . \qquad \text{VI-3}$$

It is seen that η_{PL} is equal to the area below the ψ_P curve in Fig. VI-3a enclosed between $\zeta_A = 0$ and $\zeta_A = \zeta_{AL}$.

Similarly, it can be shown that for a single tank reactor:

$$\eta_{P1} = (\psi_P \zeta_A)_1 ; \qquad \text{VI-4}$$

the index 1 refers to the outlet conditions. The latter equation also follows from the definition of the yield in Eq. II-24. Clearly, the yield obtainable with a single tank reactor is equal to the area of the rectangle with sides ψ_{P1} and ζ_{A1}.

190

In the example of Fig. VI-3a a tubular reactor gives a higher yield than a tank reactor for the same final degree of conversion; the latter reactor operates at the outlet conditions involving a low selectivity. If, on the other hand, as shown in Fig. VI-3b, the curve rises with increasing degree of conversion, a tank reactor will give a higher yield than a tubular reactor. Thus, the sign of the slope of the $\psi_P - \zeta_A$ curve presents a standard for the selection of the basic reactor type giving the highest yield. This standard is equivalent to that given earlier by DENBIGH [179] and by TRAMBOUZE and PIRET [180], who considered the sign of the quantity $d^2 \xi_P/d\xi_A{}^2$ of a reaction system. When it is negative, the formation of desired product is favoured at a low degree of conversion (tubular reactor preferable) and when it is positive most of the desired product can be made at a high degree of conversion (tank reactor preferable). In the latter case, the capacity of the reactor is necessarily small so that a larger reaction volume is always required in comparison with a tubular reactor. Whether and to what extent some of the yield has to be sacrificed to an increase in reactor capacity, e.g. by using a cascade of tank reactors, can only be judged on economic grounds.

Optimum yield in a cascade of tank reactors

The $\psi_P - \zeta_A$ graph can likewise be used for finding the yield obtainable with a cascade of tank reactors. It can easily be shown that, for the n-th reactor in a cascade, Eq. VI-4 applies in the form:

$$\eta_{Pn} - \eta_{P(n-1)} = \psi_{Pn}(\zeta_{An} - \zeta_{A(n-1)}) \,,$$

and hence for a cascade of N reactors:

$$\eta_{PN} = \sum_{n=1}^{n=N} \psi_{Pn}(\zeta_{An} - \zeta_{A(n-1)}) \,. \qquad \text{VI-5}$$

η_{PN} can thus be represented as the sum of the areas of a number of rectangles. It will be clear that the value of η_{PN} will now depend on the selection of the values of ζ_{An}; they can be chosen in such a way that the yield has a maximum value for a given number of reactors in a cascade, i.e. the sum of the areas of a given number of rectangles under the curve is a maximum.

This way of putting the problem of yield optimization was illustrated by DENBIGH [178] with regard to the production of Cyclonite (P) from Hexamine and nitric acid at constant temperature. It was found experimentally that the differential selectivity of the reaction has a maximum as a function of the acid strength of which the degree of conversion ζ (= mass of Hexamine reacted/mass of acid fed) is a measure; the final degree of conversion was set at $\zeta = 0.111$. As can be seen from Fig. VI-4, one tank reactor would give a yield $\eta_{P1} = 0.58$. With two tank reactors in cascade, a maximum value of $\eta_{P2} = 0.71$ would be obtainable with $\zeta_1 = 0.082$; since the reactors were large enough to ensure practically complete conversion of the Hexamine supplied, optimum conditions for two tank reactors could be achieved

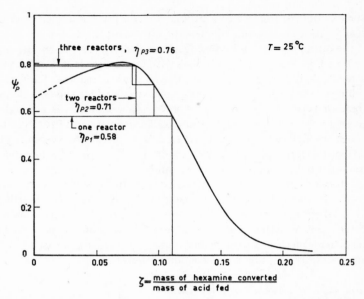

FIG. VI-4. Optimization of yield in a cascade of tank reactors for the production of Cyclonite, DENBIGH [178].

by feeding 74% (= 0.082/0.111) of the Hexamine into the first reactor and the rest into the second one.

If three reactors in cascade were used, it would be possible to increase the maximum yield still further to $\eta_{P3} = 0.76$; 71, 16, and 13% of the Hexamine feed should then be injected into the first, second and third reactor, respectively. Some of the methods which can be used for maximizing the total area of the rectangles have been indicated in DENBIGH's paper [178] and in the ensuing discussion.

In this example it should be noted that a distributed feed of one of the reactants had to be applied for proper adjustment of the composition of the reaction mixture in the different reactors. A similar case is treated in the following illustration.

ILLUSTRATION VI. 2. *Alkylation of isobutane with propylene.*

From a study by ODEN [181] on the alkylation of isobutane with propylene to light alkylate at 5°C a relation between the differential selectivity and the excess isobutane can be derived (see Fig. VI-5). It is asked to calculate the yield of light alkylate η_{P1} in a single tank reactor, and also η_{P3} for a cascade of 3 tank reactors where 50, 25 and 25% of the olefins are fed to the first, second and third reactor, respectively. The residence times are so long that the olefins are converted practically completely in each tank; the ratio of the mass feed rate of isobutane and the total feed rate of olefins is to be 5.

It can be directly concluded from Fig. VI-5 that:

$$\eta_{P1} = \frac{0.86 \times 0.20}{0.20} = 0.86,$$

192

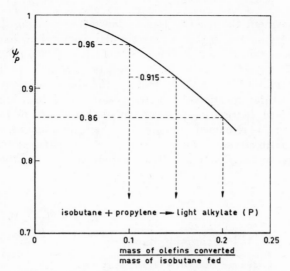

FIG. VI-5. Differential selectivity as a function of the degree of conversion in an alkylation process, ODEN [181]; Illustration VI.2.

and: $\qquad \eta_{P3} = 0.5 \times 0.96 + 0.25 \times 0.915 + 0.25 \times 0.86 = 0.924$.

To illustrate the economic implications of a change from the single tank reactor to the cascade, we will assume the difference between the manufacturing costs in the two installations to be negligibly small. If the net sales value of light alkylate ($M = 100$ kg/kmol) is 340 MU/ton and that of the by-products ($M = 100$ kg/kmol) 280 MU/ton, a sales value of 39, 410 MU/day becomes available with a daily feed of 50 tons of propylene ($M = 42$ kg/kmol) in a single tank reactor; in the second case this figure will be 39, 870 MU/day. Accordingly, an extra gross profit of 158,000 MU/year can be made with the cascade of three tank reactors, on the basis of 345 stream-days per year.

Cross-flow reactor systems

In many cases the differential selectivity of an isothermal reaction system depends on more than one composition variable; the method described above for calculating and optimizing yields is then no longer applicable. Suppose that ψ_P depends on both the reactant concentrations c_A and c_B which are not uniquely related to each other but can be varied at will, and that ψ_P is large when one of these concentrations is relatively small. It is then of interest to examine how the proper reactant concentrations can be ensured in a reactor so as to obtain a high yield of the desired product.

Problems of this kind are encountered with simultaneous reactions. In Illustration II.6 we discussed the reaction system:

$$\left.\begin{array}{l} A + B \xrightarrow{1} P \ , \ R_P = k_1 c_A c_B \\ A + A \xrightarrow{2} X \ , \ R_X = \tfrac{1}{2} k_2 c_A{}^2 \end{array}\right\} \qquad \text{VI-6}$$

A high yield can be obtained with this system if the ratio c_B/c_A is as high as

193

possible throughout the reactor. It was shown (also see Fig. II-12) that a tank reactor gives a higher yield than a tubular reactor, but that even better results can be obtained if a distributed feed of reactant A is properly applied as an additional degree of freedom. This was brought forward in a paper by VAN DE VUSSE and VOETTER [25], who for the above reactions studied the strategy of multiple injection of component A for obtaining a high yield of P.

When the feed distribution to a tubular reactor was made in such a way that the ratio c_B/c_A remained constant over the reactor length, the yield of a tank reactor with the same value of c_B/c_A could be matched, but the capacity was much higher. This can be readily understood, since the value of ψ_P

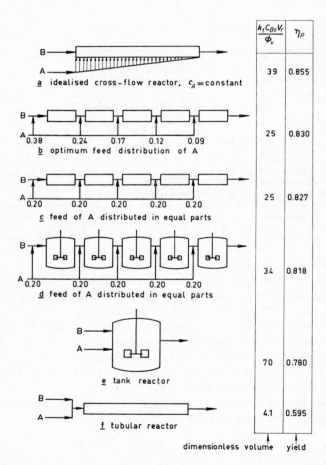

FIG. VI-6. Dimensionless reactor volume and yield for various cross-flow reactor systems; reaction VI-6, isothermal operation with $k_1 = k_2$, equal molar feed rates of A and B, final degree of conversion $\zeta_A = 0.95$ [25, 182].

then has the same value everywhere in both reactors, while the absolute reactant concentrations are, on an average, higher in the cross-flow tubular reactor.

If, on the other hand, c_A is made constant over the length of the tubular reactor, the ratio c_B/c_A averaged over the length will be greater than for a tank reactor operating with the same c_A value. Accordingly, the yield will be higher than that of a tank reactor with the same final degree of conversion of A. Its capacity will also be higher. This indicates that the cross-flow reactor has possibilities for obtaining reasonable capacities and high yields with this type of reaction. This is of importance for some catalysed gas reactions since the stirred tank is not a suitable type of reactor for these.

For practical reasons, the side injection of A should be concentrated at a limited number of feed points. MESSIKOMMER [182] investigated how reactant A should be distributed over a given number of feed points in order to obtain the maximum reactor yield η_P. He found that its value was rather insensitive to the feed distribution and that a feed of equal fractions gave almost the same result as the optimum feed distribution.

The performance of a number of reactor systems and injection policies for the above reaction have been compared in Fig. VI-6. Fig. VI-6a shows the idealized cross-flow tubular reactor in which c_A is constant over the reactor length. Fig. VI-6b and VI-6c give the results of MESSIKOMMER's calculations for 5 injection points; there is hardly any difference between the optimum and the equal feed distributions. The systems a, b, c and d all show better yields and capacities than the single tank reactor in Fig. VI-6e. The ordinary tubular reactor (f) has a much greater capacity than the tank reactor, but its yield is considerably lower. All strategies of Fig. VI-6, except d and e, can also be carried out in a semi-batch reactor.

VI.3. Optimization by means of temperature

Once it has been established in what temperature range a given reaction system can be operated, it may be asked what will be the most favourable reaction temperature or temperature sequence with respect to capacity, final conversion and yield.

For single irreversible reactions, the greatest conversion rate and hence the highest capacity are always achieved at the highest temperature which is economically and technically permissible. Particularly when great heat effects are involved, the arrangements for cooling or heating may be a much more determining factor in temperature selection than the reactor capacity.

Capacity optimization may, however, play an important part in exothermic equilibrium reactions; a compromise must then be found between the requirements of a high degree of conversion (low temperature) and those of a high average conversion rate. The various optimization problems arising with this type of reaction will be dealt with below. In conclusion, some remarks will be made on the optimization of more complex reaction systems in which especially the reactor yield is involved.

The optimization of exothermic equilibrium reactions

With this type of reaction, the conversion rate will pass through a maximum as a function of temperature when the composition of the reaction mixture is constant. At a low temperature this rate will be small, whereas a high temperature, T_e, will exist at which the mixture is in equilibrium and the conversion rate is zero. The temperature at which the conversion rate is a maximum will be somewhat lower than T_e and is determined by the condition:

$$\frac{\partial |R|_J}{\partial T} = 0 . \qquad \text{VI-7}$$

This condition can be further elaborated if the rate equation is known. Suppose we have the equilibrium reaction:

$$\nu_A A + \nu_B B \rightarrow \nu_P P + \nu_Q Q ,$$

having a production rate of P defined by:

$$R_P = k_1 a_A^{\nu_A} a_B^{\nu_B} - k_2 a_P^{\nu_P} a_Q^{\nu_Q} ,$$

with $k_1 = k_{1\infty} \exp(-E_1/RT)$, $k_2 = k_{2\infty} \exp(-E_2/RT)$ and $E_2 > E_1$. Applying Eq. VI-7, we find:

$$\frac{\partial R_P}{\partial T} = a_A^{\nu_A} a_B^{\nu_B} \frac{dk_1}{dT} - a_P^{\nu_P} a_Q^{\nu_Q} \frac{dk_2}{dT} = 0 ,$$

or

$$\frac{a_P^{\nu_P} a_Q^{\nu_Q}}{a_A^{\nu_A} a_B^{\nu_B}} = \left(\frac{k_1 E_1}{k_2 E_2} \right)_{T=T_{\text{opt}}} , \qquad \text{VI-8}$$

where T_{opt} is the temperature at which VI-7 applies. Since at equilibrium $R_P \equiv 0$, we may also write:

$$\frac{a_P^{\nu_P} a_Q^{\nu_Q}}{a_A^{\nu_A} a_B^{\nu_B}} = \left(\frac{k_1}{k_2} \right)_{T=T_e} .$$

The last two equations and the expressions for k_1 and k_2 yield:

$$\frac{T_{\text{opt}}}{T_e} = \frac{1}{1 + \dfrac{RT_e}{E_2 - E_1} \ln \dfrac{E_2}{E_1}} . \qquad \text{VI-9}$$

When the difference between the absolute temperatures T_e and T_{opt} is relatively small, Eq. VI-9 may be approximated by:

$$\frac{T_e - T_{\text{opt}}}{T_e} \approx \frac{RT_e}{-\Delta H_r} \ln \frac{E_2}{E_1} .$$

196

Application of these equations is simple in the case of a continuous *tank reactor* with a minimum volume for a given product composition and throughput; T_e and hence T_{opt} and the maximum conversion rate can be readily calculated from the composition.

The optimum temperature profile in a *tubular reactor* can be found on the assumption that the criterion VI-7 and hence also Eq. VI-9 must be valid for any cross section of the reactor. DENBIGH [179] postulated this condition in 1944 by intuitive reasoning; it can also be made acceptable in the following manner. The volume of a tubular reactor is proportional to the integral:

$$\int_0^{\zeta_{AL}} \frac{d\zeta_A}{|R|_J},$$

where R_J is a function of the initial composition, ζ_A and T for a given reaction system. For the optimum temperature policy, this integral should be a minimum, which leads to the condition:

$$\int_0^{\zeta_{AL}} \frac{\partial |R|_J}{\partial T} \frac{d\zeta_A}{|R|_J^2} = 0. \qquad \text{VI-10}$$

This relation can be observed in many ways, and it is evident that one of these is to see that $\partial |R|_J/\partial T = 0$ (compare Eq. VI-7) and the conversion rate has its maximum value as a function of temperature at any degree of conversion.

The procedure for calculating the optimum temperature profile then is as follows. First find T_e as a function of, e.g., the degree of conversion ξ_A (Curve 1 in Fig. VI-7), and then T_{opt} by means of Eq. VI-9 (Curve 2). Because of the known relation between T_{opt} and ξ_A, the conversion rate can be expressed in terms of ξ_A only; hence, the material balance (e.g., Eq. II-10) can be integrated to yield ξ_A as a function of the distance z from the reactor inlet (Curve 3 in Fig. VI-7). The optimum temperature as a function of z is obtained by combining Curves 2 and 3.

Only for very simple rate expressions is it possible to extend the above theory a little further with a general mathematical formulation. For example, in the reaction A $\rightarrow$ P with: $R_P = k_1 c_A - k_2 c_P$, $E_2 > E_1$, we may introduce the reference temperature T_R at which $k_1 = k_2 = k_R$ (also see Section IV-6, p. 130). The ratio $k_1/k_R = \varkappa$ then is a measure of the reaction temperature; the conversion rate can be written as:

$$R_P = k_R c_{A0} [\varkappa(1 - \zeta_A) - \varkappa^{E_2/E_1} \zeta_A]. \qquad \text{VI-11}$$

Application of condition VI-7 yields for the dimensionless reaction rate constant at the optimum temperature:

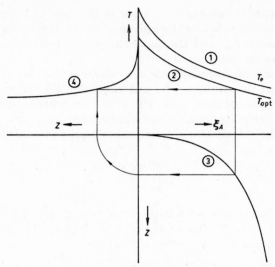

FIG. VI-7. Principle of finding the optimum temperature profile for an exothermic equilibrium reaction in a tubular reactor.

$$\varkappa_{\text{opt}} = \left[\frac{E_1(1 - \zeta_A)}{E_2 \zeta_A} \right]^{E_1/(E_2 - E_1)} . \qquad \text{VI-12}$$

By combining this result with the material balance for a *tank reactor*, it is possible, for example, to eliminate ζ_A and to find an expression for the minimum dimensionless residence time $(k_R \bar{\tau})_{\text{min}}$:

$$(k_R \bar{\tau})_{\text{min}} = \left[\left(\frac{E_2}{E_1} - 1 \right) \varkappa_{\text{opt}}^{E_2/E_1} \right]^{-1} . \qquad \text{VI-13}$$

Similar calculations for a *tubular reactor* are more involved; they were carried out by HORN for first and second order equilibrium reactions [183, 184, 185, 186]. Two of these papers [183, 186] contain tables which for various values of E_2/E_1 give the corresponding values of $\varkappa_{\text{opt}}$, ζ_A and the dimensionless reactor length. Eq. VI-12 indicates that the optimum conversion rate and temperature should be infinitely high at the inlet of the reactor ($\zeta_A = 0$); for practical reasons, however, there always is an upper temperature limit.

The theory of the optimum temperature profile was applied by various authors. CALDERBANK [187] calculated that, with an optimum temperature profile, SO_2 could be oxidized to a certain conversion level in a catalyst bed at a rate corresponding to a production of 54 tons H_2SO_4/ton catalyst per day; with the same conversion level, this figure was 11.4 for an externally cooled catalyst bed and 3.4 for a two-stage adiabatic tubular reactor with intermediate cooling. In a paper on the same subject, MARS and VAN KRE-

VELEN [188] showed that the capacity of industrial reactors for the catalytic oxidation of SO_2 has been rising steadily. Applications to the synthesis of NH_3 were published by VAN HEERDEN [89] and by ANNABLE [189]. The latter author compared the optimum temperature profile with the actual profile in an existing plant; they were sensibly different and the conversions were 22% and 19.2%, respectively. Consequently, it would be possible to increase the conversion considerably and at the same time to profit from the reduction of the recirculation of unconverted material [190].

Although the above procedures make it possible to obtain a tubular reactor having the minimum volume for a given production rate and final conversion, it is questionable whether such a design will be attractive from the practical and economic points of view. It was shown by WESTERTERP [191] that it is technically not impossible to approximate the optimum temperature profile by suitable methods of heat exchange; the investment costs may, however, be considerable and, moreover, the heat economy may be poor. The feed has to be heated to a high temperature with high quality heat which is withdrawn along the reactor length by a much colder cooling medium. In many cases, therefore, alternative temperature policies have to be considered as well, involving, for instance, the isothermal and the adiabatic tubular reactor; these can also be optimized, as will be shown below. For a given final degree of conversion, ζ_{AL}, the criterion for the highest capacity of an *isothermal tubular reactor* is given by Eq. VI-10, which is now used with the additional condition of isothermal operation. Eq. VI-10 can be solved analytically with simple rate expressions. For example, with a first order equilibrium reaction with R_P defined by Eq. VI-11 the result is:

$$-\ln\left[1 - (1 + \varkappa')\zeta_{AL}\right] = \frac{\left(\dfrac{E_2}{E_1} - 1\right)\varkappa'(1 + \varkappa')\zeta_{AL}}{\left(1 + \dfrac{E_2}{E_1}\varkappa'\right)\left[1 - (1 + \varkappa')\zeta_{AL}\right]},$$

where:

$$\varkappa' = \varkappa_{\text{opt}}^{E_2/E_1 - 1},$$

and $\varkappa_{\text{opt}}$ is the value of k_1/k_R at which the reactor volume is a minimum. Fig. VI-8 shows $\varkappa_{\text{opt}}$ according to this result as a function of E_2/E_1 for $\zeta_{AL} = 0.9$. It may be concluded from this figure that the optimum temperature for isothermal operation is intermediate between the equilibrium temperature at $\zeta_A = 0.9$ and the temperature at which the conversion rate at the reactor outlet would be a maximum. This means that there is only one cross section at which Eq. VI-7 is valid, and consequently the reactor volume will be larger than that of a tubular reactor with the optimum temperature profile under otherwise identical circumstances. HORN [183, 192] calculated the

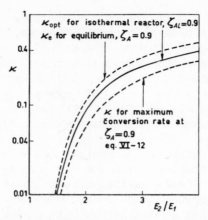

FIG. VI-8. Dimensionless forward reaction rate constant $\varkappa$ for first-order equilibrium reaction; its optimum value for an isothermal tubular reactor lies between $\varkappa_e$ (at which $R_P = 0$) and $\varkappa$ for maximum conversion rate (Eq. VI-10).

ratio of these two volumes for first order and second order exothermic equilibrium reactions. Fig. VI-9 contains some of his results showing that this ratio is not excessively large at not too high degrees of conversion. Consequently, it will not be very serious if the optimum temperature profile is not adhered to, unless the reactor volume and/or the catalyst contained in it are extremely expensive.

It was already mentioned that the establishment of the optimum temperature profile may involve technical difficulties and expensive provisions; the

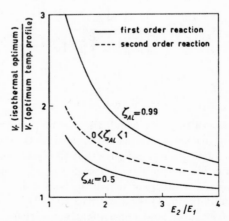

FIG. VI-9. Volume ratio of tubular reactors with optimum uniform temperature and with optimum temperature profile; the curve for the second-order equilibrium reactions is for a stoichiometric feed and independent of the degree of conversion (HORN [192]).

200

same can be true for isothermal operation, although to a lesser extent. Particularly with gas reactions in a catalytic reactor, it is much simpler, from a technical point of view, to let the reaction proceed *adiabatically*. Now, in a single adiabatic reactor the temperature and the conversion are related by the expression:

$$T = T_0 + \Delta T_{ad}\zeta_A .\qquad\qquad \text{VI-14}$$

If a certain final conversion ζ_{AL} is desired, the temperature T_L at the end of the reactor should be lower than the equilibrium temperature T_e of the product mixture. Hence, the feed temperature T_0 should be lower than T_e by an amount of the order of $\Delta T_{ad}\zeta_{AL}$. For many catalytic gas reactions this would lead to such low entrance temperatures that an excessively large reactor volume would be necessary.

In practice, this difficulty is solved by the use of a *multi-stage tubular reactor* with intermediate cooling of the reaction mixture. Such a system is shown in Fig. VI-10 together with the temperature as a function of the amount of catalyst passed by the reaction mixture. It may now be asked how, with a given final degree of conversion, the reactor volume or catalyst mass should be distributed and what would be the best entrance temperature of each section for the capacity of the system to have a maximum value.

HORN and KÜCHLER [54] provided the solution to a slightly different for-

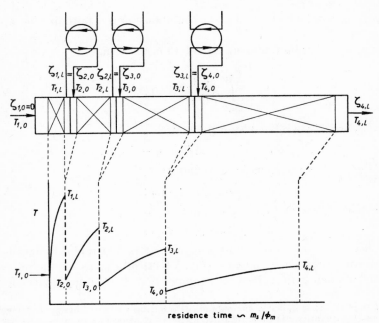

FIG. VI-10. Multi-stage adiabatic tubular reactor with cooling between sections.

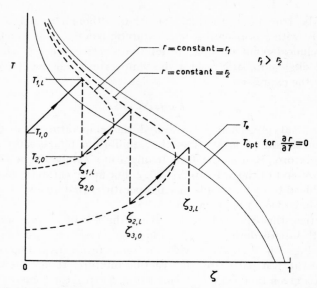

FIG. VI-11. Illustration of the conditions VI-15 and VI-16 for the optimum design of a multistage adiabatic tubular reactor for exothermic equilibrium reactions.

mulation of the same problem, i.e. that of determining the highest possible final conversion for a given number of sections and for a given entrance temperature of the first section. The conditions for this optimization appear to be:

i. For each section (index n) Eq. VI-10 in the form:

$$\int_{\zeta_{n,0}}^{\zeta_{n,L}} \frac{\partial r}{\partial T} \frac{\mathrm{d}\zeta_n}{r^2} = 0 \,,^\star \qquad\qquad \text{VI-15}$$

where ζ_n and T are related by Eq. VI-14:

$$T_n - T_{n,0} = \Delta T_{ad}(\zeta_n - \zeta_{n,0}) \;;$$

ii. Between two sections $(n-1)$ and n:

$$r_{(n-1),L} = r_{n,0} \;; \qquad\qquad \text{VI-16}$$

this condition relates $T_{n,0}$ to $T_{(n-1),L}$ since:

$$\zeta_{(n-1),L} = \zeta_{n,0} \,.$$

The significance of these conditions can best be illustrated by means of a temperature-conversion diagram (Fig. VI-11) of a given exothermic equilibrium reaction with a given feed composition. It contains a curve for T_e,

---

★ For the sake of simplicity, the subindices referring to the components have been omitted; the quantity r is to be regarded as the conversion rate in mass units per unit mass of catalyst (r_s).

202

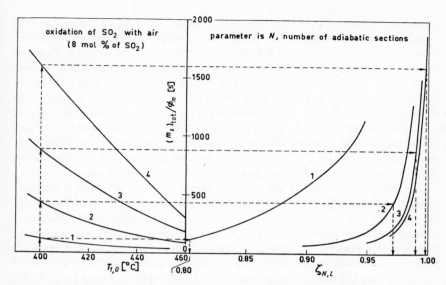

FIG. vi-12. Optimum inlet temperature and minimum amount of catalyst for the oxidation of SO_2 in a multi-stage adiabatic reactor; calculated with EKLUND's conversion rate data [196].

the temperature at which the mixture would be in chemical equilibrium, and a curve for T_{opt} at which the conversion rate is at a maximum, both for the corresponding degree of conversion. Two lines of constant conversion rate have also been drawn. The feed enters the first stage at a temperature $T_{1,0}$ ($\zeta_{1,0} \equiv 0$) and the reaction mixture is heated up proportionally to ζ in accordance with Eq. VI-14. When the $T_1 - \zeta_1$ line intersects with the curve for T_{opt}, the sign of $\partial r/\partial T$ changes from positive to negative. Condition VI-15 is fulfilled at the point with coordinates ($\zeta_{1,L}, T_{1,L}$); this point lies on the curve $r = r_1$, and Eq. VI-16 requires the reaction mixture now to be cooled to such a temperature $T_{2,0}$ that the mixture entering the second section has the same conversion rate r_1*. This procedure is then repeated until the desired number of stages has been passed. The inlet temperature of the first stage, $T_{1,0}$, is an independent parameter which has to be varied in order to find the minimum amount of catalyst needed for a certain final degree of conversion,

---

* It may occur that $T_{1,L}$ exceeds the maximum of the permissible temperature $T*$ so that only a corresponding degree of conversion $\zeta*(<\zeta_{1,L})$ can be reached in the first section. The first section then no longer has the minimum volume, since Eq. VI-15 will not apply any more. HORN [193] showed that in that case Eq. VI-16 should be replaced by:

$$\Delta T_{ad} \int_0^{\zeta*} \frac{\partial r}{\partial T} \frac{d\zeta_1}{r^2} + \frac{1}{r(\zeta*)} = \frac{1}{r_{2,0}}$$

for finding the proper entrance temperature to the second section.

203

or the maximum degree of conversion obtainable with a given amount of catalyst in a given number of sections. A typical result of such calculations is shown in Fig. VI-12. Starting from a given inlet temperature, $T_{1,0}$, the amount of catalyst is found with which a maximum degree of conversion, $\zeta_{N,L}$, is obtained. The greater the number of adiabatic sections, the more catalyst is needed for optimum operation and the corresponding increase in final conversion. The figure also shows that with a certain desired value of $\zeta_{N,L}$ the amount of catalyst can be drastically reduced by using more sections, provided the proper inlet temperature be observed. This is also clear from Fig. VI-11 since the T-ζ zig-zag history of the reaction mixture will be closer to the curve for T_{opt} as the number of stages is increased.

The above problem was also treated by ARIS [195] in a more abstract manner, taking into account the economic implications. The technical optimization problem can be further complicated by considering the possibility of intermediate cooling by the addition of cold feed to the reaction mixture between the sections. In this case, not only the temperature will drop between two sections but the degree of conversion as well. Fig. VI-13 (path 2) shows this for the catalytic oxidation of SO_2, the optimization of which was treated by BORESKOV and SLINKO [196]. SCHOENEMANN [197] worked out a similar problem for NH_3 synthesis.

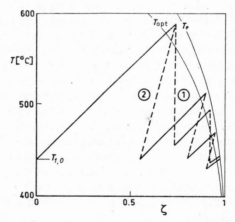

FIG. VI-13. Temperature-conversion curve for the catalytic oxidation of SO_2 in a multi-bed adiabatic reactor; 1 — three sections with intermediate indirect cooling, 2 — four sections with intermediate supply of cold feed; BORESKOV and SLINKO [196].

BARTHOLOMÉ and KRABETZ [198] reported on the calculation of a multi-bed reactor for the equilibrium reaction $H_2O + CO \rightarrow CO_2 + H_2$. They discuss, for a multi-stage adiabatic reactor, the relation between the conversion and the inlet temperature, the influence of catalyst aging on conversion, and the possibility of increasing the conversion by distributing the catalyst over several beds with intermediate indirect cooling of the reaction mixture. It appears from their work, that a deviation from the optimum distribution of catalyst in a two-bed reactor has only a small effect on the final degree of conversion, provided the inlet temperature has been properly adjusted.

It is seen that an optimum design can be made when the necessary information is available and reliable. Strictly speaking, such an optimum is then only valid for a given set of conditions regarding the feed composition and the reactor load. Since these conditions may vary in an operating installation, and particularly since the plant capacity in many cases must be increased over the rated capacity, it is important to examine the possiblity of optimization under changed conditions. Two problems of this nature were reported on by Küchler [199]. His first example relates to an equilibrium reaction carried out in an isothermal tubular reactor. At a certain load the optimum temperature is 338°C and the degree of conversion 68%. If the reactor load is increased by a factor 2.5, the degree of conversion would be 45% at the same temperature. Under the new conditions, however, the optimum reactor temperature is 358°C and the corresponding maximum conversion 55%.

In the second example mentioned by Küchler, the same reaction is carried out in an adiabatic multi-stage reactor. Table VI-1 shows the optimum conditions for two reactor loads differing by a factor of 2.7. It is seen that the optimum distribution of catalyst is only slightly different in the two cases; this is favourable since the distribution cannot be changed during plant operation. The various inlet temperatures, however, have to be drastically changed when the load is increased.

TABLE VI-1

Optimum conditions for equilibrium reaction in multi-bed adiabatic reactor at different loads, Küchler [199].

	100% load		270% load	
	% of total cat. mass	Inlet temp. °C	% of total cat. mass	Inlet temp. °C
First bed	7.6	280	9.2	320
Second bed	14.9	279	17.5	311
Third bed	27.4	279	28.7	305
Fourth bed	50.1	277	44.6	300
Final degree of conversion	90.0%		75.2%	

Temperature optimization with complex reaction systems

The occurrence of one or more reactions by which reactants or desired products are turned into wasteful products greatly complicates the problems of technical optimization. The main reason for this is that more than one concentration variable is needed for specifying the composition of the mixture and that several coupled material balance equations have to be handled. One of the mathematical techniques by which this can be done is the Lagrange multiplier technique; its elements will be outlined in Section VI.4 with reference, among other things, to temperature optimization of complex reactions. For the time being, we shall deal only with the more evident aspects of this problem.

In Section VI.2 we used the concept of differential selectivity ψ_P indicating the ratio of the production rate of useful material and the conversion rate of reactant. This quantity depends not only on composition but also on temperature, and it will be clear that the sign of the quantity $\partial\psi_P/\partial T$ is closely related to the selection of the optimum temperature.

i. In case $\partial\psi_P/\partial T > 0$, the desired reaction is favoured by a rise in temperature. Hence, the operating temperature should be selected as high as is compatible with other technical limitations; the highest possible yield is then obtained with parallel reactions and also with a system involving unwanted consecutive reactions provided the reaction mixture is discharged at the proper degree of conversion. At the same time, the high temperature ensures the highest possible capacity. As a consequence, this case does not generally present difficulties with respect to the optimum temperature.

ii. When $\partial\psi_P/\partial T < 0$, on the other hand, the yield is improved by lowering the temperature. This causes the capacity to be reduced, so that a compromise must frequently be made, the proper solution of which is again governed by the economy of the plant. For systems with two *parallel* reactions of equal order, HORN [183, 186] derived the condition for obtaining the maximum reactor capacity for a given yield. It appears that the temperature must rise with increasing conversion. This can be qualitatively understood. At a low degree of conversion the reactants still have a high concentration, and since it is important that most of them be converted to the desired product, a relatively low temperature is required. As the reactant concentration decreases, the differential selectivity is sacrificed in favour of a higher capacity and the temperature can be raised so as to enhance the conversion rate.

BILOUS and AMUNDSON [200], HORN [183] and KATZ [201] investigated optimum temperature profiles for sets of two *consecutive* reactions where the intermediate product is the one desired. In this case a gain in capacity can in principle be obtained by letting the temperature decrease with increasing conversion. At a low degree of conversion, it is mainly the first of the two reactions that occurs, and a relatively high temperature is still permissible; when some of the intermediate product has formed, however, its decomposition must be slowed down by lowering the temperature. According to HORN, the increase in capacity obtainable by this method is at most 10 to 20% of the capacity of an isothermal tubular reactor giving the same yield. This means that the problem of maximum capacity hardly comes up in the case of consecutive reactions. The temperature level influences mainly the highest obtainable yield, and not much can be done to reduce the required reactor volume. Fig. VI-14 shows, for a system of two consecutive first order reactions in a tubular reactor with the optimum temperature profile, the dimensionless residence time and the dimensionless temperature at the outlet as a function of maximum yield. If the latter is to be increased from 0.9 to 0.95, T_L/T_R must be reduced from 0.75 to 0.71, and the reactor volume has to be increased accordingly by a factor of 3.6.

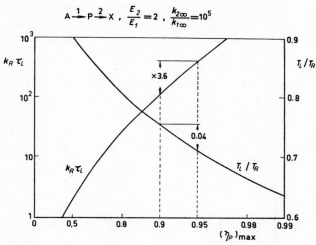

FIG. VI-14. The dimensionless residence time and the outlet temperature of a tubular reactor with an optimum temperature profile for first order consecutive reactions [183].

iii. The value of ψ_P may pass through an extreme as a function of temperature. It is, of course, only of interest for temperature optimization if this extreme, defined by $\partial\psi_P/\partial T = 0$, is a maximum. This situation can arise with more wasteful reactions than one if one of these is relatively stimulated at low temperature and another at high temperature. Some remarks on the technique of yield optimization in such systems will be made in Section VI.4 (p. 220). We shall treat below an example of this kind which has become classical.

ILLUSTRATION VI. 3. *Denbigh's problem*

DENBIGH [202] considered a reaction system of the type:

$$A + B \xrightarrow{1} P \xrightarrow{3} Q,$$
$$\downarrow^2 \qquad \downarrow^4$$
$$X \qquad \ Y$$

207

where P is an intermediate product and Q the desired product. This could e.g. be a nitration of a hydrocarbon with P and Q as mono- and dinitro compounds, respectively, and X and Y as resinous by-products. In the case to be discussed, the production rate of X with respect to that of P from the reactants increases with rising temperature; at the same time, the production of Y is favoured at a low temperature. Consequently, the temperature should be low at a low degree of conversion, and high at a high degree of conversion.

Assuming all reactions to be of the first order and on the basis of a specific selection of the numerical values of the rate constants and their temperature dependence, DEN-BIGH calculated the optimum temperatures for a cascade of two tank reactors. As an additional requirement it was postulated that the residence time in the first reactor entailed maximum concentration of P, and that the second reactor was so large as to occasion complete conversion of the reactants. The results of his calculations (Fig. VI-15) indicate that, with two tank reactors operating at the same temperature, a maximum yield $\eta_Q = 0.25$ is obtained at 53°C. When the temperature of the second reactor, T_2, is kept constant and T_1 is varied, a yield maximum is found at which T_1 is considerably lower than T_2. It is seen from Fig. VI-15 that the optimum value of T_1 is about 7°C and that T_2 should be as high as possible; in this example it is limited to 141°C. The corresponding yield has now increased to $\eta_Q = 0.53$.

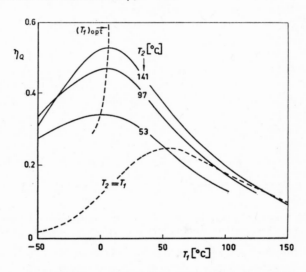

FIG. VI-15. DENBIGH's problem [202]; Illustration VI.3.

Various other workers have taken up the same problem for further yield optimization studies. HORN and TROLTENIER [185] found that the obtainable maximum yield $\eta_Q = 0.69$ in a tubular reactor with an optimized temperature profile between the limits of 7 and 141°C. Using the method of dynamic programming (see Section VI.4), ARIS [203] verified DENBIGH's calculations. He also calculated the optimum conditions for one, two and three tank reactors in cascade with an upper temperature limit of only 121°C and a restricted volume of the last reactor; the results are shown in the table on p. 209.

STOREY [204] investigated the same problem using a different mathematical method (the numerical hill-climbing technique, ROSENBROCK [205]). His optimum temperatures for a cascade of four tank reactors without volume and temperature restrictions are −15, 5, 130 and 300°C, respectively, with a final yield of $\eta_Q = 0.69$. STOREY obtained reactor-volume ratios which are rather different from those found by ARIS. The distribution of reaction volumes over different stages probably is much less critical than the temperature or the concentrations.

Number of tank reactors in cascade N	1	2	3
Optimum temperatures (°C)			
T_1	45	3	−13
T_2	—	121	15
T_3	—	—	121
Optimum volume ratios			
V_{r2}/V_{r1}	—	29	0.3
V_{r3}/V_{r1}	—	—	29
Yield of cascade η_{QN}	0.221	0.451	0.495

VI.4. Some mathematical methods of optimization

The general theory of finding an extreme value for a given function of a number of variables which are mutually dependent through a number of additional relations is beyond the scope of this book. When the number of variables is very small, say 1 or 2, the problems are reduced to finding an extreme of a curve or of a two-dimensional surface; these are solved by simple mathematical or graphic methods which can still be visualized. As the number of variables increases, thus also increasing the number of relations between them, it becomes necessary to use abstract methods, and the number of equations to be solved rises rapidly. Therefore, the actual solution of complex optimization problems is only possible with the aid of automatic computers. Owing to the simultaneous development of these machines and of applied mathematics, powerful and practical methods have become available for solving complex optimization problems. In the following we shall discuss the method of dynamic programming, the application of the Lagrange multiplier technique and the method of "steepest ascent". Although applications to reactor optimization will be considered, these methods clearly are quite general and by no means restricted to chemical reactors.

Dynamic programming

This method is mainly concerned with the optimum selection of a sequence of events. It is based on the "principle of optimality" formulated by BELL-MAN [206]: "An optimal policy has the property that whatever the initial decisions are, the remaining decisions must constitute an optimal policy with regard to the state resulting from the first decision". On the basis of this principle, an optimization problem involving the simultaneous selection of the values of a large number of parameters can be reduced to a sequence of decisions involving a smaller number of parameters.

If this principle is applied to the optimization of a cascade of N tank reactors it may be said that, if the first n reactors have been optimized, the total system will be optimal when the remaining cascade of $(N - n)$ reactors has been optimized with respect to the feed leaving the nth reactor. Reversing this argument, we may say that the remaining cascade can be optimized provided we know the feed conditions of the reactor No. $(n + 1)$. Now, these conditions are not yet known as long as the optimization problem has not been solved; accordingly, they have to be treated as variables. The procedure now is to start with the last reactor No. N and to find its optimum conditions as a function of the parameters of the feed entering into it. Next, for each combination of these parameters the reactor No. $(N - 1)$ can be optimized as a function of the feed conditions coming from No. $(N - 2)$; hence, the optimum cascade of the last two tank reactors can be found as a function of its feed parameters whereupon the procedure must be repeated with the next upstream reactor. If the flow of reaction mixture is characterized by more variables than one, the number of calculations to be made may become very great. According to ARIS, who in a recent book [207] discussed the applications to chemical reactors, the method is highly suitable for machine computation. As indicated by STOREY [204], this procedure is limited to a true sequence (or, in the case of chemical reactors, to a cascade or an ideal tubular reactor); it cannot be used for reactor problems in which recirculation or feedback occurs.

Interesting results have in the meantime been obtained by means of dynamic programming. GRÜTTER and MESSIKOMMER [208] showed that, with all *first order* reactions (including equilibrium, parallel and consecutive reactions) carried out *isothermally* in a cascade of tank reactors, maximum capacity is obtained when all reactors are of equal size. This is not so with a reaction order different from unity, but with isothermal second order reactions the capacity difference between optimum volume distribution and equal distribution appears to be small [209]. Therefore, practical as well as economic considerations indicate that all reactors in an isothermal cascade can best have the same volume. ARIS applied the theory of dynamic programming to tubular reactors [207, 210] and also to multistage adiabatic reactors [195, 207].

The two examples given below are intended to illustrate the method outlined above. They relate to very simple problems which can also be solved by more elementary methods.

ILLUSTRATION VI. 4a *The minimum reaction volume of an isothermal cascade*

It is required to find the minimum total volume and the corresponding individual volumes of a cascade of three tank reactors for a single first-order isothermal reaction [190]. The final degree of conversion is $\zeta_{A3} = 1 - c_{A3}/c_{A0} = 0.9$.

The material balances for the reactors numbered 1, 2 and 3 in the direction of flow give:

$$\frac{c_{A1}}{c_{A0}} = \frac{1}{1 + k\tau_1}, \quad \frac{c_{A2}}{c_{A1}} = \frac{1}{1 + k\tau_2} \quad \text{and} \quad \frac{c_{A3}}{c_{A2}} = \frac{1}{1 + k\tau_3}.$$

For the application of dynamic programming, we start with the third reactor, and we express $k\bar{\tau}_3$ with the last equation in terms of the variable c_{A2}/c_{A0}:

$$k\bar{\tau}_3 = \frac{c_{A2}}{c_{A3}} - 1 = \frac{c_{A2}}{c_{A0}} \times \frac{1}{0.1} - 1 .$$

This relationship is represented by the straight line in the lower half of Fig. VI-16a.

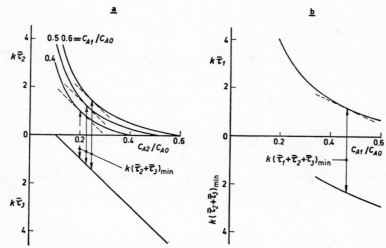

FIG. VI-16. Determination of the minimum total volume of an isothermal cascade;
Illustration VI.4a.

Now the minimum value of $k(\bar{\tau}_2 + \bar{\tau}_3)$ has to be found as a function of c_{A1}/c_{A0}. To this end we write the material balance of Reactor 2 in the form:

$$k\bar{\tau}_2 = \frac{c_{A1}}{c_{A2}} - 1 = \frac{c_{A1}}{c_{A0}} \times \frac{c_{A0}}{c_{A2}} - 1 .$$

This expression gives the curves shown in the top half of Fig. VI-16a with c_{A1}/c_{A0} as a parameter. The miminum value of $k(\bar{\tau}_2 + \bar{\tau}_3)$ can then be found in the manner indicated, and the result is plotted as a function of c_{A1}/c_{A0} in the lower half of Fig. VI-16b. Finally, $k\bar{\tau}_1$ is likewise plotted as a function of c_{A1}/c_{A0}, and the minimum distance between the two curves in Fig. VI-16b gives the minimum value of $k(\bar{\tau}_1 + \bar{\tau}_2 + \bar{\tau}_3)$ with the corresponding value of c_{A1}/c_{A0}.

It appears from this construction that:

$$k(\bar{\tau}_1 + \bar{\tau}_2 + \bar{\tau}_3)_{min} = 3.45$$
$$k(\bar{\tau}_2 + \bar{\tau}_3)_{min} = 2.30$$
$$k(\bar{\tau}_3)_{min} = 1.15$$

Hence:

$$\bar{\tau}_1 = \bar{\tau}_2 = \bar{\tau}_3 \quad \text{and} \quad \frac{c_{A1}}{c_{A0}} = \frac{c_{A2}}{c_{A1}} = \frac{c_{A3}}{c_{A2}} = 0.465 .$$

This result could have been obtained more quickly by ordinary calculus since c_{A1}/c_{A0} and c_{A2}/c_{A0} can easily be eliminated from the material balances in the case of a first order reaction. The above method may be useful with other rate expressions or with empirical conversion rates.

211

ILLUSTRATION VI. 4b. *The minimum reaction volume of a nonisothermal cascade*

An equilibrium reaction with first order kinetics is carried out in a cascade of 2 tank reactors. The reaction is A → P, and the following relations apply:

$$c_A + c_P = c_{A0}, \quad R_P = k_1 c_A - k_2 c_P,$$

$$k_1 = k_{1\infty} e^{-E_1/RT}, \quad k_2 = k_{2\infty} e^{-E_2/RT}, \quad \frac{E_2}{E_1} = 2.$$

Find the minimum total reaction volume and the corresponding reactor temperatures when $c_{A2}/c_{A0} = 0.1$.

We introduce as a measure of temperature $\varkappa = k_1/k_R$, where k_R is the value of $k_1 = k_2$ at the reference temperature T_R (also see Section IV.6 and Eq. VI-11). The material balances of the two reactors can now be written in the form:

$$k_R \bar{\tau}_1 = \frac{1 - c_{A1}/c_{A0}}{(\varkappa + \varkappa^2) c_{A1}/c_{A0} - \varkappa^2}, \tag{a}$$

and:

$$k_R \bar{\tau}_2 = \frac{c_{A1}/c_{A0} - c_{A2}/c_{A0}}{(\varkappa + \varkappa^2) c_{A2}/c_{A0} - \varkappa^2}. \tag{b}$$

Since c_{A2}/c_{A0} has been fixed at the value 0.1, $k_R \bar{\tau}_2$ is, in principle, still a function of the two variables c_{A1}/c_{A0} and $\varkappa$. Now, one of the variables can be eliminated in this case because at each value of c_A/c_{A0} there is an optimum temperature (corresponding with $\varkappa_{opt}$) at which the conversion rate is at a maximum. For $\varkappa_{opt}$ we have here from Eq. VI-12:

$$\varkappa_{opt} = \frac{c_A/c_{A0}}{2(1 - c_A/c_{A0})}. \tag{c}$$

With this equation we find for the second tank, where $c_{A2}/c_{A0} = 0.1$:

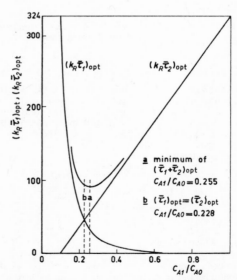

FIG. VI-17. Finding the minimum volume of a cascade of two tank reactors for an equilibrium reaction; Illustration VI.4b.

$$\varkappa_{\text{opt}} = \frac{0.1}{2 \times 0.9} = \frac{1}{18} ,$$

and from Eq. (b):

$$(k_R \bar{\tau}_2)_{\text{opt}} = 360 \frac{c_{A1}}{c_{A0}} - 36 .$$

This relation is given by the straight line in Fig. VI-17.
The combination of Eqs. (a) and (c) gives for the first tank reactor:

$$(k_R \bar{\tau}_1)_{\text{opt}} = \frac{4(1 - c_{A1}/c_{A0})^2}{(c_{A1}/c_{A0})^2} ,$$

which is the curve in Fig. VI-17. In this graph, the sum of $(k_R \bar{\tau}_1)_{\text{opt}}$ and $(k_R \bar{\tau}_2)_{\text{opt}}$ has a minimum at $c_{A1}/c_{A0} = 0.255$, from which the following conditions follow:

$$k_R \bar{\tau}_1 = 34.4 , \quad k_R \bar{\tau}_2 = 55.9 , \quad k_R(\bar{\tau}_1 + \bar{\tau}_2)_{\text{min}} = 90.2 ,$$

$$\varkappa_1 = 0.171 , \quad \varkappa_2 = 0.0556 .$$

It is seen that the first reactor has a smaller volume than the second. It can now be asked whether the capacity will be much decreased if two tanks of equal volume are selected. It can be read from the graph (case b) that then $c_{A1}/c_{A0} = 0.228$, with:

$$k_R \bar{\tau}_1 = 46.0 , \quad k_R \bar{\tau}_2 = 46.0 , \quad k_R(\bar{\tau}_1 + \bar{\tau}_2) = 92.0 ,$$

$$\varkappa_1 = 0.148 , \quad \varkappa_2 = 0.0556 .$$

Only a very small increase in the total volume is found; the first tank is larger than in the optimal case and the degree of conversion is higher at a lower temperature. Here, too, it appears that the distribution of reactor volumes is not a very effective variable for optimization of the capacity. In this example, $k_R(\bar{\tau}_1 + \bar{\tau}_2) \leqslant 100$ (i.e., at the most 10% more than the minimum value) when $\bar{\tau}_1/\bar{\tau}_2$ varies from 1.7 to 0.2; when $\bar{\tau}_1/\bar{\tau}_2 = 0$ or ∞, we have only one tank reactor with $(k_R \bar{\tau})_{\text{opt}} = 324$.

In case this calculation has to be made for more than two tank reactors in a cascade, the beginning will be essentially the same, but the above conditions for the system of two tanks will have to be obtained as a function of feed composition. The same procedure can then be carried out for the third tank from the outlet, and so on.

The Lagrange multiplier technique

This is a general mathematical method for finding the extreme value of a given function of a certain number of variables between which additional relations exist. To illustrate the principle of the method, let us assume that the extremes have to be found of a function $M(x, y)$, while x and y are related by the condition $f(x, y) = 0$. If y cannot be solved explicitly from the latter equation, it is possible to form a linear combination of $M(x, y)$ and $f(x, y)$:

$$M(x,y) - \lambda f(x,y) ,$$

in which the factor λ (the Lagrange parameter) has yet to be determined in such a way that the quantity $(M - \lambda f)$ is extreme for a point (x, y) which obeys $f(x, y) = 0$. In that case, $M(x, y)$, too, will be extreme. Consequently, the conditions for an extreme in $M(x, y)$ can be obtained from:

and

$$\left.\begin{array}{l} \dfrac{\partial}{\partial x} [M(x,y) - \lambda f(x,y)] = 0 \\[2mm] \dfrac{\partial}{\partial y} [M(x,y) - \lambda f(x,y)] = 0 . \end{array}\right\} \qquad \text{VI-17}$$

These equations, together with $f(x, y) = 0$, furnish the values of λ, x and y for which $M(x, y)$ is extreme.

HORN (see, e.g., [183, 184, 211]) used this method extensively for the optimization of chemical reactors. In view of the great importance of the results obtained by him, we shall treat the theory in greater detail below, first for a cascade of tank reactors (i) and then for a tubular reactor (ii).

i. Cascade of N tank reactors

We shall consider a reaction in which the composition of the reaction mixture is determined by the concentrations of two species A and P, c_A and c_P. As usual, the conditions in tank reactor No. n and at its outlet will be indicated by the index n; they are determined by the composition, c_{An} and c_{Pn}, by the average residence time, $\bar{\tau}_n$, and by the temperature T_n. It will be assumed that the inlet composition of the cascade, c_{A0} and c_{P0}, is fixed and not a variable of the problem; this assumption is not essential but merely a simplification.

The quantity to be optimized will generally be a function of the composition of the reaction mixture leaving the last tank reactor (conversion, yield) and of the total average residence time $\bar{\tau}$ in the cascade (capacity):

$$M = M(c_{AN}, c_{PN}, \bar{\tau}) . \qquad \text{VI-18}$$

This function is meant to be representative of the merits of the plant performance; it is sometimes called the "objective function" or, in economic problems, the "cost function".

Now, in a system with given rate equations and with a given feed composition, c_{AN}, c_{PN} and $\bar{\tau}$ are determined entirely by the values of $\bar{\tau}_n$ and T_n in each of the given total of N reactors. Accordingly, M can, in principle, be written as a function of these "primary variables":

$$M = M^*(\bar{\tau}_1 \dots \bar{\tau}_N, T_1 \dots T_N) . \qquad \text{VI-19}$$

However, the function M^* cannot be explicitly expressed in terms of these variables. The relation between c_{AN}, c_{PN} and $\bar{\tau}$ and the primary variables $\bar{\tau}_n$ and T_n (and c_{A0} and c_{P0}) is governed by the following set of $(2N + 1)$ equations:

$$0 = c_{A(n-1)} - c_{An} + \bar{\tau}_n R_{An} , \quad n = 1 \dots N , \qquad \text{VI-20}$$
$$0 = c_{P(n-1)} - c_{Pn} + \bar{\tau}_n R_{Pn} , \quad n = 1 \dots N \qquad \text{VI-21}$$

and:

$$0 = \sum_{n=1}^{n=N} \bar{\tau}_n - \bar{\tau} . \qquad \text{VI-22}$$

Applying the multiplier method developed by LAGRANGE, a linear combination, F, can be made of $M(c_{AN}, c_{PN}, \bar{\tau})$ and Eqs. VI-20, 21 and 22:

$$F = M(c_{AN}, c_{PN}, \bar{\tau}) - \sum_{n=1}^{n=N} \lambda_{An}(c_{A(n-1)} - c_{An} + \bar{\tau}_n R_{An}) -$$
$$- \sum_{n=1}^{n=N} \lambda_{Pn}(c_{P(n-1)} - c_{Pn} + \bar{\tau}_n R_{Pn}) - \lambda_\tau \left(\sum_{n=1}^{n=N} \bar{\tau}_n - \bar{\tau} \right) , \qquad \text{VI-23}$$

214

for which the following relations are valid:

$$\frac{\partial M^*(\bar{\tau}_n, T_n)}{\partial(\bar{\tau}_1 \dots \bar{\tau}_N, T_1 \dots T_N)} = \frac{\partial F}{\partial(\bar{\tau}_1 \dots \bar{\tau}_N, T_1 \dots T_N)}, \qquad \text{VI-24}$$

and:

$$0 = \frac{\partial F}{\partial(c_{A1} \dots c_{AN}, c_{P1} \dots c_{PN}, \bar{\tau})}. \qquad \text{VI-25}$$

The partial derivative of the objective function with respect to one of the *primary* variables can be calculated with Eq. VI-24. The $(2N + 1)$ Lagrange parameters λ_{An}, λ_{Pn} and λ_τ needed for this calculation are determined by Eq. VI-25.

Now, if M^* has an extreme value, all partial derivatives of Eq. VI-24 must vanish. Accordingly, with optimum conditions:

$$\frac{\partial F}{\partial(\bar{\tau}_1 \dots \bar{\tau}_N, T_1 \dots T_N)} = 0. \qquad \text{VI-26}$$

Eqs. VI-17, given in the introduction, are rather simple forms of Eqs. VI-26 and 25.

Eqs. VI-25 and VI-26 yield the following relations:

$$\frac{\partial F}{\partial c_{An}} = 0 = -\lambda_{A(n+1)} + \lambda_{An}\left(1 - \bar{\tau}_n \frac{\partial R_{An}}{\partial c_A}\right) - \lambda_{Pn}\bar{\tau}_n \frac{\partial R_{Pn}}{\partial c_A},$$
$$n = 1 \dots (N - 1) ; \quad \text{VI-27}$$

$$\frac{\partial F}{\partial c_{Pn}} = 0 = -\lambda_{P(n+1)} + \lambda_{Pn}\left(1 - \bar{\tau}_n \frac{\partial R_{Pn}}{\partial c_P}\right) - \lambda_{An}\bar{\tau}_n \frac{\partial R_{An}}{\partial c_P},$$
$$n = 1 \dots (N - 1) ; \quad \text{VI-28}$$

$$\frac{\partial F}{\partial \bar{\tau}_n} = 0 = -\lambda_{An}R_{An} - \lambda_{Pn}R_{Pn} - \lambda_\tau, \quad n = 1 \dots N ; \qquad \text{VI-29}$$

$$\frac{\partial F}{\partial T_n} = 0 = \left(-\lambda_{An}\frac{\partial R_{An}}{\partial T} - \lambda_{Pn}\frac{\partial R_{Pn}}{\partial T}\right)\bar{\tau}_n, \quad n = 1 \dots N ; \qquad \text{VI-30}$$

$$\frac{\partial F}{\partial c_{AN}} = 0 = \frac{\partial M}{\partial c_{AN}} + \lambda_{AN}\left(1 - \bar{\tau}_N \frac{\partial R_{AN}}{\partial c_A}\right) - \lambda_{PN}\bar{\tau}_N \frac{\partial R_{PN}}{\partial c_A}; \quad \text{VI-31}$$

$$\frac{\partial F}{\partial c_{PN}} = 0 = \frac{\partial M}{\partial c_{PN}} + \lambda_{PN}\left(1 - \bar{\tau}_N \frac{\partial R_{PN}}{\partial c_P}\right) - \lambda_{AN}\bar{\tau}_N \frac{\partial R_{AN}}{\partial c_P}; \quad \text{VI-32}$$

$$\frac{\partial F}{d\bar{\tau}} = 0 = \frac{\partial M}{\partial \bar{\tau}} + \lambda_\tau. \qquad \text{VI-33}$$

The above relations, together with Eqs. VI-20 and 21, form a set of $(6N + 1)$ equations permitting the evaluation of the $(6N + 1)$ unknowns (i.e., c_{An},

c_{Pn}, $\bar{\tau}_n$, T_n, λ_{An}, λ_{Pn} and λ_τ) with which an extreme in the objective function M is obtained. It should be noted that the above equations are restricted in the sense that only two concentrations have been supposed to be needed for specifying the composition of the reaction mixture; the feed composition has been assumed constant, and intermediate feed or withdrawal has not been considered. Also, M has not been supposed to depend on the individual temperatures of the various reactors; however, if the objective function were influenced by the heat economy of the plant, a dependence on these temperatures would be possible. The same method as indicated above could be used since there are no restrictions regarding the number of variables.

Only in very simple cases can the $(6N + 1)$ equations be solved analytically; when this is the case, the optimization problem may also be solved by more direct methods (see, e.g., Illustration VI. 4c). In more complex problems, the simultaneous solution of $(6N + 1)$ equations containing $(6N + 1)$ unknowns is a typical task for a computer. The various routines available for this consist essentially of a sequence of successive approximations, so that numerous calculations have to be made. An elementary application of the above theory will be given below.

ILLUSTRATION VI. 4c. *The maximum yield for first order consecutive reactions in one tank reactor*

It is required to find the condition for maximum yield of P for two consecutive first order reactions $A \xrightarrow{1} P \xrightarrow{2} X$ in a continuous tank reactor for the two following cases:
    (a) Optimum load at a given reaction temperature;
    (b) Optimum reaction temperature at a given load.
The feed contains neither P nor X.

We have:
$$R_A = -k_1 c_A, \quad R_P = k_1 c_A - k_2 c_P,$$

while the quantity to be optimized, $M = c_{P1}/c_{A0}$, is a function of c_{A1}, c_{P1} and $\bar{\tau}$. The equations to be solved are:

$$0 = c_{A0} - c_{A1} - k_1 \bar{\tau} c_{A1}, \tag{cf.VI-20}$$

$$0 = -c_{P1} + k_1 \bar{\tau} c_{A1} - k_2 \bar{\tau} c_{P1}, \tag{cf.VI-21}$$

$$0 = \lambda_{A1}(1 + k_1 \bar{\tau}) - \lambda_{P1} k_2 \bar{\tau}, \tag{cf.VI-31}$$

$$0 = \frac{1}{c_{A0}} + \lambda_{P1}(1 + k_2 \bar{\tau}), \tag{cf.VI-32}$$

$$0 = \lambda_{A1} k_1 c_{A1} - \lambda_{P1}(k_1 c_{A1} - k_2 c_{P1}), \tag{a} \quad \text{(cf.VI-29)}$$

$$0 = \lambda_{A1} c_{A1} \frac{dk_1}{dT} - \lambda_{P1}\left(c_{A1}\frac{dk_1}{dT} - c_{P1}\frac{dk_2}{dT}\right). \tag{b} \quad \text{(cf.VI-30)}$$

The last equation may be omitted in solving problem (a). The first two equations give:

$$\frac{c_{A1}}{c_{A0}} = \frac{1}{1 + k_1 \bar{\tau}}, \quad \frac{c_{P1}}{c_{A0}} = \frac{k_1 \bar{\tau}}{(1 + k_1 \bar{\tau})(1 + k_2 \bar{\tau})},$$

and the next two:

$$\lambda_{A1} = \frac{-k_1 \bar{\tau}}{1 + k_1 \bar{\tau}}\lambda_{P1}, \quad \lambda_{P1} = \frac{-1}{c_{A0}(1 + k_2 \bar{\tau})}.$$

216

After substitution of these expressions into Eq. (a), we find that the residence time for maximum yield is:

$$\bar{\tau}_{opt} = (k_1 k_2)^{-\frac{1}{2}}. \tag{c}$$

In solving problem (b), Eq. (a) is not relevant since it was obtained by differentiation with respect to $\bar{\tau}$, which is assumed constant in this case. The expressions for c_{A1}, c_{P1}, λ_{A1} and λ_{P1} are now substituted into Eq. (b). The final result is that the maximum yield is produced at the temperature where:

$$(1 + k_1\bar{\tau})\frac{dk_1}{dT} = k_1\bar{\tau}(1 + k_2\bar{\tau})\frac{dk_2}{dT}. \tag{d}$$

In this simple case, the results (c) and (d) could have been found directly by calculating the maximum value of c_{P1}/c_{A0} as a function of $\bar{\tau}$ and T since an expression for c_{P1}/c_{A0} was available containing these two variables only. This example must, therefore, be regarded as an illustration of the method. It should be noted that the λ's have a physical significance. In this case we have:

$$-c_{A0}\lambda_{A1} = c_{P1}/c_{A0} = \eta_{P1} \quad \text{(yield)},$$
$$-c_{A0}\lambda_{P1} = c_{P1}/(c_{A0} - c_{A1}) = \sigma_{P1} \quad \text{(selectivity)}.$$

ii. Ideal tubular reactor

The behaviour of a tubular reactor (without feed distribution or product removal) can be approached by taking a cascade of tank reactors of equal size and by letting the total number of reactors, N, go to infinity and the residence time of each reactor to zero. This property can be used in deriving the expressions for optimum conditions in a tubular reactor from the theory for the cascade.

We shall again assume that the composition of the reaction mixture is determined by the two concentrations c_A and c_P and that the function to be optimized depends on the composition of the reaction mixture at the outlet, c_{AL} and c_{PL}, and on the total residence time τ_L:

$$M = M(c_{AL}, c_{PL}, \tau_L).$$

If the residence time τ is taken as a measure of the distance from the feed end of the reactor, the conversion equations VI-20 and VI-21 become (with $\varrho = $ constant):

$$0 = -dc_A + R_A d\tau, \qquad \text{VI-34}$$
$$0 = -dc_P + R_P d\tau. \qquad \text{VI-35}$$

The auxiliary function F defined by Eq. VI-23 now becomes:

$$F = M(c_{AL}, c_{PL}, \tau_L) + \int_{\tau=0}^{\tau=\tau_L} \lambda_A(\tau)[dc_A - R_A d\tau] +$$
$$+ \int_{\tau=0}^{\tau=\tau_L} \lambda_P(\tau)[dc_P - R_P d\tau]. \quad \text{VI-36}$$

The Lagrange parameters λ_A and λ_P are now functions of τ. An extreme in F — and hence equally in M as well — is formed by making the partial derivatives of F equal to zero with respect to c_A, c_P and T. The results are:

217

$$\frac{\partial F}{\partial c_A} = 0 \to 0 = \frac{d\lambda_A}{d\tau} + \lambda_A \frac{\partial R_A}{\partial c_A} + \lambda_P \frac{\partial R_P}{\partial c_A}, \star \qquad \text{VI-37}$$

$$\frac{\partial F}{\partial c_P} = 0 \to 0 = \frac{d\lambda_P}{d\tau} + \lambda_A \frac{\partial R_A}{\partial c_P} + \lambda_P \frac{\partial R_P}{\partial c_P}, \star \qquad \text{VI-38}$$

$$\frac{\partial F}{\partial T} = 0 \to 0 = \lambda_A \frac{\partial R_A}{\partial T} + \lambda_P \frac{\partial R_P}{\partial T}. \qquad \text{VI-39}$$

In addition to these three equations we have the boundary conditions:

$$\frac{\partial F}{\partial c_{AL}} = 0 = \frac{\partial M}{\partial c_{AL}} + \lambda_{AL}, \qquad \text{VI-40}$$

$$\frac{\partial F}{\partial c_{PL}} = 0 = \frac{\partial M}{\partial c_{PL}} + \lambda_{PL}, \qquad \text{VI-41}$$

$$\frac{\partial F}{\partial \tau_L} = 0 = \frac{\partial M}{\partial \tau_L} - \lambda_{AL}R_{AL} - \lambda_{PL}R_{PL}, \qquad \text{VI-42}$$

which come in the place of Eqs. VI-31, 32 and 33. From the 5 differential equations VI-34, 35, 37, 38 and 39 with their boundary conditions VI-40, 41 and 42, the relationship between τ, c_A, c_P, λ_A, λ_P and T can be found for which M will be extreme. Several methods of solution can be followed (HORN and TROLTENIER [185], HORN [192]), but computer aid will generally be necessary.

It is possible to eliminate c_A, c_P and T from the 5 differential equations in the following manner:

$$(\text{VI-37}) \times dc_A \to \frac{d\lambda_A}{d\tau} dc_A + \lambda_A \frac{\partial R_A}{\partial c_A} dc_A + \lambda_P \frac{\partial R_P}{\partial c_A} dc_A = 0$$

$$(\text{VI-38}) \times dc_P \to \frac{d\lambda_P}{d\tau} dc_P + \lambda_A \frac{\partial R_A}{\partial c_P} dc_P + \lambda_P \frac{\partial R_P}{\partial c_P} dc_P = 0$$

$$(\text{VI-39}) \times dT \to \qquad\qquad \lambda_A \frac{\partial R_A}{\partial T} dT + \lambda_P \frac{\partial R_P}{\partial T} dT = 0$$

$$\frac{d\lambda_A}{d\tau} dc_A + \frac{d\lambda_P}{d\tau} dc_P + \lambda_A dR_A + \lambda_P dR_P = 0$$

When dc_A and dc_P are substituted by using Eqs. VI-34 and 35, it is found that the following condition must be met along the reactor:

$$d(\lambda_A R_A + \lambda_P R_P) = 0,$$

or, with Eq. VI-42:

$$\lambda_A R_A + \lambda_P R_P = \frac{\partial M}{\partial \tau_L}. \qquad \text{VI-43}$$

If we are not interested in the capacity of the reactor but only in the yield, M will not be a function of τ_L and $\partial M/\partial \tau_L = 0$. λ_A and λ_P can then be elim-

---

$\star$ These equations, which are analogous with Eqs. VI-27 and 28, are obtained from VI-36 after the integrals $\int \lambda_A dc_A$ and $\int \lambda_P dc_P$ have been partially integrated.

inated from Eqs. VI-39 and VI-43 to give:

$$\frac{1}{R_A}\frac{\partial R_A}{\partial T} = \frac{1}{R_P}\frac{\partial R_P}{\partial T}, \quad \text{or} \quad \frac{\partial}{\partial T}\left(\frac{R_P}{R_A}\right) = 0. \qquad \text{VI-44}$$

This condition simply states that the differential selectivity ψ_P (defined by Eq. VI-2) should be a maximum at any cross section in the reactor. As already discussed in Section VI.3 (p. 207), it implies that the highest or lowest permissible temperature is the optimum temperature if there is no maximum in ψ_P. Interesting possibilities of temperature optimization exist if ψ_P has a maximum as a function of T within the permissible temperature range (see, e.g., Illustration VI.4d).

Another group of problems where the parameters λ can be rather easily eliminated without the restriction $\partial M/\partial \tau_L = 0$ is encountered when the conversion rates are *linear functions* of the concentrations. In such case we can use the property that:

$$c_A\frac{\partial R_A}{\partial c_A} + c_P\frac{\partial R_A}{\partial c_P} = R_A, \qquad \text{VI-45}$$

if, e.g., R_A is linear in c_A and c_P.

The derivation of the optimum conditions will be shown below for the case where the two components A and P characterize the reaction mixture; it can be extended to more components. This is of some importance since the assumption of first order or linearized kinetics will in many cases provide a good approximation of practical circumstances and therefore a good estimate of optimum conditions.

If we write Eqs. VI-37 and VI-38 in the form:

$$0 = c_A\frac{d\lambda_A}{d\tau} + \lambda_A\frac{dc_A}{d\tau} - \lambda_A\frac{dc_A}{d\tau} + \lambda_A c_A\frac{\partial R_A}{\partial c_A} + \lambda_P c_A\frac{\partial R_P}{\partial c_A},$$

$$0 = c_P\frac{d\lambda_P}{d\tau} + \lambda_P\frac{dc_P}{d\tau} - \lambda_P\frac{dc_P}{d\tau} + \lambda_A c_P\frac{\partial R_A}{\partial c_P} + \lambda_P c_P\frac{\partial R_P}{\partial c_P},$$

and if we take the sum of these two equations, we obtain:

$$0 = \frac{d}{d\tau}(\lambda_A c_A + \lambda_P c_P) + \lambda_A\left(c_A\frac{\partial R_A}{\partial c_A} + c_P\frac{\partial R_A}{\partial c_P} - \frac{dc_A}{d\tau}\right) +$$

$$+ \lambda_P\left(c_A\frac{\partial R_P}{\partial c_A} + c_P\frac{\partial R_P}{\partial c_P} - \frac{dc_P}{d\tau}\right).$$

The last two terms in this equation are now zero because of the material balances VI-34 and VI-35 and of Eq. VI-45 for linear rate expressions. Accordingly:

$$\frac{d}{d\tau}(\lambda_A c_A + \lambda_P c_P) = 0, \qquad \text{VI-46}$$

and:

$$\lambda_A c_A + \lambda_P c_P = \lambda_{AL} c_{AL} + \lambda_{PL} c_{PL}.$$

λ_A and λ_P can be calculated from Eqs. VI-46 and VI-39. After substitution of these calculated values into VI-43 and using the values given by Eqs. VI-40 and VI-41 for λ_{AL} and λ_{PL} we find:

$$\frac{R_A \dfrac{\partial R_P}{\partial T} - R_P \dfrac{\partial R_A}{\partial T}}{c_A \dfrac{\partial R_P}{\partial T} - c_P \dfrac{\partial R_A}{\partial T}} = \frac{-\dfrac{\partial M}{\partial \tau_L}}{c_{AL} \dfrac{\partial M}{\partial c_{AL}} + c_{PL} \dfrac{\partial M}{\partial c_{PL}}}. \qquad \text{VI-47}$$

It is seen that this expression is reduced to Eq. VI-44 when the cost function does not contain the capacity (or τ_L) as a variable.

The above theory was worked out in a more general form by HORN [192], who applied Eq. VI-47 in calculating optimum temperature profiles for various reactions. Analogous calculations were made by BILOUS and AMUNDSON [200] for first and second order consecutive reactions in tubular reactors.

ILLUSTRATION VI. 4d. *Temperature optimization of three parallel reactions*

It is asked to find the optimum conditions in a tubular reactor for the three parallel first order reactions:

$$A \xrightarrow{1} P, \quad R_P = k_1 c_A = c_A k_{1\infty} \exp{(-E_1/RT)}$$
$$A \xrightarrow{2} X, \quad R_X = k_2 c_A = c_A k_{2\infty} \exp{(-E_2/RT)}$$
$$A \xrightarrow{3} Y, \quad R_Y = k_3 c_A = c_A k_{3\infty} \exp{(-E_3/RT)}.$$

The activation energy E_1 lies in between the values of E_2 and E_3 so that the undesired side reactions 2 and 3 will dominate at low and high temperatures, respectively. The unconverted reactant A will be recovered and added to the feed. The by-products X and Y have no economic value.

We shall require the gross profit per molar unit of P produced to be a maximum. The total gross profit of the plant per unit time will be supposed to be:

$$\Phi_v[c_{PL}C_P - (c_{A0} - c_{AL})C_A] - V_r C_f - \Phi_v C_0,$$

where
Φ_v = volumetric throughput,
C_P = sales value of one kmol of P,
C_A = cost of one kmol of A,
C_f = fixed costs per unit of reaction volume,
C_0 = variable costs per unit of throughput.
The profit per kmol of P then becomes:

$$M(c_{AL}, c_{PL}, \tau_L) = C_P - \frac{c_{A0} - c_{AL}}{c_{PL}} C_A - \frac{\tau_L}{c_{PL}} C_f - \frac{C_0}{c_{PL}}.$$

It is seen that, for a high value of M, the selectivity $[c_{PL}/(c_{A0} - c_{AL})]$ and c_{PL} should be high and τ_L not too large.

Selecting A and P as the characteristic components for which $R_A = -(k_1 + k_2 + k_3)c_A$ and $R_P = k_1 c_P$, we find for the left-hand side of Eq. VI-47:

$$\frac{k_1 - (k_1 + k_2 + k_3) \dfrac{dk_1}{d(k_1 + k_2 + k_3)}}{\dfrac{c_P}{c_A} + \dfrac{dk_1}{d(k_1 + k_2 + k_3)}}.$$

The right-hand side of Eq. VI-47 becomes, in view of the above cost function M:

$$\frac{C_f}{c_{A0}C_A + \tau_L C_f + C_0} = C.$$

C happens to be independent of c_{AL} and c_{PL} in this case, but it varies with τ_L. Substitution of these expressions into Eq. VI-47 yields the following condition:

$$\frac{c_P}{c_A} C = k_1 - (k_1 + k_2 + k_3 + C) \frac{dk_1}{d(k_1 + k_2 + k_3)}. \tag{a}$$

Fig. VI-18 shows the latter function of T for a given set of conversion rate constants indicated, with $C = 0$ and with a positive value of C.

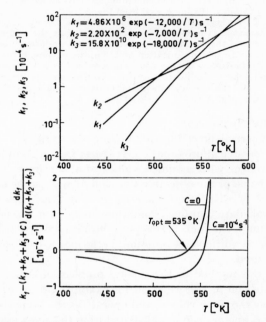

FIG. VI-18. Yield optimization of three parallel first order reactions; Illustration VI.4d.

If the chemicals A and P are very expensive and the fixed costs relatively low, the reactor capacity may be a rather unimportant parameter, and consequently $C \approx 0$. Equation (a) is then reduced to:

$$\frac{d}{d\tau}\left(\frac{k_1}{k_1 + k_2 + k_3}\right) = 0, \qquad \text{(see Eq. VI-44)}$$

which means that an optimum temperature exists irrespective of the degree of conversion. Accordingly, the best procedure is to operate isothermally at the temperature which follows from the latter equation:

$$T_{\text{opt}} = \frac{E_2 - E_3}{R \ln\left[\dfrac{k_{2\infty}(E_2 - E_1)}{k_{3\infty}(E_1 - E_3)}\right]}. \tag{b}$$

For the k's indicated in Fig. VI-18, we find $T_{\text{opt}} = 535°\text{K}$, in accordance with the intersection of the curve for $C = 0$ with the abscissa. It can be shown similarly that the

221

maximum yield is obtained by isothermal operation for the reactions:

$$A \xrightarrow{1} P \underset{3}{\overset{2}{<}} \begin{matrix} X \\ Y \end{matrix} \quad \text{and} \quad A \underset{1}{\overset{2}{\rightleftarrows}} P \xrightarrow{3} X \ ,$$

provided E_1 lies in between E_2 and E_3 and the reactor capacity is not a cost parameter (HORN and TROLTENIER [186]).

If the reactor capacity does play a part in the optimization problem, C has a positive value. Consequently, the curve representing the right-hand side of Eq. (a) is lowered (see Fig. VI-18 for $C = 10^{-4}$ s^{-1}). At the same time, the left-hand side of (a) has a positive value proportional to c_P/c_A. It can be seen from Fig. VI-18 that a higher temperature is required in this case than is given by Eq. (b), and that the temperature should be slightly raised as c_P/c_A increases. It is intuitively understood that the temperature must be raised because it is only then that average reaction rates are faster and, consequently, the capacity is higher. In this optimization problem, the value of C cannot be fixed beforehand since it contains τ_L, which in turn is determined by the temperature profile in the reactor. Hence, the optimum temperature profile must be found by successive approximation, in each step of which the material balances have to be used for calculating the final conversion of A and the yield of P.

The method of "steepest ascent"

This is a numerical procedure for finding the extreme of an objective function by successive approximation. It starts from a complete solution of the reactor problem with assumed values of the primary variables. The corresponding value of the objective function M will not be optimal. If it is now known how M will change when the primary variables are changed, it is possible to calculate improved conditions under which a new value of M nearer the optimum is found. If this procedure is repeated a sufficient number of times, the conditions for optimum performance can be approached as closely as is desired.

In applying this method to the general problem of a cascade of N tank reactors as stated on p. 214, we start, for example, on the assumption that all reactors have the same volume and operate at the same temperature T_n. The values of c_{An} and c_{Pn} can be calculated from the given inlet composition and from the material balances; the objective function $M(c_{AN}, c_{PN}, \bar{\tau})$ can therefore be evaluated for this non-optimal cascade. In order to know in what direction the primary variables have to be changed, the partial derivatives of M, i.e. of $M^*(\bar{\tau}_1 \dots \bar{\tau}_N, T_1 \dots T_N)$ (see Eq. VI-19), have to be known under the conditions first assumed. To find these derivatives, the Lagrange method has to be used in the form given by Eqs. VI-24 and VI-25. This set of equations provide the values of λ_{An}, λ_{Pn} and λ_τ to be used in VI-24 for finding the values of $\partial M^*/\partial \bar{\tau}_n$ and $\partial M^*/\partial T_n$ associated with the arbitrarily selected non-optimal cascade.

Now, if we suppose that the value of M^* will come closer to the extreme by the increase of an assumed residence time $\bar{\tau}_n$, the best way to arrive at an improved value $\bar{\tau}'_n$ from the residence time $\bar{\tau}_n$ is:

$$\bar{\tau}'_n = \bar{\tau}_n + \varepsilon_\tau \frac{\partial M^*}{\partial \bar{\tau}_n} . \qquad \qquad \text{VI-48}$$

Similarly, an improved temperature, T'_n, will be obtained with:

$$T_n' = T_n + \varepsilon_T \frac{\partial M^*}{\partial T_n}. \qquad \text{VI-49}$$

These equations constitute the basis of the method of steepest ascent. Once a set of new $\bar{\tau}'_n$ and T'_n values has been obtained, the whole procedure can be repeated a number of times until M^* does not change by more than a prescribed small amount.

The factors ε_τ and ε_T have to be selected in a judicious manner. If they are taken too small, a great many cycles may be needed to arrive at the final solution; if they are taken too large an overshoot of the optimum values of $\bar{\tau}_n$ and T_n may occur.

Many calculations obviously have to be carried out before optimum conditions are arrived at. However, the method appears to be very suitable for automatic computers. As an additional advantage, the machine can print out information concerning non-optimal conditions in the course of the computation. From these data, an idea can be obtained of the flexibility of the plant with regard to deviations from the best operating policy. It also is an easy matter to take into account additional complicating factors contained in the problem, such as temperature limits or limited tank sizes.

Among the various authors who employed the method of steepest ascent in reactor optimization studies we mention HORN and TROLTENIER [185].

In concluding this section it may be said that, thanks to the various mathematical techniques and the computing aids nowadays available, any optimization problem can be solved, provided the problem is realistic and properly stated. The difficulties of optimization lie mainly in providing the pertinent data and in an adequate construction of the objective function M. This kind of information is quite specific for the process under consideration and for the plant environment. It cannot generally be obtained from *a priori* considerations. Carefully systematized data amassed from previous experience with similar processes and plants will have to guide improvements based on optimization.

EXPERIMENTAL REACTORS

In carrying out the calculations discussed in this book, the chemical engineer must rely on dependable information regarding the chemical reaction rates involved. These data have to be procured in the chemical or physico-chemical laboratory by means of investigations with suitable *experimental reactors*. It is not at all necessary that an experimental reactor is of the same type as the industrial reactor; it is much more important that one of the *model reactor* types is approached and that it is operated *isothermally*. With a batch reactor the experimental results are obtained in the form of the composition of the reaction mixture as a function of time. With a tank reactor and a tubular reactor the product composition can be determined as a function of reactor load (or residence time, $\bar{t}$ or τ_L). The variables in such experiments generally are the temperature, the composition of the feed (which may consist of different streams, miscible or not) and, for catalytic reactions, the amount or concentration of catalyst.

With the results of such kinetic measurements a kinetic model should be set up which represents the relationship between the chemical reaction rate and its influencing variables, with sufficient accuracy for engineering purposes. Such a model does not need to be a true representation of the reaction mechanism, although some insight into this mechanism will be very helpful in many cases. Proper interpretation of chemical kinetic measurements with a view to practical applications is the main theme of the book by JUNGERS and associates [13]. Heterogeneous gas reactions with solid catalyst and the influence of adsorption and desorption in such processes were thoroughly treated by HOUGEN and WATSON [12].

The realization of an experimental reactor the behaviour of which is approximately the same as that of an isothermal model reactor frequently presents difficulties of a practical nature. The measures that can be taken to obviate such difficulties may be derived from the material discussed in Chapters III, IV and V. In the following we shall briefly review the main problems involved, namely, the residence time distribution, the supply or removal of heat and the problems connected with mass transfer and interfacial area in heterogeneous systems.

Residence time distribution

An experimental reactor should either have no spread in reaction or residence times (batch reactor and ideal tubular reactor, respectively), or a very well-defined residence time distribution function (such as in an ideal tank reactor). In this respect, the well-mixed batch reactor is a suitable experimental reactor, in particular for reactions which proceed at such a slow rate that the composition of the reaction mixture as a function of time can be accurately measured. The continuous tank reactor is to be preferred for faster reactions; it has the advantage that the conversion rate is measured directly for a well-defined composition of the reaction mixture. With liquid-liquid reactions, for example, the tank reactor has the advantage that the hold-up and the residence time distribution of both phases are well-determined quantities. However, a drawback of the tank reactor for liquid-liquid and gas-liquid systems is that interfacial areas cannot as yet be accurately predicted. The principle of the tank reactor would also be very desirable for the investigation of not overly fast homogeneous and heterogeneous gas reactions, but it is not yet frequently used in view of difficulties connected with mixing and heat transfer.

The tubular reactor is appropriate for the kinetic study of fast reactions and particularly of homogeneous and heterogeneous gas reactions. Its great disadvantage is that the conversion rate is not measured in a straightforward manner but that an average over the reactor length is obtained ("integral reactor"). In order to avoid this problem, use is frequently made of a short tube length or a high reactor load with which a low degree of conversion and almost constant conditions over the reactor length can be achieved ("differential reactor"). This procedure requires a high precision of the composition measurements (see, e.g., RIETEMA [212]). If a short tube section is used for this purpose the result may furthermore be influenced by a considerable spread in residence time distribution.

In general it can be said that with turbulent flow in a relatively long empty tube ($L/d_t > 100$) the effect of longitudinal dispersion may be disregarded. The ideal tubular reactor is approximated with flow through a packed tube when $Re_p > 10$, $d_t/d_p > 10$ and $L/d_p \gg 20$ (see Section III.9). With respect to the residence time distribution of the gas, the fluidized bed reactor is a poor experimental reactor unless the height-diameter ratio is large. A separate check of the residence time distribution is advisable even under these circumstances. The main advantage of a fluidized bed reactor is its temperature homogeneity.

The supply or removal of heat

In an experimental reactor, the reaction should proceed under isothermal conditions as much as possible. This involves high demands on the control of the amount of heat to be exchanged in a batch reactor or a tubular reactor since the conversion rate varies as a function of time or of position, respectively. When the cooling or heating medium has a constant temperature, T_c, it is advisable to make the difference between the reaction temperature and T_c as small as possible; a large variation in heat flux then involves only a small absolute change in the reaction temperature. This can only be achieved when the product of the over-all heat transfer coefficient and the heat exchange surface per unit volume is sufficiently high. This means, in the case of a tubular reactor, that the pipe diameter may have to be small and that the cooling or heating medium should have practically the same temperature as the desired value of the reaction temperature.

Another manner in which temperature differences can be diminished is by reducing the conversion rate. With heterogeneous reactions in a fixed bed catalytic reactor, this can be done, for example, by diluting the catalyst phase with inert material having a reasonably high thermal conductivity. In this way, radial temperature differences can be more or less suppressed; mathematical corrections for a radial temperature distribution, if still existing, were discussed by FROMENT, PIJCKE and GOETHALS [213]. Better isothermal operation can also be achieved by lowering the reactant concentration, either by dilution with inert material or, in the case of gases, by a reduction of the pressure (LE GOFF, BONNETAIN and LETORT [214]).

With a continuous tank reactor, the desired reaction temperature can be obtained by imparting a properly selected temperature to the feed stream and/or by heat exchange between the reactor contents and a cooling or heating medium. Here, it is not necessary to keep the temperature difference for the heat exchange small, but local temperature differences in the reaction mixture have to be avoided, for example by adequate agitation.

Mass transfer and interfacial area

One of the most important questions to be investigated in experimental reactors for heterogeneous systems is whether or not physical phenomena influence the conversion rate, and if so, to what extent this occurs. The purpose of laboratory, bench-scale or pilot plant reactor studies, therefore, should be to disentangle the chemical kinetics of the reaction from the measured conversion rates. Results of this nature (which are often hard to obtain) constitute the only proper basis for scaling up to the dimensions of an industrial reactor, in which the state of dispersion, and accordingly the influence of physical phenomena, may be different from that prevailing in the experimental reactor. The latter is especially true when mobile interfaces between the phases are involved, such as in gas-liquid and liquid-liquid systems.

With *relatively slow* reactions, it is frequently possible to eliminate the physical rate-determining factors by reducing the scale of dispersion and by providing for a sufficiently large interfacial area. For heterogeneous reactions catalysed by a catalyst deposited on a porous solid carrier, such conditions may be achieved by means of a high flow rate around the pellets of catalyst and by making the particles so small as to render diffusional resistance in the pores relatively unimportant. At the same time, experiments should be included with the same catalytic material having the particle size to be used in practice.

The kinetics of rather slow homogeneous reactions in a liquid which is contacted by another non miscible liquid or a gas containing one of the reactants can be studied in an agitated vessel. If it is found that the conversion rate becomes constant as the interfacial area is increased (such as by stronger agitation or by a change in phase ratio), it is highly probable that the effect of mass transfer has been eliminated; see, e.g., VIALLARD [215]. Such a degree of dispersion may not be attainable for the same reaction when carried out on an industrial scale; allowance must then be made for the influence of mass transfer in the manner indicated in Section V.3. To this end, the product of the mass transfer coefficient and the specific interfacial area, βA_v, has to be known. It appears that the prediction of A_v is generally much less reliable than that of β. For slow reactions where the correction to be applied is still small, this may not be a cause for great concern. However, with faster reactions the conversion rate becomes more and more proportional to A_v, so that a knowledge of this quantity is then of primary importance, both in an experimental reactor and in an industrial reactor.

An indication regarding the relative influence of a physical mass transfer resistance on *moderately fast reactions* can be obtained by performing experiments at different temperatures. The apparent activation energy of the reaction will be high when the chemical reaction rate is controlling, and it will decrease as a function of rising temperature when the effects of diffusion and mass transfer come into play. The interpretation can be guided by the theories discussed in Section V.4 for heterogeneous reactions and in Section V.3 for homogeneous reactions. When performing such experiments the size of the interfacial area and the flow conditions in the adjoining phases should remain constant with varying temperature. This cannot be realized by dispersing a gas or a liquid in a liquid which is agitated by conventional means. WESTERTERP [103] showed that, with gas-liquid systems, successful use can be made of an experimental arrangement in which gas bubbles are rising through a liquid contained in a narrow tube. The size of the bullet-shaped bubbles can be kept constant; their rate of rise and the liquid flow behaviour around them are independent of temperature.

For the quantitative investigation of *fast* homogeneous reactions in gas-liquid and liquid-liquid systems, a kinetic experiment will have to be directed to a study of mass transfer combined with chemical reaction. It is of primary importance that the size of the interfacial area and the flow conditions are accurately known. For gas absorption with chemical reaction, this has resulted in equipment in which the absorption takes place in a laminar liquid film or in a laminar liquid jet. Several studies have been published on the use of this technique for the evaluation of the chemical kinetics (see, among other authors, DANCKWERTS and KENNEDY [216], NIJSING, HENDRIKSZ and KRAMERS [126] and KRAMERS, BLIND and SNOECK [217]). There is a need for similar techniques to be used with liquid-liquid systems.

227

Some recommended experimental reactor types are listed in the table below. This survey does not pretend to be complete. In particular for complex reaction systems, it should be carefully considered what design of an experimental reactor would give the best chance of a proper interpretation of the experimental results.

Some recommended experimental reactors

Reaction mixture	Experimental reactor	Remarks
Gas	Tubular reactor	Integral or differential
Liquid	Batch reactor; tank reactor; tubular reactor	Slow reactions; moderately fast reactions; fast reactions
Solid	Batch fluidized bed	Inert gas or liquid for fluidization
Gas-liquid	Gas-liquid contactor★; laminar film or jet	Slow reactions; fast reactions
Liquid-liquid	Batch reactor★; tank reactor★; film reactor	Good agitation, no settling of dispersed phase; fast reactions
Gas-solid	Tubular reactor	Integral or differential with fixed bed
Liquid-solid	Batch reactor; tubular reactor	Good dispersion of solids; fixed or fluidized bed

★ Interfacial area must be known.

THE DYNAMIC BEHAVIOUR OF AN AUTOTHERMAL
TANK REACTOR

Only the steady state characteristics of continuous flow reactors have been considered in this book. In practice, nonstationary performance due to disturbances is equally important. Intentional disturbances are applied in starting and stopping operations and when a change is made in the operating conditions; the designer and the operator have to be aware of the resulting transient conditions. Unintentional disturbances such as variations in feed conditions, in steam pressures, etc., have to be counteracted by automatic control; the dynamic response of the plant to such disturbances largely determines the control system to be used and the dynamic characteristics of the required controllers.

With *isothermal* reactor operation, a change in feed rate or in feed composition will result in a gradual change of the conversion from one value to another. The time interval in which the transition occurs will then be of main interest. Due to the introduction of time as a new independent variable, ordinary differential equations now have to be solved for tank reactors (which in the steady state were described by means of algebraic equations). MASON and PIRET [35, 218] applied these to the starting-up of isothermal cascades of tank reactors; on the basis of their study they recommend procedures for rapidly attaining on-stream conditions in a cascade. Partial differential equations have to be solved for the treatment of the transient behaviour of isothermal tubular reactors (which in the steady state were described by means of ordinary differential equations). Solutions for particular cases can be readily obtained by means of modern calculation aids, even when the conversion rate expressions are nonlinear functions of the concentrations.

With *nonisothermal* operation, the transient behaviour of a reactor may show temperature excursions which temporarily or permanently lead to undesired reactor conditions. This is a result of coupling between the material and energy balances. The simultaneous solution of two ordinary nonlinear differential equations presents difficulties with respect to the treatment of the steady state operation of tubular reactors (compare the discussion on the parametric sensitivity of tubular reactors in Section IV.4); it can be imagined that the corresponding nonstationary problems must be rather intractable. On the other hand, the dynamic behaviour of an autothermally operating tank reactor belongs to a class of less complicated problems. AMUNDSON and

229

associates [86, 87, 219, 220, 221] did pioneering work in this field which was reviewed by Foss [222]. HOFTIJZER and ZWIETERING [93] applied the theory to a polymerization reaction carried out in a single tank reactor. The salient points of the theory of the unsteady autothermal tank reactor will be outlined below.*

The equations governing the dynamic behaviour of a tank reactor are essentially the material balances (cf. Eqs. I-1 and II-12):

$$\frac{d(\varrho V_r w_{J1})}{dt} = \Phi_{m0} w_{J0} - \Phi_{m1} w_{J1} + r_{J1} V_r \,, \qquad \text{A-1}$$

and the energy balance (cf. Eq. IV-1):

$$\frac{d(\varrho V_r u_1)}{dt} = \Phi_{m0} h_0 - \Phi_{m1} h_1 + UA(T_c - T_1) \,. \qquad \text{A-2}$$

It is now assumed that the density, ϱ, and the reaction volume, V_r, remain constant so that $\Phi_{m0} = \Phi_{m1} = \Phi_m$. We furthermore consider a single reaction the extent of which is expressed by the relative degree of conversion of a reactant A: $\zeta \equiv (w_{A0} - w_{A1})/w_{A0}$. The index 1 indicating the conditions in the reactor and at its outlet will be omitted. Upon introduction of the average residence time, $\bar{\tau} = \varrho V_r / \Phi_m$, Eq. A-1 becomes:

$$\frac{d\zeta}{d(t/\bar{\tau})} = -\zeta + \frac{\bar{\tau}|r|_A}{\varrho w_{A0}} \,. \qquad \text{A-3}$$

Eq. A-2 can be worked out by using the expressions IV-5 and IV-6 for u and h. If we further assume that $u \approx h$ (liquid) and that c_p and $(\Delta h_r)_A$ are constant, we may write for Eq. A-2:

$$\frac{dT}{d(t/\bar{\tau})} - \frac{w_{A0}(\Delta h_r)_A}{c_p} \frac{d\zeta}{d(t/\bar{\tau})} = T_0 - T + \frac{w_{A0}(\Delta h_r)_A}{c_p} \zeta +$$
$$+ \frac{UA\bar{\tau}}{\varrho c_p V_r} (T_c - T) \,. \qquad \text{A-4}$$

A further simplification can be obtained by introducing the adiabatic temperature rise (for complete conversion of A):

$$\Delta T_{ad} = -(\Delta h_r)_A w_{A0}/c_p \,,$$

and the heat exchange time constant τ':

$$\tau' = \varrho c_p V_r / UA \,, \dagger$$

and by eliminating the term with $d\zeta/d(t/\bar{\tau})$ in Eq. A-4 by means of Eq. A-3. The result is:

---

* The manner of treatment was suggested to us by Dr. W. J. BEEK.
† This is the time constant connected with the exponential approach of the reactor temperature to T_c when no reaction occurs and the flow is stopped. $\tau' = \infty$ for an adiabatic reactor.

$$\frac{\mathrm{d}T}{\mathrm{d}(t/\bar{\tau})} = T_0 - T - \Delta T_{ad} \frac{\bar{\tau}|r|_A}{\varrho w_{A0}} + \frac{\bar{\tau}}{\tau'} (T_c - T) . \qquad \text{A-5}$$

As explained in Section IV.5, not more than three solutions of Eqs. A-3 and A-5 are possible in the steady state. These solutions could be visualized by plotting the function ζ and the straight line $[T - T_0 + (T - T_c)\bar{\tau}/\tau']$ in a $\zeta - T$ graph and looking for the intersections (cf. Figs. IV-11 and IV-12). The intermediate solution was unstable and the other two were called statically stable. The upper stable solution is of main interest since it is associated with the highest degree of conversion; this point will be given the index s.

In describing nonstationary behaviour use may be made of a $\zeta - T$ plane for a study of what happens when the reactor conditions deviate from a stable solution. Provided the conversion rate is a known function of ζ and T, the values of $\mathrm{d}\zeta/\mathrm{d}(t/\bar{\tau})$ and $\mathrm{d}T/\mathrm{d}(t/\bar{\tau})$ can be calculated from Eqs. A-3 and A-5 for each point (ζ, T); hence, it is possible in principle to approximate a sequence of (ζ, T) combinations and corresponding times along which a stable solution is eventually reached from an arbitrary starting point. If we are interested only in the $\zeta - T$ path, the time can be eliminated from Eqs. A-3 and A-5, which results in:

$$\frac{\mathrm{d}\zeta}{\mathrm{d}T} = \frac{-\zeta + \dfrac{\bar{\tau}|r|_A}{\varrho w_{A0}}}{T_0 - T - \Delta T_{ad} \dfrac{\bar{\tau}|r_A|}{\varrho w_{A0}} + \dfrac{\bar{\tau}}{\tau'} (T_c - T)} . \qquad \text{A-6}$$

We shall now examine more closely the possible $\zeta - T$ paths after a change in operating conditions. It is accordingly assumed that at a certain moment the reactor works in a point (ζ, T) which is not a statically stable state corresponding to the new set of conditions. If the new conditions do not change, one of the stable states will ultimately be attained. We shall concern ourselves mainly with the manner in which the new upper stable point (ζ_s, T_s) is reached. For this discussion, we shall adopt the conversion rate expression for a first order reaction:

$$|r|_A = k \varrho w_{A0}(1 - \zeta) .$$

As in the approximation used in Section IV.4, page 113, we now write for k:

$$k = k_\infty \exp(-E/RT) =$$
$$= k_\infty \exp(-E/RT_s) \times \exp\left[\frac{E}{RTT_s}(T - T_s)\right] \approx$$
$$\approx k_s \exp\left[\frac{E}{RT_s^2}(T - T_s)\right] = k_s e^{\Delta\vartheta}.$$

The above approximation is permissible in the vicinity of the upper stable solution belonging to the new operating conditions after a change has been brought about. At its temperature T_s the reaction rate constant is k_s; the quantity $\Delta\vartheta$ is the dimensionless deviation from this temperature. If we

231

furthermore introduce:

$$\Delta\vartheta_0 = (T_0 - T_s)E/RT_s^2 ,$$

$$\Delta\vartheta_c = (T_c - T_s)E/RT_s^2 ,$$

$$\Delta\vartheta_{ad} = \Delta T_{ad}E/RT_s^2 ,$$

Eq. A-6 becomes:

$$\frac{d\zeta}{d\Delta\vartheta} = \frac{-\zeta + k_s\bar{\tau}(1 - \zeta)e^{\Delta\vartheta}}{-(1 + \bar{\tau}/\tau')\Delta\vartheta + \Delta\vartheta_{ad}k_s\bar{\tau}(1 - \zeta)e^{\Delta\vartheta} + \Delta\vartheta_0 + \bar{\tau}/\tau' \Delta\vartheta_c} . \quad \text{A-7}$$

In the upper stable solution ($\Delta\vartheta = 0$), both $d\zeta/dt$ (Eq. A-3) and dT/dt (Eq. A-5) are zero, and consequently the nominator and the denominator of Eq. A-7 must vanish. This gives the well-known relations:

$$k_s\bar{\tau} = \zeta_s/(1 - \zeta_s) ,$$

and:

$$\Delta\vartheta_0 + \frac{\bar{\tau}}{\tau'} \cdot \Delta\vartheta_c = -\Delta\vartheta_{ad}k_s\bar{\tau}(1 - \zeta_s) = -\Delta\vartheta_{ad}\zeta_s .$$

Substitution of these into Eq. A-7 yields the general formula for first order reactions:

$$\frac{d\zeta}{d\Delta\vartheta} = \frac{-\zeta + \dfrac{\zeta_s}{1 - \zeta_s}(1 - \zeta)e^{\Delta\vartheta}}{-\left(1 + \dfrac{\bar{\tau}}{\tau'}\right)\Delta\vartheta + \dfrac{\Delta\vartheta_{ad}\zeta_s}{1 - \zeta_s}(1 - \zeta)e^{\Delta\vartheta} - \Delta\vartheta_{ad}\zeta_s} . \quad \text{A-8}$$

The slope of the $\zeta - \Delta\vartheta$ path can be calculated from Eq. A-8 for each point in a $\zeta - \Delta\vartheta$ plane, as shown in Fig. A-1. The locus of all points where $d\zeta/d\Delta\vartheta = 0$ is found when the nominator of Eq. A-8 is zero. In Fig. A-1, this is Curve 1, which corresponds to the heat production curve in Fig. IV-11a. Curve 2 is found by putting the denominator equal to zero; it is the locus of all points for which $d\zeta/d\Delta\vartheta = \infty$. The heat removal line corresponding to Fig. IV-11b is given in this system by the equation (Line 3):

$$\zeta = \zeta_s + \left(1 + \frac{\bar{\tau}}{\tau'}\right)\frac{\Delta\vartheta}{\Delta\vartheta_{ad}} .$$

This line has a slope of arctan $[(1 + \bar{\tau}/\tau')/\Delta\vartheta_{ad}]$. For points of the $\zeta - \Delta\vartheta$ path lying on this line, we have $d\zeta/d\Delta\vartheta = 1/\Delta\vartheta_{ad}$, as can be derived from Eq. A-8.

The value of $d\zeta/d\Delta\vartheta$ can also be calculated at several other points. Some results have been indicated by the arrows in Fig. A-1 for a chosen combination of ζ_s, $\Delta\vartheta_{ad}$ and $(1 + \bar{\tau}/\tau')$. An impression can be obtained from these regarding the manner in which a stable situation is reached after a disturbance.

It is seen from Fig. A-1 that, starting from a high degree of conversion on the left of Curve 2, both ζ and $\Delta\vartheta$ will invariably decrease. If the starting

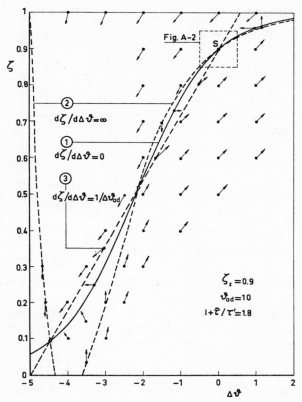

FIG. A-1. The $\zeta - \Delta\vartheta$ plane for a first order exothermic reaction in a cooled tank reactor.

point is relatively far from Curve 2 the reaction will be extinguished; if it is sufficiently near, the $\zeta - \Delta\vartheta$ path will vertically cross Curve 2 above the unstable steady solution, and it will then pass through Curve 1 (horizontally) and through Curve 3 (with a slope $1/\Delta\vartheta_{ad}$). In this case, the conversion and the temperature will again rise, cross Curves 2 and 1 to the right of the upper stable operating point, and again turn to the left to reach this point S. Apparently, if one starts from a moderate degree of conversion and from a $\Delta\vartheta$-value to the right of Curve 2, the reactor temperature will pass through a maximum value which may be much higher than T_s. This feature may be undesirable in particular cases (such as when an exothermic side reaction will occur at this high temperature) and special precautions must be taken in the starting-up of such a system. On the other hand, with a low conversion and a temperature in the vicinity of Curve 2 as a start, the conversion will temporarily rise, pass through a maximum and eventually reach the lower stable point; in such case the ignition of the reaction has not succeeded.

It is possible to divide the $\zeta - \Delta\vartheta$ plane into a part from which only the

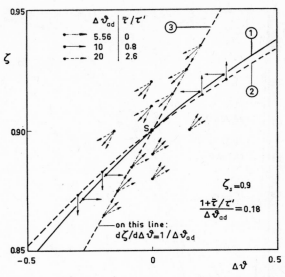

FIG. A-2. The region around the statically stable operating point S in Fig. A-1.

lower stable point can be reached and a part from which only the upper stable point is reached. The dividing line lies slightly to the left of Curve 2 above the unstable point, and slightly to the right of Curve 2 below the unstable point. It cannot easily be constructed with the method given above. In fact, the best way to trace the $\zeta - \Delta\vartheta$ paths for a given problem is by using an analog computer. This was done by AMUNDSON, whose paper [219] contains a number of results in the form of graphs like Fig. A-1.

It can be deduced from Fig. A-1 that the stable point S is approached by a turning movement. The region around S has been enlarged in Fig. A-2 to allow closer inspection of this phenomenon. Curves 1, 2 and 3 are identical with those in Fig. A-1. However, three possible combinations of $\Delta\vartheta_{ad}$ and $\bar{\tau}/\tau'$ are considered in Fig. A-2. It is seen that, with adiabatic operation ($\bar{\tau}/\tau' = 0$), $d\zeta/d\Delta\vartheta$ for points lying on Line 3 coincides with this line. Consequently, with an adiabatic autothermal reactor the point S will always be reached along Line 3, either from below or from above. With the cooled reactor ($\bar{\tau}/\tau' > 0$), Line 3 can be crossed and the $\zeta - \Delta\vartheta$ path can approach S by a spiral movement (e.g., $\bar{\tau}/\tau' = 0.8$). However, when the reactor is very strongly cooled (e.g., $\bar{\tau}/\tau' = 2.6$), Fig. A-2 shows that S cannot be reached although it is a *statically* stable point. If the arrows for this case are followed, it is found that the $\zeta - \Delta\vartheta$ path will ultimately turn around S in a limit cycle; this results in a steady oscillation of the reactor conditions. One could say intuitively that such a limit cycle will not occur if the value of $d\zeta/d\Delta\vartheta$ on Line 3 is greater than the tangent of the slope of Curve 2 in the point S. This would lead to the following condition of the *dynamic* stability of S:

234

$$\frac{1}{\Delta\vartheta_{ad}} > (1 - \zeta_s) - \frac{1 - \zeta_s}{\Delta\vartheta_{ad}\zeta_s}\left(1 + \frac{\bar{\tau}}{\tau'}\right). \qquad \text{A-9}$$

A more precise examination of the stability conditions of S can be made by considering the region so close to S that Eqs. A-3 and A-5 can be expressed as linear functions of $(\zeta - \zeta_s)$ and $\Delta\vartheta$. If we put:

$$\zeta - \zeta_s \equiv \Delta\zeta, \ e^{\Delta\vartheta} = 1 + \Delta\vartheta ,$$

and neglect small second-order terms, we find from Eq. A-3:

$$\frac{d\Delta\zeta}{d(t/\bar{\tau})} = -\frac{1}{1 - \zeta_s}\Delta\zeta + \zeta_s\Delta\vartheta \equiv a_{11}\Delta\zeta + a_{12}\Delta\vartheta , \qquad \text{A-10}$$

and from Eq. A-5:

$$\frac{d\Delta\vartheta}{d(t/\bar{\tau})} = -\frac{\Delta\vartheta_{ad}\zeta_s}{1 - \zeta_s}\Delta\zeta + \left[\Delta\vartheta_{ad}\zeta_s - \left(1 + \frac{\bar{\tau}}{\tau'}\right)\right]\Delta\vartheta \equiv a_{21}\Delta\zeta + a_{22}\Delta\vartheta. \ \text{A-11}$$

The solution of these equations has the form:

$$\Delta\zeta = b_{11}\,e^{p_1 t/\bar{\tau}} + b_{12}\,e^{p_2 t/\bar{\tau}} ,$$

$$\Delta\vartheta = b_{21}\,e^{p_1 t/\bar{\tau}} + b_{22}\,e^{p_2 t/\bar{\tau}} ,$$

in which p_1 and p_2 are defined by:

$$p_{1,2} = \frac{a_{11} + a_{22}}{2}\left[1 \pm \sqrt{1 - \frac{4(a_{11}a_{22} - a_{12}a_{21})}{(a_{11} + a_{22})^2}}\right] .$$

The solution is stable if $\Delta\zeta$ and $\Delta\vartheta$ approach zero with increasing time. This only occurs when the real parts of p_1 and p_2 are negative. Hence, the stability conditions are:

$$-a_{11} - a_{22} > 0 , \qquad \text{A-12}$$

and:

$$a_{11}a_{22} - a_{12}a_{21} > 0 . \qquad \text{A-13}$$

Inserting the values for the coefficients a from Eqs. A-10 and A-11, we find from Eq. A-13:

$$-\frac{1}{1 - \zeta_s}\left[\Delta\vartheta_{ad}\zeta_s - \left(1 + \frac{\bar{\tau}}{\tau'}\right)\right] + \Delta\vartheta_{ad}\frac{\zeta_s^2}{1 - \zeta_s} > 0 ,$$

or:

$$\frac{1 + \bar{\tau}/\tau'}{\Delta\vartheta_{ad}} > \zeta_s(1 - \zeta_s) . \qquad \text{A-14}$$

This condition states that at the point S the slope of Line 3 (in Fig. A-1) must be greater than that of Curve 1. This can be easily verified from the equations for these lines. Apparently, Eq. A-14 is the condition for static stability which was already mentioned in Section IV.5.

The other condition, A-12, becomes:

$$\frac{1}{1 - \zeta_s} - \Delta\vartheta_{ad}\zeta_s + 1 + \frac{\bar{\tau}}{\tau'} > 0 \,,$$

or:

$$\frac{1}{\Delta\vartheta_{ad}\zeta_s} > (1 - \zeta_s) - \frac{1 - \zeta_s}{\Delta\vartheta_{ad}\zeta_s}\left(1 + \frac{\bar{\tau}}{\tau'}\right). \qquad \text{A-15}$$

The right-hand side of A-15 is the tangent to Curve 2 at the point S (compare Eq. A-9). Apparently, the left-hand term does not represent the value of $d\zeta/d\Delta\vartheta$ on Line 3, as was surmised in deriving Eq. A-9. It appears to be the value of $d\zeta/d\Delta\vartheta$ when the $\zeta - \Delta\vartheta$ path crosses the line $\Delta\vartheta = 0$; this can be verified by substituting $\Delta\vartheta = 0$ into Eq. A-8.

For an adiabatic reactor, the conditions A-15 and A-14 are identical; there will always be static and dynamic stability, as was also shown in Fig. A-2. Applying Eq. A-15 to the two other cases illustrated in Fig. A-2, we calculate:

$$\Delta\vartheta_{ad} = 10 \to \frac{1}{9} > \frac{0.72}{9} \,,$$

$$\Delta\vartheta_{ad} = 20 \to \frac{1}{18} \not> \frac{1.54}{18} \,.$$

Hence, it follows that the system is dynamically unstable in the latter case. Such a situation should be avoided in practice. This can be done by properly selecting the reactant concentrations in the feed which determine the value of ΔT_{ad}. For example, it can be easily verified that the last two tank reactors of the cascade treated in Illustrations IV.3 and IV.5 are stable not only statically but in the dynamic sense as well.

LIST OF REFERENCES

Chapter I

1. Bird, R. B., W. E. Stewart and E. N. Lightfoot: "Transport Phenomena", Wiley, New York (1960).
2. Hougen, O. A., K. M. Watson and R. A. Ragatz: "Chemical Process Principles", II, "Thermodynamics", 2nd ed., Wiley, New York (1959).
3. Denbigh, K. G.: "The Principles of Chemical Equilibrium", University Press, Cambridge (1961).
4. Damköhler, G.: "Einfluss von Diffusion, Strömung und Wärmetransport auf die Ausbeute bei chemisch-technischen Reaktionen", Der Chemie-Ingenieur, III-1, Akad. Verlagsges., Leipzig (1937). (VDI, Leverkusen, 1957).
5. Frank-Kamenetski, D. A.: "Stoff- und Wärmeübertragung in der chemischen Kinetik", transl. fr. Russian, Springer, Berlin (1959).
6. Krevelen, D. W. van: Chem. Eng. Sci. 8: 5 (1958).
7. Hougen, O. A., K. M. Watson and R. A. Ragatz: "Chemical Process Principles", I, "Material and Energy Balances", 2nd ed., Wiley, New York (1954).
8. Smith, J. M.: "Chemical Engineering Kinetics", McGraw-Hill, New York (1956).
9. Reid, R. C., and T. K. Sherwood: "Properties of Gases and Liquids", McGraw-Hill, New York (1958).
10. Hougen, O. A. and K. M. Watson: "Chemical Process Principles", II, "Thermodynamics", 1st ed., Wiley, New York (1947).
11. Krevelen, D. W. van, and H. A. G. Chermin: Chem. Eng. Sci. 1: 66, 238 (1951–52).
12. Hougen, O. A. and K. M. Watson: "Chemical Process Principles", III, "Kinetics and Catalysis", Wiley, New York (1947).
13. Jungers, J. C., with J. C. Balaceanu, F. Coussemant, F. Eschard, A. Giraud, M. Hellin, P. Leprince and G. E. Limido: "Cinétique chimique appliquée", Société des Editions Technip, Paris, (1958).
14. Letort, M.: Chem. Eng. Sci. 8: 18 (1958).
15. Schweyer, H. E.: "Process Engineering Economics", McGraw-Hill, New York (1955).
16. Wicke, E.: Z. Elektrochem. 57: 460 (1953).
17. Brötz, W.: "Grundrisz der chemischen Reaktionstechnik", Verlag Chemie, Weinheim (1958).
18. Walas, S. M.: "Reaction Kinetics for Chemical Engineers", McGraw-Hill, New York (1959).

Chapter II

19. Smith, D. F.: J. Am. Chem. Soc. 47: 1862 (1925).
20. Venkateswarlu, C., M. Satyanarayana and M. N. Rao: Ind. Eng. Chem. 50: 973 (1958).
21. Eldridge, J. M. and E. L. Piret: Chem. Eng. Progr. 46: 290 (1950).
22. Jenney, T. M.: Chem. Eng. 62: 198 (1955).
23. Jones, R. W.: Chem. Eng. Progr. 47: 46 (1951) .
24. Weber, A. P.: Chem. Eng. Progr. 49: 26 (1953).
25. Vusse, J. G. van de and H. Voetter: Chem. Eng. Sci. 14: 90 (1961).
26. McMullin, R. B.: Chem. Eng. Progr. 44: 183 (1948).
27. Chermin, H. A. G. and D. W. van Krevelen: Chem. Eng. Sci. 14: 58 (1961).

28. WEBER, A. B. R.: Doctoral Thesis, Techn. Univ., Delft (1957).
29. HUIBERS, D. TH. A.: Doctoral Thesis, Techn. Univ., Delft (1960).
30. WATERMAN, H. I., C. BOELHOUWER and D. TH. A. HUIBERS: "Process Characterization", Elsevier, Amsterdam (1960).

Chapter III

31. DANCKWERTS, P. V.: *Chem. Eng. Sci.* **2**: 1 (1953).
32. KRAMERS, H. and G. ALBERDA: *Chem. Eng. Sci.* **2**: 173 (1953).
33. BROTHMAN, A., A. P. WEBER and E. Z. BARISH: *Chem. Met. Eng.* **7**: 111 (1943).
34. VUSSE, J. G. VAN DE: *Chem. Eng. Sci.* **4**: 178, 209 (1955).
35. MASON, D. R. and E. L. PIRET: *Ind. Eng. Chem.* **42**: 817 (1950).
36. WESTERTERP, K. R. and P. LANDSMAN: *Chem. Eng. Sci.* **17**: 363 (1962).
37. CHOLETTE, A. and L. CLOUTIER: *Can. J. Chem. Eng.* **37**: 105 (1959).
38. WEHNER, J. F. and R. H. WILHELM: *Chem. Eng. Sci.* **6**: 89 (1959).
39. LAAN, E. TH. VAN DER: *Chem. Eng. Sci.* **7**: 187 (1958).
40. FAN, L. T. and R. C. BAILIE: *Chem. Eng. Sci.* **13**: 63 (1960).
41. LEVENSPIEL, O. and K. B. BISCHOFF: *Ind. Eng. Chem.* **51**: 1431 (1959).
42. LEVENSPIEL, O. and K. B. BISCHOFF: *Ind. Eng. Chem.* **53**: 313 (1961).
43. LEVENSPIEL, O.: *Chem. Eng. Sci.* **17**: 576 (1962).
44. SCHOENEMANN, K.: *Dechema-Monogr.* **21**: 203 (1952).
45. HOFMANN, H.: Doctoral Thesis, Techn. Univ., Darmstadt (1955).
46. DANCKWERTS, P. V.: *Chem. Eng. Sci.* **8**: 93 (1958).
47. ZWIETERING, T. N.: *Chem. Eng. Sci.* **11**: 1 (1959).
48. KRAMERS, H.: *Chem. Eng. Sci.* **8**: 45 (1958).
49. DENBIGH, K. G.: *J. Appl. Chem.* **1**: 227 (1951).
50. CLELAND, F. A. and R. H. WILHELM: *A. I. Ch. E. Journal* **2**: 489 (1956).
51. VIGNES, J. P. and P. J. TRAMBOUZE: *Chem. Eng. Sci.* **17**: 73 (1962).
52. HOVARKA, R. B. and H. B. KENDALL: *Chem. Eng. Progr.* **56** (8): 58 (1960).
53. RIETEMA, K.: *Chem. Eng. Sci.* **8**: 103 (1958).
54. HORN, F. and L. KÜCHLER,: *Chem. Ing. Techn.* **31**: 1 (1951).
55. GREENHALGH, R. E., R. L. JOHNSON and H. D. NOTT: *Chem. Eng. Progr.* **55** (2): 44 (1959).
56. JAHNKE, E. and F. EMBDE: "Tables of Functions", Dover Publ., New York (1945).
57. CURL, R. L.: *A. I. Ch. E. Journal* **9**: 175 (1963).
58. MADDEN, A. J. and G. L. DAMERELL: *A. I. Ch. E. Journal* **8**: 233 (1962).
59. MILLER, R. S., J. L. RALPH, R. L. CURL and G. D. TOWELL: *A. I. Ch. E. Journal* **9**: 196 (1963).
60. HOFMANN, H.: *Chem. Eng. Sci.* **14**: 193 (1961).
61. TAYLOR, G. I.: *Proc. Roy. Soc.* **A219**: 186 (1953).
62. DEEMTER, J. J. VAN, J. J. BROEDER and H. A. LAUWERIER: *Appl. Sci. Res.* **A5**: 374 (1956).
63. TAYLOR, G. I.: *Proc. Roy. Soc.* **A223**: 446 (1954).
64. TICHACEK, L. J., C. H. BARKELEW and T. BARON: *A. I. Ch. E. Journal* **3**: 439 (1957).
65. SJENITZER, F.: *The Pipeline Engineer* D-31 (Dec. 1958).
66. CROOCKEWIT, P., C. C. HONIG and H. KRAMERS: *Chem. Eng. Sci.* **4**: 111 (1955).
67. STEMERDING, S., F. J. ZUIDERWEG, J. G. VAN DE VUSSE, V. B. THEGZE, R. J. WALL, K. E. TRAIN and R. B. OLNEY: *Erdölzeitschrift* **77**: 401 (1961).
68. WESTERTERP, K. R. and W. H. MEYBERG: *Chem. Eng. Sci.* **17**: 373 (1962).
69. McHENRY, K. W. and R. H. WILHELM: *A. I. Ch. E. Journal* **3**: 83 (1957).
70. CAIRNS, E. J. and J. M. PRAUSNITZ: *Chem. Eng. Sci.* **12**: 20 (1960).
71. HIBY, J. W.: Paper C71, Symposium on the Interaction Between Fluids and Particles, London (June 1962).
72. BERNARD, R. A. and R. H. WILHELM: *Chem. Eng. Progr.* **46**: 233 (1950).
73. LATINEN, G. A.: Doctoral Thesis, Princeton University (1951).
74. JOSSELIN DE JONG, G. DE: *Trans. Geoph. Un.* **39**: 67 (1958).
75. SAFFMANN, P. G.: *Chem. Eng. Sci.* **11**: 125 (1959).
76. CAIRNS, E. J. and J. M. PRAUSNITZ: *A. I. Ch. E. Journal* **6**: 400, 554 (1960).
77. KRAMERS, H., M. D. WESTERMANN, J. H. DE GROOT and F. A. A. DUPONT: Paper B1, Symposium on the Interaction Between Fluids and Particles, London (June 1962).

78. DEEMTER, J. J. VAN: *Chem. Eng. Sci.* **13**: 143 (1961).
79. REMAN, G. H.: *Chem. and Ind.* (London): 46 (1955).
80. WEBER, H.: Doctoral Thesis, Techn. Univ., Darmstadt (1960).
81. STEMERDING, S.: *Chem. Eng. Sci.* **14**: 209 (1961).
82. JARDINE, P.: Doctoral Thesis, Univ. Delaware (1957).
83. HANHART, J., H. KRAMERS and K. R. WESTERTERP: *Chem. Eng. Sci.* (in press).

Chapter IV

84. PERONA, J. J. and G. THODOS: *A. I. Ch. E. Journal* **3**: 230 (1957).
85. BARKELEW, C. H.: *Chem. Eng. Progr. Symp. Ser. No. 25*, **55**: 37 (1959).
86. BILOUS, O. and N. R. AMUNDSON: *A. I. Ch. E. Journal* **2**: 117 (1956).
87. AMUNDSON, N. R.: *De Ingenieur* **67**: Ch. 73 (1955).
88. WAGNER, C.: *Chem. Ing. Techn.* **18**: 28 (1945).
89. HEERDEN, C. VAN: *Ind. Eng. Chem.* **45**: 1242 (1953).
90. HEERDEN, C. VAN: *Chem. Eng. Sci.* **8**: 133 (1958).
91. MERTENS DE WILMARS, E.: *Génie chim.* (Belg.) **78** (4): 93 (1957).
92. WESTERTERP, K. R.: *Chem. Eng. Sci.* **17**: 423 (1962).
93. HOFTIJZER, P. J. and T. N. ZWIETERING: *Chem. Eng. Sci.* **14**: 241 (1961).
94. DEMARIA, F., J. E. LONGFIELD and C. BUTLER: *Ind. Eng. Chem.* **53**: 259 (1961).
95. ROLLMAN, W. F.: U. S. Pat. 2, 604, 479.

Chapter V

96. BOND, W. N. and D. A. NEWTON: *Phil. Mag.* **4**: 24, 889 (1927); **5**: 794 (1928).
97. KRONIG, R. and J. C. BRINK: *Appl. Sci. Res.* **A2**: 143 (1950).
98. GARNER, F. H. and D. HAMMERTON: *Chem. Eng. Sci.* **3**: 1 (1954).
99. LINTON, M. and K. L. SUTHERLAND: *Chem. Eng. Sci.* **12**: 214 (1960).
100. BOUSSINESQ, J.: *J. de Math. pure et appl.* **6** (1): 285 (1905).
101. GRIFFITH, R. M.: *Chem. Eng. Sci.* **12**: 198 (1960).
102. CALDERBANK, P. H. and M. B. MOO-YOUNG: *Chem. Eng. Sci.* **16**: 39 (1961).
103. WESTERTERP, K. R., L. L. VAN DIERENDONCK and J. A. DE KRAA: *Chem. Eng. Sci.* **18**: 157 (1963); K. R. WESTERTERP: Doctoral Thesis, Techn. Univ., Delft (1962).
104. HOFMANN, H.: *Chem. Eng. Sci.* **14**: 56 (1961).
105. TRAMBOUZE, P. J.: *Chem. Eng. Sci.* **14**: 161 (1961).
106. SCHOENEMANN, K. and H. HOFMANN: *Chem. Ing. Techn.* **29**: 665 (1957).
107. SCHOENEMANN, K.: *Chem. Eng. Sci.* **8**: 161 (1957).
108. HOFMANN, H.: *Chem. Eng. Sci.* **8**: 113 (1957).
109. SCHOENEMANN, K.: *Chem. Eng. Sci.* **14**: 39 (1961).
110. LEWIS, W. K. and W. G. WHITMAN: *Ind. Eng. Chem.* **16**: 1215 (1924).
111. HATTA, S.: *Technol. Repts., Tôhoku Imp. U.* **10**: 119 (1932).
112. KREVELEN, D. W. VAN and P. J. HOFTIJZER: *Rec. Trav. Chim. Pays-Bas* **67**: 563 (1948).
113. VUSSE, J. G. VAN DE: *Chem. Eng. Sci.* **16**: 21 (1961).
114. POTTER, O. E.: *Trans. Instn. Chem. Engrs.* **36**: 415 (1958).
115. FRIEDLANDER, S. K. and M. LITT: *Chem. Eng. Sci.* **7**: 229 (1958).; *Appl. Sci. Res.* **A8**: 403 (1959).
116. ACRIVOS, A.: *Chem. Eng. Sci.* **13**: 57 (1960).
117. MEYERINK, E. S. C. and S. K. FRIEDLANDER: *Chem. Eng. Sci.* **17**: 121 (1962).
118. DANCKWERTS, P. V.: *Trans. Far. Soc.* **46**: 300, 701 (1950).
119. CHAMBRÉ, P. L. and J. D. YOUNG: *The Physics of Fluids* **1**: 48 (1958).
120. BRIAN, P. L. T., J. F. HURLEY and E. H. HASSELTINE: *A. I. Ch. E. Journal* **7**: 226 (1961).
121. SHERWOOD, T. K. and R. L. PIGFORD: "Absorption and Extraction", McGraw-Hill, New York (1952).
122. KREVELEN, D. W. VAN and P. J. HOFTIJZER: *Chem. Eng. Sci.* **2**: 145 (1953).
123. DANCKWERTS, P. V.: *Appl. Sci. Res.* **A3**: 385 (1953).
124. KREVELEN, D. W. VAN and P. J. HOFTIJZER: *Chim. Ind.*, XXIème congrès int. Chim. Ind.: 168 (1948).
125. NIJSING, R. A. T. O. and H. KRAMERS: *Chem. Eng. Sci.* **8**: 81 (1958).

126. NIJSING, R. A. T. O., R. H. HENDRIKSZ, and H. KRAMERS: *Chem. Eng. Sci.* **10**: 88 (1959).
127. NARSIMHAN, G.: *Chem. Eng. Sci.* **16**: 7 (1961).
128. DENBIGH, K. G. and G. S. G. BEVERIDGE: *Trans. Instn. Chem. Engrs.* **40**: 23 (1962).
129. THIELE, E. W.: *Ind. Eng. Chem.* **31**: 916 (1939).
130. ZELDOWITCH, J. B.: *Acta Physicochim. URSS* **10**: 583 (1939).
131. WAGNER, C.: *Z. phys. Chem.* **A193**: 1 (1943).
132. WICKE, E.: *Angew. Chem.* **19**: 57, 94 (1947).
133. KREVELEN, D. W. VAN: *Chem. Weekbl.* **47**: 427 (1951).
134. THOENES, D. and H. KRAMERS: *Chem. Eng. Sci.* **8**: 271 (1958).
135. RICHARDSON, J. F. and J. SZEKELY: *Trans. Instn. Chem. Engrs.* **39**: 212 (1961).
136. WHEELER, A.: "Catalysis", Vol. II, Reinhold, New York (1955).
137. WICKE, E.: *Z. Elektrochem.* **60**: 774 (1956).
138. WICKE, E. and K. HEDDEN: *Z. Elektrochem.* **57**: 636 (1953).
139. HEDDEN, K.: *Chem. Eng. Sci.* **14**: 317 (1961).
140. CHIEH CHU and O. A. HOUGEN: *Chem. Eng. Sci.* **17**: 167 (1962).
141. CARBERRY, J. J.: *A. I. Ch. E. Journal* **7**: 350 (1961).
142. SCHILSON, R. E. and N. R. AMUNDSON: *Chem. Eng. Sci.* **13**: 226 (1961).
143. CARBERRY, J. J.: *Chem. Eng. Sci.* **17**: 675 (1962).
144. LOON, W. VAN: Doctoral Thesis, Techn. Univ., Delft (1952).
145. HELD, E. F. M. VAN DER: *Chem. Eng. Sci.* **14**: 300 (1961).
146. WICKE, E.: *Z. Elektrochem.* **65**: 267 (1961).
147. WICKE, E.: *Chem. Eng. Sci.* **8**: 61 (1958).
148. VULIS, A.: "Thermal Regimes of Combustion", transl. fr. Russian, McGraw-Hill, New York, (1961).
149. HEDDEN, K.: *Chem. Ing. Techn.* **30**: 125 (1958).
150. OELE, A. P.: *Chem. Eng. Sci.* **8**: 146 (1958).
151. KRAMERS, H.: *Physica*, **12**: 61 (1946).
152. YAGI, S. and D. KUNII: *A. I. Ch. E. Journal* **3**: 373 (1957).
153. WILHELM, R. H., W. C. JOHNSON, R. WYNKOOP and D. W. COLLIER: *Chem. Eng. Progr.* **44**: 105 (1948).
154. BUNNELL, D. G., H. B. IRVIN, R. W. OLSON and J. M. SMITH: *Ind. Eng. Chem.* **41**: 1977 (1949).
155. COBERLY, C. A. and W. R. MARSHALL: *Chem. Eng. Progr.* **47**: 141 (1951).
156. MAEDA, S.: *Technol. Repts., Tôhoku Imp. U.* **16**(2): 1 (1952).
157. PLAUTZ, D. A. and H. F. JOHNSTONE: *A. I. Ch. E. Journal* **1**: 193 (1955).
158. SCHWARTZ, C. E. and J. M. SMITH: *Ind. Eng. Chem.* **45**: 1209 (1953).
159. YAGI, S. and N. WAKAO: *A. I. Ch. E. Journal* **5**: 79 (1959).
160. KLING, G.: *Chem. Ing. Techn.* **31**: 705 (1959).
161. LEVA, M.: *Ind. Eng. Chem.* **42**: 2498 (1950).
162. BARON, T.: *Chem. Eng. Progr.* **48**: 118 (1952).
163. WILHELM, R. H., W. C. JOHNSON and F. S. ACTON: *Ind. Eng. Chem.* **35**: 562 (1943).
164. GROSSMAN, L. M.: *Trans. Am. Inst. Chem. Engrs.* **42**: 535 (1946).
165. CHAMBRÉ, P. L. and L. M. GROSSMAN: *Appl. Sci. Res.* **A5**: 245 (1956).
166. CHAMBRÉ, P. L.: *Appl. Sci. Res.* **A9**: 157 (1960).
167. KJAER, J.: "Measurement and Calculation of Temperature and Conversion in Fixed Bed Catalytic Reactors", J. Gjellerups Forlag, Copenhagen (1958).
168. BEEK, J.: "Design of packed catalytic reactors", in "Advances of Chemical Engineering." Vol. 3, 203–271, Academic Press, New York (1962).
169. LÜCK, G.: *Allg. Wärmetechnik*, **3**: 176 (1952).
170. REBOUX, P: "Phénomènes de fluidisation", Association Française de Fluidisation, Paris (1954).
171. LEVA, M.: "Fluidisation", McGraw-Hill, New York (1959).
172. ZENZ, F. A. and D. F. OTHMER: "Fluidization and Fluid-particle Systems," Reinhold, New York (1960).
173. Conference on Fluidization Technology, *J. Appl. Chem.* **2**, Suppl. Issue No. 1 (1952); Symposium on Fluidization, *Trans. Instn. Chem. Engrs.* **39**: 166–240 (1961).
174. LEWIS, W. K., E. R. GILL LAND and W. GLASS: *A. I. Ch. E. Journal* **5**: 419 (1959).
175. MATHIS, J. F. and C. C. WATSON: *A. I. Ch. E. Journal* **2**: 518 (1956).
176. MAY, W. G.: *Chem. Eng. Progr.* **55**: 49 (1959).

177. YAGI, S. and D. KUNII: *Chem. Eng. Sci.* **16**: 364, 372, 380 (1961).

Chapter VI

178. DENBIGH, K. G.: *Chem. Eng. Sci.* **14**: 25 (1961).
179. DENBIGH, K. G.: *Trans. Far. Soc.* **40**: 352 (1944).
180. TRAMBOUZE, P. J. and E. L. PIRET: *A. I. Ch. E. Journal* **5**: 384 (1959).
181. ODEN, E. C.: *Petr. Refiner* **29**(4): 103 (1950).
182. MESSIKOMMER, B. H., Proc. Int. Seminar on "Analogue Computation Applied to the Study of Chemical Processes", Brussels (November 1960).
183. HORN, F.: Doctoral Thesis, Techn. Univ., Vienna (1958).
184. HORN, F.: *Chem. Eng. Sci.* **14**: 77 (1961).
185. HORN, F. and U. TROLTEN ER: *Chem. Ing. Techn.* **32**: 382 (1960).
186. HORN, F and U. TROLTEN ER: *Chem. Ing. Techn.* **33**: 413 (1961).
187. CALDERBANK, P. H.: *Chem. Eng. Progr.* **49**: 585 (1953).
188. MARS, P. and D. W. VAN KREVELEN: *Chem. Eng. Sci.* **3**: Spec. Suppl.: 41 (1954).
189. ANNABLE, D.: *Chem. Eng. Sci.* **1**: 145 (1952).
190. WESTERTERP, K. R. and W. J. BEEK: *De Ingenieur* **73**: Ch. 15 (1961).
191. WESTERTERP, K. R.: *De Ingenieur* **73**: Ch. 69 (1961).
192. HORN, F.: *Z. Elektrochem.* **65**: 209 (1961).
193. HORN, F.: *Z. Elektrochem.* **65**: 295 (1961).
194. EKLUND, R. B.: "The Rate of Oxidation of Sulphur Dioxide with a Commercial Vanadium Catalyst", Almqvist and Wiksell, Stockholm (1956).
195. ARIS, R.: *Chem. Eng. Sci.* **12**: 243 (1960).
196. BORESKOV, G. K. and M. G. SLINKO: *Chem. Eng. Sci.* **14**: 259 (1961).
197. SCHOENEMANN, K.: *Génie Chim.* (Belg.) **38**: 163 (1960).
198. BARTHOLOMÉ, E. and R. KRABETZ: *Z. Elektrochem.* **65**: 224 (1961).
199. KÜCHLER, L.: *Chem. Eng. Sci.* **14**: 11 (1961).
200. BILOUS, O. and N. R. AMUNDSON: *Chem. Eng. Sci.* **5**: 81, 115 (1956).
201. KATZ, S.: *Ann. New York Ac. Sci.* **84**: 441 (1960).
202. DENBIGH, K. G.: *Chem. Eng. Sci.* **8**: 125 (1958).
203. ARIS, R.: *Chem. Eng. Sci.* **12**: 56 (1960).
204. STOREY, C.: *Chem. Eng. Sci.* **17**: 45 (1962).
205. ROSENBROCK, H. H.: *Computer Journal* **3**(3): 175 (1960).
206. BELLMAN, R.: "Dynamic Programming", Oxford Univ. Press. London (1957)
207 ARIS, R : "The Optimal Design of Chemical Reactors", Acad. Press, New York (1961); also see *Z. Elektrochem.* **65**: 229 (1961).
208. GRÜTTER, W. F. and B. H. MESSIKOMMER: *Helv. Chim. Acta* **44**: 285 (1961).
209. GRÜTTER, W. F. and B. H. MESSIKOMMER: *Helv. Chim. Acta* **43**: 2182 (1960).
210. ARIS, R.: *Chem. Eng. Sci.* **13**: 18 (1960).
211. HORN, F.: *Chem. Eng. Sci.* **15**: 176 (1961).

Appendix I

212. RIETEMA, K.: *Chem. Eng. Sci.* **14**: 3 (1961).
213. FROMENT, G., H. PIJCKE and G. GOETHALS: *Chem. Eng. Sci.* **13**: 180 (1961).
214. LE GOFF, P., L. BONNETAIN and M. LETORT: *Chem. Eng. Sci.* **14**: 290 (1961).
215. VIALLARD, A.: *Chem. Eng. Sci.* **14**: 183 (1961).
216. DANCKWERTS, P. V. and A. M. KENNEDY: *Trans. Instn. Chem. Engrs.* **32S**: 54 (1954).
217. KRAMERS, H., M. P. P. BLIND and E. SNOECK: *Chem. Eng. Sci.* **14**: 115 (1961).

Appendix II

218. MASON, D. R. and E. L. PIRET: *Ind. Eng. Chem.* **43**: 1210 (1951).
219. BILOUS, O. and N. R. AMUNDSON: *A. I. Ch. E. Journal* **1**: 513 (1955).
220. ARIS, R. and N. R. AMUNDSON: *Chem. Eng. Sci.* **7**: 121, 132, 148 (1958).
221. SHEAN-LIN, L., and N. R. AMUNDSON: *Z. Elektrochem.* **65**: 276 (1961).
222. FOSS, A. S.: *Chem. Eng. Progr. Symp. Ser.* **55** (25): 47 (1959).

AUTHOR INDEX

ACRIVOS, A., 153
ACTON, F. S., 180
ALBERDA, G., 65
AMUNDSON, N. R., 116, 117, 165, 230, 234
ANNABLE, D., 199
ARIS, R., 204, 208, 210, 230

BAILIE, R. C., 80
BALACEANU, J. C., 12, 224
BARISH, E. Z., 66
BARKELEW, C. H., 93, 113, 115
BARON, T., 93, 180
BARTHOLOMÉ, E., 204
BEEK, J., 180
BEEK, W.J., 199, 230
BELLMAN, R., 209
BERNARD, R. A., 95
BEVERIDGE, G. S. G., 156
BILOUS, O., 116, 206, 220, 230, 234
BIRD, R. B., 1, 3
BISCHOFF, K. B., 80
BLIND, M. P. P., 227
BOELHOUWER, C., 52
BOND, W. N., 139
BONNETAIN, L., 226
BORESKOV, G. K., 204
BOUSSINESQ, J., 140
BRIAN, P. L. T., 153
BRINK, J. C., 139
BROEDER, J. J., 92
BROTHMAN, A., 66
BRÖTZ, W., 21
BUNNELL, D. G., 177
BUTLER, C., 133

CAIRNS, E. J., 95, 96
CALDERBANK, P. H., 140, 198
CARBERRY, J. J., 165, 168
CHAMBRÉ, P. L., 153, 180
CHERMIN, H. A. G., 7, 50
CHIEH CHU, 164
CHOLETTE, A., 76
CLELAND, F. A., 86
CLOUTIER, L., 76
COBERLY, C. A., 177
COLLIER, D. W., 176
COUSSEMANT, F., 12, 224
CROOCKEWIT, P., 94

CURL, R. L., 89

DAMERELL, G. L., 89
DAMKÖHLER, G., 1, 180
DANCKWERTS, P. V., 65, 74, 78, 83, 153, 154, 227
DE GROOT, J. H., 96
DE JOSSELIN de JONG, G., 96
DE KRAA, J. A., 140, 227
DEMARIA, F., 133
DENBIGH, K. G., 1, 86, 92, 156, 189, 191, 192, 197, 207
DUPONT, F. A. A., 96

EKLUND, R. B., 203
ELDRIDGE, J. M., 33
EMBDE, F., 88
ESCHARD, F., 12, 224

FAN, L. T., 80
FOSS, A. S., 230
FRANK-KAMENETSKI, D. A., 1, 160
FRIEDLANDER, S. K., 153
FROMENT, G., 226

GARNER, F. H., 139
GILLILAND, E. R., 183
GIRAUD, A., 12, 224
GLASS, W., 183
GOETHALS, G., 226
GREENHALGH, R. E., 87
GRIFFITH, R. M., 140
GROSSMAN, L. M., 180
GRÜTTER, W. F., 210

HAMMERTON, D., 139
HANHART, J., 97
HASSELTINE, E. H., 153
HATTA, S., 147
HEDDEN, K., 164, 173
HELLIN, M., 12, 224
HENDRIKSZ, R. H., 155, 227
HIBY, J. W., 73, 95
HOFMANN, H., 82, 92, 97, 144
HOFTIJZER, P. J., 133, 147, 151, 153, 154, 155, 230
HONIG, C. C., 94